D1189826

Brittle Behavior of Engineering Structures

Brittle Behavior of

Prepared for the
Ship Structure Committee
Under the general direction of the
Committee on Ship Steel
National Academy of Sciences—National Research Council

Engineering Structures

By EARL R. PARKER

Professor of Metallurgy
and Chairman, Division of Mineral Technology
University of California, Berkeley

NEW YORK · JOHN WILEY & SONS, INC.

London · Chapman & Hall, Limited

Library of Congress Catalog Card Number: 57–5928

Printed in the United States of America

Dedicated to FINN JONASSEN

who, in his capacity as Technical Director of the Committee on Ship Steel, was instrumental in developing the idea of this book. His skillful, patient leadership guided the Project Advisory Committee and author through the trying days of organizing, writing, and rewriting the text. His untimely death saddened the hearts of all who knew this fine man.

Foreword

The usual approach to the design of large steel structures has not been realistic, as the numerous failures during the past decade have attested. These failures have been frequent and often spectacular. They were usually brittle, whereas structural steel is normally considered to be a ductile material, the casualties frequently occurring with explosive suddenness and at nominal stresses computed to be far below the yield point of the material.

Prompted by the large number of failures in welded steel merchant ships that occurred in the winter of 1942–1943, an extensive investigation into the causes of these failures was initiated by the Secretary of the Navy. Failures and the attendant circumstances were studied, research programs were begun, and scientific thought throughout the world was stimulated by the challenging nature of the problem. The research activity and general high level of interest continued after the end of World War II and still exist today.

After the war, however, it became more apparent with the passage of time that the brittle fracture problem was not peculiar to the welded merchant ships built during the war. Brittle failures were reported in steel plate structures such as bridges, penstocks, oil storage tanks, and gas transmission pipelines. Furthermore, a study of failures that occurred late in the Nineteenth and in the first four decades of the Twentieth Century exposed a great number that had previously not been associated with the phenomenon of brittle fracture.

It was established, therefore, that the problem was common to all steel plate structures, whether riveted or welded, and that it had been with us for over 70 years, even though only properly identified in the past 10 or 15. However, the available knowledge on the subject was scattered. Hence the demands of the engineer for research data that would be of assistance in avoiding future catastrophic failures could, in many cases, not be satisfied, not because pertinent experimental or analytical work had not been performed but because most of the results of this work were not generally available.

The interagency Ship Structure Committee,* which has supported the major portion of the postwar brittle fracture research conducted in this country, recognized this problem as early as 1948. At that time there were discussions regarding the possibility of collecting and analyzing the results of the many different tests for "notch toughness" that had been performed under a number of research projects, many of them on a single group of pedigreed steels, during the preceding 4 or 5 years. Accordingly, the Ship Structure Committee requested the National Academy of Sciences–National Research Council to "prepare a monograph or monographs summarizing the research work accomplished in the improvements of hull structures of ships or on subjects related thereto." The Academy–Research Council, through its Committee on Ship Steel, then appointed an advisory committee for the specific purpose of overseeing the preparation of a volume such as that visualized by the Ship Structure Committee.

Whereas the original objective of the book had been comparatively narrow (as evidenced by the short working title, "Notch Bar Monograph"), the Project Advisory Committee immediately suggested that the objective be broadened: "To present the present day knowledge of the phenomenon of brittle behavior of metals and its manifestation in engineering structures." It was with this purpose that the present book was prepared, the material being directed primarily at practicing engineers, metallurgists, and others concerned with the behavior of metals. It should be recognized, however, that even though the knowledge in this area has advanced tremendously in the last decade, it is still inadequate to permit the preparation of a satisfactory engineering design textbook on the subject.

The Advisory Committee considers itself most fortunate in having been able to obtain the services of Professor Earl R. Parker as the author of this book. Professor Parker's long association with the problem, his considerable active work in the field, and his familiarity with pertinent and related disciplines combine to provide a background not far short of ideal.

This monograph was prepared under the terms of contract NObs-

* The Ship Structure Committee is composed of the following member agencies:
Bureau of Ships, Department of the Navy.
Military Sea Transportation Service, Department of the Navy.
United States Coast Guard, Treasury Department.
Maritime Administration, Department of Commerce.
American Bureau of Shipping.

50148, BuShips Project NS-731-034, between the Bureau of Ships, Department of the Navy, and the National Academy of Sciences—National Research Council. The opinions expressed herein do not necessarily represent those of the Ship Structure Committee or of its member agencies. The manuscript was reviewed piecemeal several times in the course of preparation and in its complete final form and approved for publication by the Project Advisory Committee.

THE PROJECT ADVISORY COMMITTEE

Members of the Project Advisory Committee:

John R. Low, Jr., Chairman
Research Laboratory
General Electric Company

Maxwell Gensamer
Professor of Metallurgy
Acting Associate Dean, Faculty of Engineering
School of Mines
Columbia University

LeVan Griffis
Director, Mechanics Research Department
American Machine and Foundry Company

Lloyd R. Jackson
Technical Director
Battelle Memorial Institute

Noah Kahn
Head Metallurgist
Material Laboratory
New York Naval Shipyard

John M. Lessells
President, Lessells and Associates, Inc.
Associate Professor of Mechanical Engineering, Emeritus
Massachusetts Institute of Technology

Richard H. Raring
National Advisory Committee for Aeronautics

Saylor C. Snyder
Director, Product Development
Research and Technology Division
United States Steel Corporation

Robert D. Stout
Professor of Metallurgy
Lehigh University

Finn Jonassen *
Technical Director
Committee on Ship Steel
National Academy of Sciences—National Research Council

Fred C. Bailey
Lessells and Associates, Inc.
Formerly Assistant Technical Director
Committee on Ship Steel
National Academy of Sciences—National Research Council

* Deceased 2/19/55.

Preface

This book was written for the purpose of summarizing the available information on the brittle behavior of steel in engineering structures. It contains a discussion of the theories and mechanism of failure, a review of test methods used for evaluating relative brittleness, interpretations and summaries of test results, a discussion of the effects of welding and composition variations on notch toughness, and a report of service failures.

The writing was done under the supervision of the Advisory Committee, whose names appear in the Foreword to this book. Without the advice and help of this group, this book could not have been written. Most of the credit for this textbook goes to this Committee. Each member helped with the necessary rewriting, not just once but time after time until a satisfactory draft of each chapter was obtained. Through the numerous meetings held to discuss and debate the subject material for the book, the author developed a deep appreciation for the breadth and depth of knowledge of the Committee members. They are all specialists of high standing.

In addition to the Committee members, other people were also involved in the preparation of the manuscript, and appreciation of their efforts is hereby expressed. Ta-Cheng Ku did a good deal of work on the literature review that preceded the preparation of the manuscript. T. H. Hazlett aided with the editorial work on about half of the chapters. Gloria Pelatowski made drafts of all the drawings presented herein. E. G. Thomsen provided invaluable aid in the preparation of all chapter drafts. Without the assistance of these able and willing workers, the completion of this text would have been long delayed, and the quality would have suffered.

EARL R. PARKER

May, 1957

Contents

CHAPTER

1

Introduction

On January 16, 1943, a T-2 tanker lying quietly at her fitting-out pier at Portland, Oregon, suddenly cracked in a brittle manner . . . "without warning and with a report that was heard for at least a mile. . . ." The sea was calm, the weather mild, her computed deck stress was only 9900 psi (see Fig. 1.1). There seemed to be no reason why she should have broken in two, but she did. At the time some speculated that the fracture occurred because the ship was welded; others postulated that it was due to internal stresses introduced during assembly; the quality of the steel was suspected, and the appropriateness of the design was questioned.

Investigations shed little light upon the matter; there was no satisfactory explanation for the fracture. It was known, however, that brittle behavior of large welded steel structures was not a new phenomenon. It had been observed before but had not demanded serious attention even though there had been occasional reports of welded bridges failing spontaneously, of storage tanks cracking, and of penstocks breaking. It soon became apparent that the accelerated construction of large monolithic-type structures during the early years of World War II, particularly of ships, had merely increased the number of such fractures, causing alarm for the safety of men and equipment. During the ensuing years a simple solution for the trouble was sought in vain. It is true, even after a decade of intensive research, that there is no *simple* solution. The role played by residual stresses,

Fig. 1.1 Photograph of a T-2 tanker that failed at pier.

steel composition, fatigue, welding, and design are still subject to debate. Means for improving the steel to minimize the probability of brittle fracture are finally evolving, but only after years of investigation. It has also been shown that welding, frequently considered a culprit, was not solely responsible for brittle behavior of large structures. Design and workmanship also play important roles that are still being evaluated. The importance of each of these factors and their interrelations are discussed in detail in the following chapters.

The intricate nature of the brittle fracture problem soon became apparent to the early investigators; consequently several large research projects were organized throughout the country. Part of this work was assigned to university laboratories, where testing facilities were available; other projects were conducted in government and industrial laboratories. These investigations involved great effort and required the complete cooperation of the steel companies, the welding industry, the design engineers, the construction groups, and the university staffs. Wartime stress fused these groups into a close-knit organization with a common objective—to solve the brittle fracture problem. The steel industry furnished both standard and special steels; the welding people provided special electrodes and valuable data; designers and construction groups contributed their knowledge and skill to forward the ends of the investigations; universities supplied well equipped laboratories and trained personnel for carrying out the testing and analysis. In all, it was a very satisfying adventure in cooperative enterprise.

The background of knowledge did not accumulate rapidly. Brittle behavior, never studied extensively prior to that time, had to be produced and controlled in large laboratory specimens before the numerous contributing factors could be isolated and studied. No one knew what types of specimens should be employed, nor how the test results could be interpreted in a practical manner. Hence it was necessary to make a vast number of tests on many steels, using many types of specimens. There was not even any assurance that two types of specimens would evaluate the relative merits of steels or of a welding procedure in the same way. Furthermore, structural applications covered the entire gamut of conditions. The behavior of a single specimen could, perhaps, be correlated with its structural counterpart, but it could not be expected to foretell the behavior of slightly different designs. For example, a laboratory specimen containing a longitudinal butt weld might be expected to behave during test like a loaded pressure vessel with a similar weld. However, such a correlation could be expected to hold only when the plate thickness, the welding conditions, and the state of stress were duplicated exactly. Moreover, simple laboratory specimens could not be expected to reveal the behavior of complicated structures altered by the presence of attached fittings.

Obviously what was needed for the success of the investigation was a clear understanding of the principles involved. This has been a long time in coming. Enough facts, however, have finally been accumulated and at last the general pattern of behavior seems to be resolved.

To avoid brittle fractures, the engineer must employ a new set of design criteria. The conventional approach to a design problem, involving the assumption that the standard tensile test data can be used as a basis for design stress calculations, must be modified when the possibility of brittle fracture is present. A new yardstick must be employed to indicate the merits of the metal. Just what this measurement should be has been difficult to determine. The only agreement in the past has been that it must be some kind of notched bar test, but there has been little accord about the choice of a specific specimen or the use of the data obtained therewith.

The design of large welded steel structures must be approached with a new viewpoint if the probability of a brittle failure is to be minimized. Some understanding of the concepts of triaxial stress systems and a knowledge of how triaxial tensile stresses affect the plastic behavior of steel are essential for the designer of welded structures. A discussion of the nature and theory of fracture has therefore been included in Chapters II and III to ensure an understanding of the causes of service failures.

Steel can fracture by two distinctly different modes. Its behavior can be ductile or brittle, depending upon the conditions of loading. This behavior is not unique with steel but has its counterpart in many other metals, such as molybdenum, tungsten, and zinc, and in nonmetals, such as tar and glass. For example, tar will flow under load when warm, particularly if loaded slowly, but when cold or when loaded rapidly it breaks in a brittle manner. There is a pronounced temperature dependence involved in the brittle fracture of tar or glass; this is also true for steel. Similarly, the behavior of tar and glass is markedly affected by changes in strain rate; so is the behavior of steel. The generality of the phenomenon makes an understanding of the fundamental principles somewhat easier.

Plastic flow is dependent only upon the shear stresses acting on the deforming material; ductile behavior and shear-type fractures also depend upon such stresses. Conversely, brittle behavior and cleavage-type fractures are caused by high tensile stresses. Whether a material will flow plastically or fracture in a brittle manner depends upon two things: (1) the ratio of maximum shear stress to maximum tensile stress and (2) the flow and fracture characteristics of the material. Metals that flow at a low stress level and fracture only at high stresses will always be ductile. If, however, a ductile material is retreated so that its yield strength approaches its fracture strength, its behavior may become altered to the extent that brittleness may ensue. In hot-rolled mild steel, for example, three factors are of major importance in this regard. The addition of carbon to iron introduces hard brittle particles of iron carbide, which are embedded in the iron crystals; they restrict plastic flow. As a consequence, the yield strength of the steel is raised when the carbon content is increased; the tendency toward brittle behavior is also increased. The second factor of importance is the strain rate, an increase of which will cause an increase in the yield strength. There is an associated increase in brittleness; steel, like glass or tar, requires time for flow to be initiated. The third factor involves notches, which lower the ratio of shear stress to normal stress. Thus it becomes evident that increasing the carbon content, loading at a rapid rate, or introducing notches all act to suppress plastic flow and hence to promote brittle behavior. Other factors having important effects on brittle behavior are metallurgical structure, deoxidation practice, and cooling rate.

Conventional design practice permits the use of working stresses that are some fraction of the yield strength or ultimate strength, as determined by a standard tensile test. When a stronger structure of the same proportions is required, it is customary to use a higher strength steel. The strength of hot-rolled structural steels is largely dependent upon the carbon content. Hence, if conventional practice were followed, a higher carbon steel would be substituted for its weaker counterpart. *Such a steel, while superior in a tension test, is inferior in a structure containing notches.* Experiments have shown that an increase in the carbon content in steel of only *0.10 per cent* will raise the temperature at which brittle behavior becomes possible by *25 to 50 F.* Hence it is not surprising to find that structures often become more susceptible to brittle behavior when made "stronger" by the use of a higher carbon steel. The trend at present is toward the use of lower carbon steels for those structures in which brittle fracture is a definite possibility. However, many other factors are also involved and consequently the subject must be treated at considerable length; this has been done in subsequent portions of the text.

Before proceeding with the discussion, it is necessary to introduce some of the nomenclature involved; additional details are given in Chapter II. Confusion arises from the multiplicity of terms used to describe fractured specimens or structures. The words *cleavage, shear, brittle, ductile, tough, crystalline, granular, fibrous, chevron, herringbone,* and *shear lip* all appear in the literature. Frequently the same kind of fracture is described by entirely different words by two observers. This, of course, leads to unnecessary confusion and should be avoided. An agreement about the usage of descriptive words is essential, but as yet there is no official group concerned with this problem. The terms used in this book are those most generally accepted by engineers familiar with the subject.

There are three ways in which a fracture can be described—by its *mode,* by its *behavior,* or by its *appearance.* The *mode* of fracture refers to the manner or form of separation, i.e., whether it follows the crystal boundaries, the slip planes of the individual crystals in the aggregate, or their cleavage planes. *Behavior* refers to the action of the metal prior to separation, i.e., whether the fracture was preceded by extensive deformation and hence would be characterized as ductile, or whether it occurred before any significant amount of plastic flow and would be characterized as brittle. The *appearance* refers to what one sees when observing the fracture surface. The mode of fracture can usually be discerned from the appearance of the fracture surface. Cleavage failures generally have a granular or crystalline appearance, because each crystal tends to fracture on a single plane, but this plane will vary slightly in angle from one crystal to the next in the aggregate. The flat fracture planes reflect light, so that each grain appears bright when viewed from the proper angle. Thus a polycrystalline specimen that has fractured by cleavage will seem to sparkle when rotated in the hand. Shear fractures, on the other hand, have a dull gray fibrous appearance, devoid of obvious detail. This may be due to the sliding of the fracture surfaces over each other as separation proceeds, thereby producing scratches or striations. The appearance of both cleavage and shear fractures is shown in Fig. 2.2 in Chapter II.

Experiments have shown that a fracture can follow two distinctly different paths in traversing a crystal of iron. The body centered cubic structure of this metal contains many planes, two families of which are important in fracture studies—(1) the cube faces and (2) the slip planes that traverse the cube. Cleavage fractures follow the cube planes of the individual crystalline grains. Failure in this case occurs without translation on these planes; they merely peel apart like sheets of mica. Brittle behavior is associated with the cleavage mode of separation in which the metal does not flow plastically to any significant degree before breaking.

In iron the phenomenon of plastic flow is restricted to planes containing a cube diagonal direction. Three such planes are known to function as slip planes in iron. Fracture may occur on these planes; but when it does, it is the result of a shearing action involving translation of adjacent planes. Consequently, the shear mode of fracture in steel is invariably associated with plastic flow.

Plastic flow and fracture are, however, two separate phenomena; and it is to be expected that a cleavage type fracture can, under certain circumstances, be preceded by large amounts of plastic flow. Thus a cleavage fracture may sometimes be associated with relatively ductile behavior.

NOTCH EFFECTS

Under what conditions can brittle fracture occur? The general principles indicate that any loading condition involving a low ratio of maximum shear stress to maximum normal stress tends to promote brittle behavior in steel. Certain design practices introduce unfavorable stress systems into structures and hence should be avoided or modified whenever possible. Even with satisfactory designs, however, structural discontinuities in the form of notches may be introduced inadvertently during construction. These discontinuities provide the conditions necessary to introduce low shear and high tensile stresses. Examples of such discontinuities are incompletely penetrated weld joints, weld cracks, base metal or underbead cracks, and accidental notches.

How does a notch act to change the state of stress from simple uniaxial tension to triaxial tension? This is a basic question because the important features of the brittle fracture of mild steel can be understood only after the action of a notch is clear. It is worth while to dwell upon this point at some length. Reference to Figs. 1.2, 1.3, and 1.4 will be helpful in this regard. When a uniformly distributed tensile load is applied to an unnotched plate, the stress is uniform across the section. Since there are no transverse forces acting in this simple case, the bar is free to undergo contraction, as governed by Poisson's ratio, in both the width and thickness directions. A notched

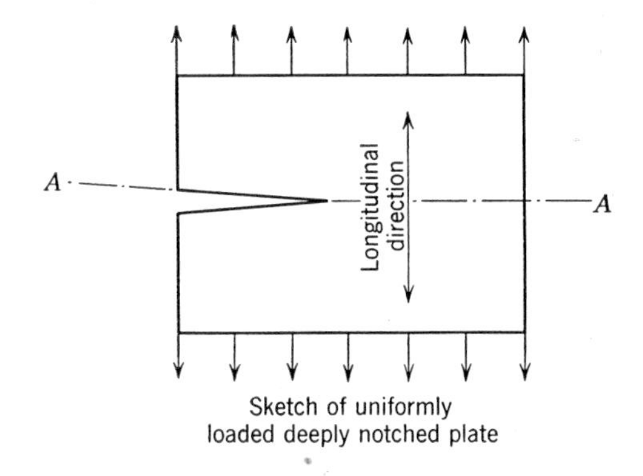

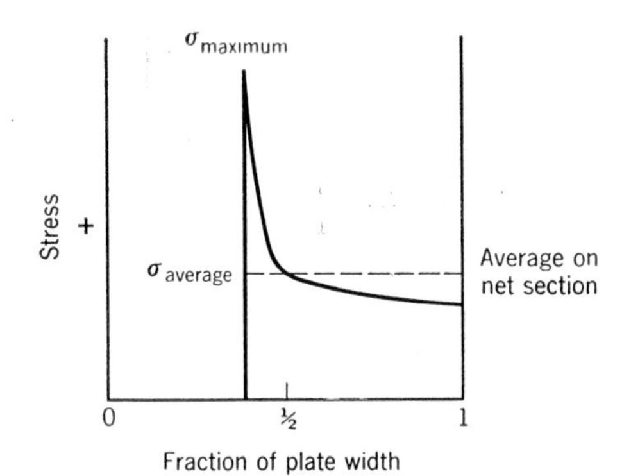

Fig. 1.2 Schematic diagram showing deeply notched plate and longitudinal stress distribution produced by a uniformly distributed load.

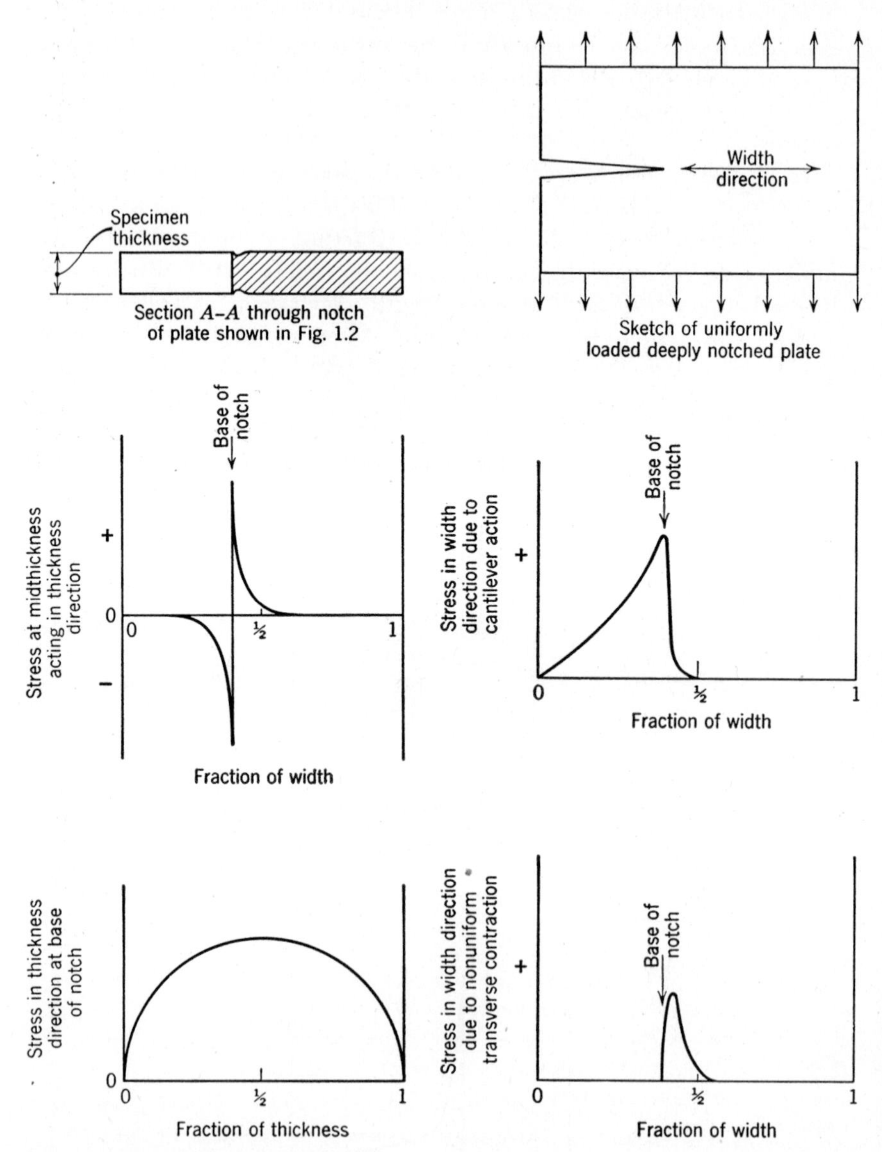

Fig. 1.3 Schematic diagram showing section through notch of plate sketched in Fig. 1.2 and distribution of normal stresses acting in the thickness direction. These stresses are due to restricted contraction in the thickness direction.

Fig. 1.4. Schematic diagram showing uniformly loaded deeply notched plate and distribution of normal stresses acting in the width direction. These stresses are due to "cantilever beam" action and to restricted contraction in width direction.

specimen subjected to simple tensile loading, such as that illustrated in Fig. 1.2, has a much more complex stress system acting near the apex of the notch. There is, of course, the well known stress concentration effect as indicated in the figure. The tensile stress acting in the longitudinal direction at the base of the notch may be several times the average value but drops abruptly to zero at the notch opening. Also, it decreases rapidly as the distance from the notch increases. It is often thought that the stress raising effect of a notch is the primary cause of trouble. However, this is not true for brittle fractures of mild steel, as is easily demonstrated. When sharply notched specimens made geometrically similar and from the same material are tested at different temperatures, the thicker ones break in a brittle manner at ordinary temperatures, whereas the thinner ones remain ductile even at low temperatures. The stress concentration factor is the same in all thicknesses of plate. However, cracking occurs at the notch apex after very little general elongation, particularly when the notch is sharp. Once a crack forms, the specimens are no longer geometrically similar; the stress concentration, which is primarily dependent upon the notch acuity, is thus substantially independent of plate thickness. When the crack forms, however, the stress state becomes less favorable for thicker plate because of the high component of tensile stress that develops in the thickness direction of the thicker plate. In service it has been observed that the incidence of failures in thin plates (e.g., ¼-in.) is much lower than in thicker ones (e.g., 1-in.). It should be kept in mind, however, that the notch toughness of thick hot-rolled plates is inferior to that of thin plates because of metallurgical as well as geometrical factors.

What does the thickness have to do with the state of stress at the base of a notch? Qualitatively the answer is straightforward. A notch introduces a complex state of stress, with tensile components acting in both thickness and width directions. Since the stress acting in the thickness direction must fall to zero at each face of the plate, it follows that the maximum value of this stress must depend upon the plate thickness. In practice it appears that thicknesses as small as a few tenths of an inch are sufficient to introduce substantial stresses in this direction. Actually the problem is quite complicated because the ratio of notch radius to plate thickness is involved. Fig. 1.3 shows a section through the notched part of the plate shown in Fig. 1.2. The longitudinal stress shown in Fig. 1.2, being zero across the notch and abnormally high in the region near the notch apex, tends to produce different degrees of lateral contraction in adjacent regions. The portion cut by the notch, being unstressed, tries to maintain its dimensions in the thickness direction, while the attached highly stressed metal beyond the notch apex tries to contract a substantial amount. The unstressed metal near the base of the notch prevents the adjacent highly stressed portion from contracting as much as it should; hence tension stresses are developed in the thickness direction in the stressed metal near the notch base. This, of course, causes compression stresses to develop in the thickness direction on the notch side of the apex. These stresses must drop to zero at each plate face because there is no external load applied there. Sketches illustrating the nature of the thickness direction stresses (for the notched specimen shown in Fig. 1.2) are shown in Fig. 1.3. It is characteristic of fractured notched plates to show various amounts of thinning ranging from a maximum at or near the notch apex, as shown schematically in section A-A of Fig. 1.3, to values approaching zero away from the notch.

Tensile stresses in the width direction can exist for two reasons, one a direct result of the loading, the other a secondary stress developed by local differences in the amount of lateral contraction. A uniformly distributed load tends to open a sharp deep crack as indicated in Fig. 1.4, producing a cantilever beam type of deflection. This generates a tensile stress acting in the width direction on the face of the notch. This stress has its maximum at the notch apex, as indicated on the graph in the same figure. The other action responsible for the generation of width direction stresses is somewhat more obscure. It arises in the load carrying portion of the metal near the notch base and is due to the gradient of longitudinal stress in the *longitudinal direction*. The longitudinal stress is a maximum at the notch apex and drops rapidly to the average value as the longitudinal distance is increased. Thus the metal at the notch base tends to contract in the width direction more than the regions above and below the notch. Since continuity is retained, the metal that tends to contract cannot freely do so, and thus stresses in the width direction are generated. The distribution of this stress is also shown schematically in Fig. 1.4.

It is evident that a sharp deep notch not only acts as a stress raiser but greatly alters the state of stress locally. Uniaxial tensile loading of a specimen containing a notch may thus create a local state of triaxial tension with a consequent dangerous lowering of the maximum shear stress to maximum tensile stress ratio.* The sharper and deeper the notch, and the thicker the plate, the lower the ratio.

The exact ratio of shear to normal stress that can be tolerated with-

* The relationships between the various stress components in triaxial stress systems are developed in Chapter II.

out inducing brittle behavior varies for each steel, and even for each condition of heat treatment or cold work for a given steel.

Furthermore, there is no simple or straightforward means for controlling this stress ratio, so that it is impossible to obtain a quantitative measurement of the sensitivity of a steel to brittle behavior in terms of the principal stresses. This is unfortunate because indirect means must be employed for evaluating the relative brittleness of steels. The only satisfactory way of doing this at present is by means of notch-toughness tests conducted at several temperatures. These tests indicate the temperature (or temperature range) over which changes in behavior take place. The results of these tests cannot be interpreted directly in terms of design requirements. This, however, may not be a permanent shortcoming because contemporary investigations indicate that there is a correlation between notch-toughness test results and service performance in at least one field of application.

All sharp deep notches in thick plates are potential brittle fracture nuclei. How sharp and how deep any notch must be in any thickness of plate to initiate a fracture depends upon many factors. Of these, temperature is of paramount importance. With a given geometry and for a specific strain rate there is always a temperature above which brittle fractures will not occur in mild steel. This temperature is in reality a temperature range, but for convenience it is defined and described as a "transition temperature."

There are several criteria currently in use to define a transition temperature. It has been found experimentally that when a given type of specimen, whether it be a standard unnotched tensile specimen or a Charpy bar, is tested over a wide enough temperature range there is a change in behavior at some temperature; with certain specimens the change is abrupt, with others it occurs gradually over a wide temperature range. As illustrated in Fig. 1.5(*a*), for example, unnotched tensile specimens made from hot-rolled 0.2 per cent carbon steel remain ductile almost down to liquid air temperature, but as this temperature is approached the ductility drops rapidly to almost zero. The mode of fracture changes from shear to cleavage; there is a corresponding change in the appearance from the gray silky surface characteristic of shear to the coarse crystalline type associated with cleavage. Obviously, then, the transition temperature can be defined in terms of the fracture mode as judged from the fracture appearance. This is called the fracture-appearance criterion, commonly abbreviated to "fracture criterion."

Another criterion for the transition temperature is based on the lack of ductility, for example, when the ductility drops to some specified low value. This is called the ductility-transition temperature, as indicated in Fig. 1.5(*a*). For a given type of test specimen, a lower temperature is usually obtained for the ductility transition than is found for the fracture-appearance transition.

Another commonly used measure of transition temperature is the temperature corresponding to the energy halfway between the maximum and minimum values. The multiplicity of criteria presently in use makes correlation of published data difficult. The complications are discussed more fully in Chapter V; for the present it is sufficient to consider the transition temperature as a dividing line between relatively ductile and relatively brittle behavior. Fig. 1.5(*b*) shows the three transition temperatures for the same steel as determined with V-notched Charpy specimens.

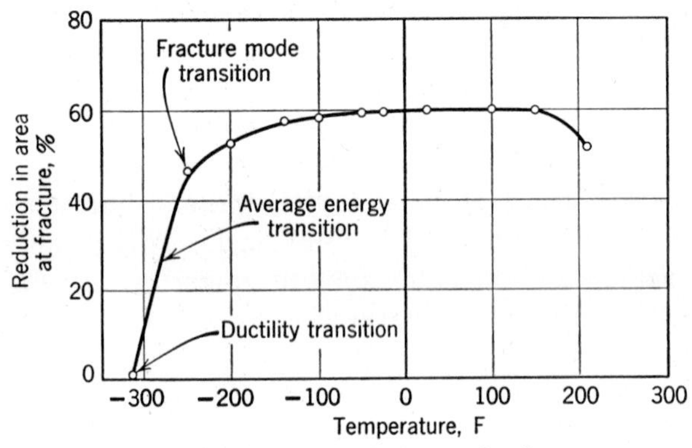

(*a*) Data for unnotched 0.505-in. diameter tensile specimens

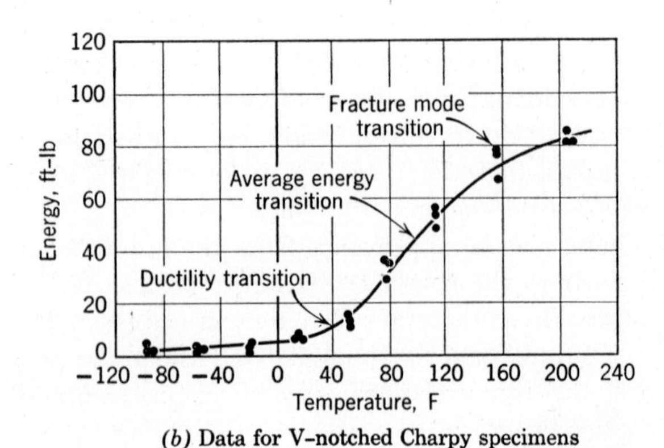

(*b*) Data for V-notched Charpy specimens

Fig. 1.5 Data for a hot-rolled 0.2% carbon steel showing the transition from ductile to brittle behavior as the testing temperature is lowered.

Since the transition temperature for a given mild steel may range from liquid air temperature for unnotched ½-in. diameter cylindrical tensile specimens to above room temperature for sharply notched bars, how can engineers use transition temperature data for design purposes? Only recently has satisfactory progress along this line been made. Tests on many plates taken from structures that failed in service have indicated that a correlation between notched bar data and service failures is possible. However, the problem still remains relatively complex. It seems that various types of notched specimens can be used to supply useful information. For example, when the energy absorbed by a V-notch Charpy specimen is below a critical value at the operating temperature, brittle fractures may initiate at nominal stresses below those normally considered safe. Whether or not a crack, once started, will propagate depends upon many factors such as the toughness of the steel, the average stress in the structure, the amount of stored energy, and the details of the structural design. In general, the conditions are such that a crack can continue to grow more easily than it can start. This, of course, leads to the spectacular catastrophic type of failure found too often in large structures.

It is important to realize at the outset that no single magic number can be used in procurement specifications to automatically preclude brittle behavior. The engineer must be cognizant of the effects on transition temperature of chemical composition, heat treatment, type of welding electrode, preheat, postheat, notches, design, energy available in the system, and many other factors before he can hope to cope with the problem.

COMPOSITION OF STEEL

A number of investigations have been conducted to reveal the effects of alloying elements on notch-toughness behavior. It must be remembered, however, that secondary effects may sometimes be involved because alloying may cause changes in microstructure, which may in turn appreciably influence behavior. Sufficient test data have been accumulated to show how the transition temperature is affected by varying the major elements normally found in structural steel, namely, carbon, manganese, phosphorus, sulphur, silicon, and nitrogen. The effects do seem to vary, depending upon the test specimen and, particularly, upon the criterion of transition temperature that is employed. This variation is perhaps to be expected and will be discussed in more detail in a later chapter. At present it will suffice to indicate only the general effects of these elements on transition temperature.

In hot-rolled or in normalized AISI 1020 steel, an increase in carbon has been found to raise the transition temperature appreciably. Also, the maximum energy that a ductile notched specimen is capable of absorbing is markedly lowered as the carbon content is increased. Phosphorus is even more effective than carbon in raising the transition temperature. Sulphur has a complex effect because the insoluble sulphides produce small fissures in the steel when it is deformed, thus altering the stress conditions. It does not, however, seem to be particularly deleterious from the standpoint of brittle fracture. Silicon seems to have a slightly beneficial effect on the transition temperature when amounts up to about 0.3% are added. This limit is not well established, however, and by some criteria no improvement at all is indicated. Silicon contents beyond about 0.5% raise the transition temperature. Results obtained on the effect of nitrogen are not consistent. Small amounts have been found in some cases to have no effect but in others nitrogen was found to raise the transition temperature appreciably.

Manganese is the only really beneficial element intentionally added in rather large quantities to structural carbon steel. It will be seen later that the improvement in transition temperature may be only 2 F, or it may be as much as 8 F for each 0.1% increase in the manganese content, depending upon the criterion for notch toughness selected. It is also important to note that the maximum energy absorbed is not affected by manganese. It therefore appears that for a given class of structural steel, the manganese should be on the high side and the carbon on the low side for optimum notch toughness; this conclusion seems to be justified by experience.

Aluminum has in some instances been found to be beneficial in hot-rolled steel, especially when added in amounts of 0.1% or more. Possibly some improvement in notch toughness may be obtained with the usual quantity of about 0.05% used for deoxidation, but its benefits in such low concentrations are somewhat doubtful. It is fairly well established that aluminum is especially beneficial when present with 0.15 to 0.30% silicon. Fully deoxidizing steel with silicon and aluminum lowers the transition temperature significantly. The transition temperature of a hot-rolled, aluminum-killed steel can usually be substantially lowered by normalizing because of the grain refinement that generally results from this treatment.

It is well known that ferrite grain size has an appreciable effect on transition temperature, an increase in ASTM ferrite grain size number (decrease in grain size) being associated with a decrease in transition temperature. Also, the influence of microstructure on notch-toughness behavior is very substantial. For example, the keyhole Charpy 15 ft-lb transition temperature may be lowered 200 F by quenching and tempering a steel, although such a heat treatment is not practical on hot-rolled structural carbon steel. The range of microstructures and compositions encountered in commercial practice makes it impossible to predict the brittle behavior characteristics of a steel from a knowledge of its AISI or ASTM classification alone. Special tests must be performed to evaluate each heat, and then the test results must be interpreted in the light of the service conditions under which the material is to operate.

WELDING

Defective welding has played a major role in initiating brittle behavior in large structures. Weld defects are common because the numerous variables in welding are difficult to control. In a weld, steel is melted, its composition is altered, and it is solidified in only a few seconds. The problem of quality control of such a process is a formidable one. It involves control of elusive metallurgical factors as well as workmanship and design. It is not surprising to find that poor quality control has been responsible for many brittle failures originating at welded joints. It should be appreciated, however, that most welds *do not* fail in service and that all welded structures contain defects but few are serious. Also, superior electrodes have been developed in recent years, so that it is now possible to make a weld that will perform better than ordinary mild steel plate material. This is an exceptional condition, however, attained only with selected materials and carefully controlled techniques. Many ordinary welded joints have mechanical properties that are inferior to those of rolled plate.

It should be pointed out that, with any of the standard welding practices now in use, the probability of the occurrence of a brittle fracture under normal conditions is relatively low. However, to minimize disastrous service failures, it is necessary for more engineers to learn the statistics about such failures and to be able to evaluate the effects of design and welding procedure on the brittle behavior of structural materials.

Briefly the problems of weldability can be classified into two groups —those of making sound welds, generally referred to as joinability; and those of serviceability, dealing with the mechancial performance of the weldment.

Joinability is the problem of welding engineers and construction men. Once they have discharged their task, it is the design engineer who must assume the responsibility for service performance. What, then, governs serviceability? The basic factors are (1) chemical composition, (2) microstructure, and (3) structural discontinuities. The first is controlled primarily by the selection of the electrode type but is also influenced by the welding procedure. The second is a function of the cooling rate and composition; the third is dependent upon both the design of the joint and the skill of the welder.

The elements that affect the quality of rolled plates (e.g., carbon, phosphorus, and sulphur) also influence the properties of welds; in addition, the quality of the weld metal is markedly affected by gases. Oxygen, nitrogen, and hydrogen can and often do have profound effects on weld metal properties. The presence of the gaseous elements is hard to detect, and the quantity absorbed is difficult to control.

The chemical composition of weld metal, however, generally contains a favorable balance of manganese and carbon. Ordinarily the carbon content of mild steel welds is low, about 0.1 per cent, and the manganese is usually maintained at a fairly high level. The high manganese and the low carbon contents tend to minimize brittleness. Nevertheless, many welds are made brittle by faulty welding procedures.

The microstructure of a weld deposit is controlled by two factors, (1) the chemical composition and (2) the cooling rate. With a given composition, the microstructure (and hence the mechanical properties) may be altered over a wide range by variations in cooling rate or by post-welding heat treatment. The toughest deposits are made with slow cooling rates or by subsequent normalizing; brittleness is promoted by fast cooling.

Much can be done about improving the quality of welded joints from the mechanical point of view. In this field contributions are possible from both welder and designer. Undercuts, incomplete penetration, slag inclusions, weld cracks, underbead cracks, and gas holes are examples of notches introduced by the welder. The engineer may contribute to the hazard by designing joints that cannot be welded with 100 per cent penetration, by specifying improper electrodes or procedures, by failing to specify the type of electrode to be used, or by not requiring the removal of surface contaminants. Alleviation of the brittle fracture problem is possible only through the intelligent cooperation of all persons involved. One unwitting or unwilling worker can undo all of the creative efforts of the remainder of the team. It is not possible to ensure against brittle behavior merely by the writing of specifications. Judgment in design and selection of materials combined with diligence in supervision must be relied upon.

RESIDUAL STRESSES

It is a well known fact that welding introduces residual stresses in a structure. Whether or not such stresses can or do contribute to brittle behavior of large structures is still a subject for debate. There is no doubt, however, that welding stresses are troublesome. Even when cracking does not occur, distortion caused by welding stresses is often a major problem of construction. Warping can be so severe in certain cases that the proper fitting of parts is impossible. The causes of distortion and methods for controlling it can best be understood after the origin and nature of welding stresses have become clear.

Welding stresses are not caused solely by the freezing and shrinkage of the weld metal, as is sometimes believed. As a matter of fact, stresses of the same nature and magnitude can be introduced into a plate or structure without any welding at all. For example, it is possible to generate radial tensile stresses in a flat plate by merely torch heating a spot in the center to 700 F. Local heating of a spot on a large plate causes the metal to expand. Only the heated spot tends to expand, however, when the surrounding metal remains cool. The heated spot tends to become larger but cannot expand freely in the plane of the plate because the surrounding cool metal resists this action. This restraint to expansion causes biaxial compression stresses to develop in the heated volume; the hotter the spot, the higher the stress level. At a sufficiently high temperature the stress reaches the yield point of the steel, and the metal begins to flow plastically. Flow can take place in one direction only, that perpendicular to the plane of the plate, because there is no restraint in this direction. This causes a thickening or upsetting in the heated region. When the plate has cooled and again resumes a condition of uniform temperature, the upset spot remains permanently thicker. Since the volume remains unchanged, a shortening must have occurred in all directions in the plane of the plate. The upset region must, therefore, be stretched elastically in all radial directions in order to maintain continuity. Thus radial tensile stresses result from local heating. Similar upsetting during welding is a primary cause of welding stresses.

As a second example, the effect of locally heating one edge of a thick wide plate will be considered. Again heating to about 700 F with an acetylene torch can be employed to introduce "welding stresses" without any metal fusion. The heating must be rapid, however, because large temperature gradients are required for the generation of residual stresses. When a large torch is moved along the edge of a plate, the metal in the heated region expands. Again, since only a small volume is hot at any time, the expansion of the heated material is restrained along the edge. Expansion or plastic flow can occur in either of the two unrestrained directions normal to the edge, and so upsetting occurs whenever temperatures are high enough to induce compressive yielding. If the heating is done progressively along the plate edge from one end to the other, the material along this entire length will become thicker. After cooling, the upset edge will be too short to conform to the longer adjacent portion of the plate. The longer longitudinal elements remain attached to the shorter upset edge and thus prevent free contraction to an unstressed length. Thus residual tensile stresses are induced along a plate edge by local heating. A tension zone thus generated is not necessarily narrow; it may extend into the plate for several inches.

A longitudinal butt weld joining two large flat plates has associated with it a residual stress pattern of the type shown in Fig. 1.6. The tension zone of the longitudinal stress, i.e., the one acting in the direction of the weld, extends into the plate for a distance equal to several times the width of the weld. Beyond this region the stress becomes compressive, with a maximum value somewhere around one-fifth of the yield strength. The maximum value of the residual tensile stress is the yield strength of the metal. This is generally about 40,000 psi for the weld zone of mild steel but sometimes reaches values as high as 60,000 psi.

The stress acting transverse to the direction of the weld is generally rather small in unrestrained plates but may reach relatively high values, even up to the yield strength, when a plate is welded into a rigid structure. In unrestrained plates there is relatively little constraint in the transverse direction, and hence the induced stress is generally only about 5000 psi.

The limited constraint present is provided by the portion already welded, which is insufficient to produce yield point stress. Near the ends of the plate the transverse stress becomes compressive because of end effects.

The vital question is—Can such stresses cause or contribute to brittle failure? There is little doubt that certain classifications of welding stresses can and do cause fracture; about other types of stresses there is some uncertainty. There is one welded assembly that can be expected to crack regularly. Frequently it is convenient for accessibility to cut door- or window-like openings in bulkheads or walls of large welded structures. To complete the structure, a tight-fitting plate is welded in the opening. Stresses introduced by the welding frequently cause cracks to form. In fact, it is very difficult to prevent cracking

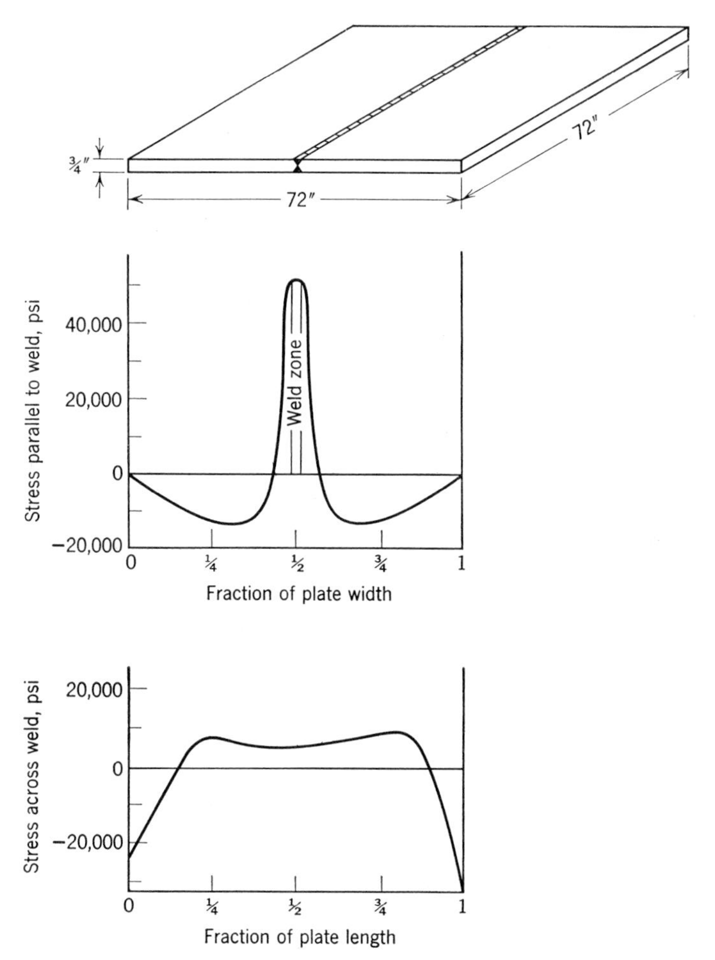

Fig. 1.6 Sketch of butt welded steel plate and typical residual stress patterns found in this kind of weldment.

when openings of this type are welded shut. Such stresses are somewhat different from those generated in unrestrained butt welded plates; they have been called "reaction stresses" to distinguish them from the unrestrained butt weld type, which are called "residual stresses." These terms are arbitrary and are not universally agreed upon but serve the useful purpose of distinguishing stresses extending over relatively long distances from those of shorter extent. Reaction stresses can be relaxed by separating two parts of a structure by a single cut, whereas residual stresses cannot. For example, if a plate in an opening is welded at the top and bottom but not at the sides, stresses are developed in the vertical direction that may be as high as the yield point. The stress will be uniform along the entire length of the panel because each cross section will have to carry the same load as that carried by the neighboring sections. The panel will be loaded like a tension member in a truss. A single cut (or crack) across the panel will relax the stress throughout its entire length. A crack in a 6-ft long panel subjected to yield point stress could open 0.072 in. from the stress relaxation alone.

Examination of the behavior of unrestrained plates joined by a longitudinal weld, in which the longitudinal stress is equal to the yield point value, reveals that when a 6-ft long panel is cut across at the midlength the crack will open less than 0.007 in. This radical difference in behavior is a consequence of the fact that stresses in a butt weld are relaxed for only a short distance back from the cut. Within 9 in. the stress again builds up to the maximum value. The reason for this is that the tension zone is directly attached to the nearby compression zone in the butt welded plate and hence cannot contract freely; this is not so in the panel.

Residual welding stresses may be relieved by two basic methods—one thermal, the other mechanical. Thermal stress relief of steel consists in heating the welded assembly to 1100–1200 F, holding for a few hours, and cooling rather slowly. At this temperature mild steel cannot sustain high stresses, and hence the stress relaxes by creep or flow of the metal. This is a very effective means for removing welding stresses and is in common use. One of the biggest assets of thermal stress relieving, however, is the beneficial tempering of the weld- and heat-affected zone. The less ductile metal in these regions is toughened by the treatment because of favorable alterations in the microstructure produced by the exposure to high temperature. It is easy to show that the greater part of the improvement produced by thermal stress relieving is due to the metallurgical changes and not to the relaxation of welding stresses. This distinction can be demonstrated by relaxing the stress mechanically, which does not alter the microstructure, and comparing the results obtained with the two stress relieving processes.

Mechanical stress relieving is accomplished by stretching plastically the regions containing tension stresses until they are increased enough in length to compensate for the shortness responsible for the tension stress. There are several ways in which this can be done. Circumferential seams in a pressure vessel can be stretched with internal pressure. A longitudinal butt weld in a simple plate can be loaded in a tensile machine until the weld zone is elongated enough to correspond to the length of the adjacent regions. After unloading there can be no stress because of the length equality of all elements. A structure such as a ship, which can neither be loaded hydraulically nor stretched in a machine, can be stress relieved by a recently developed process called "low temperature stress relieving." It consists in heating two bands adjacent to and parallel with the weld to a controlled low temperature, e.g., 350 F, while keeping the weld zone cool. The heated zone expands, pulling with it the tension zone. The tension zone, being at its yield stress, flows plastically, thereby becoming longer. After the temperature returns to normal, the stress will be relaxed because of the stretching.

DESIGN

The design of a welded structure is somewhat more critical than the design of an equivalent riveted unit. This is not true from the standpoint of determining section sizes nor from the viewpoint of assembly—if anything these procedures are easier when welding is used. The difference is that a riveted structure made of mild steel designed to operate at a stress of 17,000 psi can be expected to perform satisfactorily at this stress level for years. Not so with improperly designed or poorly constructed welded structures. The T-2 tanker shown in Fig. 1.1 had a tensile stress in the deck of less than 10,000 psi calculated from the load at the time she broke in two, and she was designed to carry considerably higher load stresses. A number of welded bridges which have fractured and fallen would probably not have done so if they had been riveted. Long welded pipelines have failed in a brittle manner because of defects introduced during manufacture or installation.

The design of welded structures involves more than designing to a working stress of about one half of the yield strength of the material employed. The conventional factors of safety obviously cannot be used directly in the design of welded structures; something more must be considered. How can the structure be safeguarded against brittle fracture? Unfortunately, there is no simple number like a factor of safety that can be employed for this purpose. Out of a large number of structures built alike, a certain few fail while the vast majority do not. For example, out of hundreds of thousands of welded joints in a long pipeline, only a very small percentage fail. But small as the fraction is, it represents an enormous expense to the builder and to the operator. The difference between successful performance and failure is evidently small. It is conceivable that with small changes in material or welding practice, most of the troublesome fractures could be avoided.

Laboratory tests have been made on a variety of structures in which design details have been varied to determine the influence of such changes on the strength and brittle behavior of welded structures. As a result of these tests, which incidentally were very costly, it has been possible to establish the advantage of certain design details. For example, the easiest and cheapest way to join three mutually perpendicular plates to make an opening like a hatch opening in a ship is to butt the square edges together and weld them. This is commonly done, but it has the great disadvantage of making the junction very rigid. Under such conditions plastic flow is inhibited, and brittle behavior becomes more probable. A small but significant percentage of structures with such openings made with structural carbon steel may fail in a brittle manner at normal temperatures when stressed in the neighborhood of 20,000 psi. Ductility can be introduced and the load carrying capacity more than doubled if the design is altered so that square corners are avoided. One of the best ways of doing this is to use a section in the corner which has been preformed to have curvature in each of the three perpendicular planes. It may be helpful in visualizing this construction to think of the flared end of a horn.

One of the basic features of design to obviate brittle fractures is to *avoid rigid connections whenever possible*. Even the addition of reinforcing pads welded onto pressure vessels or tanks to "strengthen" the structure at the place where a pipe is joined may promote brittle behavior because of the increased rigidity thereby introduced.

The big question of how to obtain a quantitative measure of the relative brittleness of materials that can be used as a design criterion remains to be answered. It has been found that the plates in ships in which the fractures started had, with few exceptions, a V-notch Charpy impact value of less than 10 ft-lb at the temperature of failure. A crack once started, however, could continue to propagate through plates having higher Charpy values; apparently, cracks can continue to propagate in plates subjected to normal service stresses even when the V-notch Charpy value at the failure temperature is as high as 20 ft-lb. These figures are quoted only as examples; there are many factors that must be considered in the selection of materials and procedures. Not the least of these is the fact that if a very restrictive Charpy impact specification were imposed, it might be impossible to obtain the quantity of steel needed for large construction projects. Even if such steel were available in sufficient quantities, satisfactory service performance would still not be assured if factors such as damage caused by arc strikes, improper welding, and poor fits were not carefully controlled. The added precautions of proper selection of electrodes and welding procedures, combined with intelligent design for welding, are essential for preventing brittle failures. The fact that steels having very low Charpy values remain ductile to −100 F if no structural discontinuities are present emphasizes the need for good design and quality control.

CHAPTER II

Elementary Concepts of Fracture

Fracture is the separation of a continuous body into two or more parts, such separation being induced by the presence of a stress. This phenomenon is an everyday occurrence and should, it seems, be well understood; however, this is not so. The physical laws that govern fracture are still among nature's well guarded secrets, but this lack of knowledge does not imply complete ignorance of the subject. Experimenters for many years have been collecting data about fracture, with the result that a great deal is known about this type of failure.* Experimental data are numerous, and, although sometimes seemingly inconsistent, they can be resolved into a rather simple pattern. It is the objective of this chapter to present the important concepts of fracture, illustrated with appropriate experimental results, and to develop a consistent picture of fracture.

TERMINOLOGY

The literature has been somewhat confused by the use of conflicting and ambiguous terminology. For example, brittle fracture of mild steel has been described by different investigators as brittle, cleavage, crystalline, or granular; ductile fracture has been described by such terms as ductile, silky, shear, or fibrous. Since it is essential that the

* The terms "fracture" and "failure" will be used interchangeably throughout the remainder of this chapter even though the two words are not strictly synonymous, fracture being but one type of failure.

meanings of such terms be clearly understood, the significance of each will be discussed in some detail.

It should be noted in the beginning that only three basic types of fracture have been observed. Two of these traverse the grains of a polycrystalline aggregate; the third follows the grain boundaries. The path of fracture at ordinary temperatures is normally through the crystals rather than around them. Hence, the grain boundary type can be discussed briefly and dismissed from further consideration. Grain boundary separation is characteristic of the behavior of materials subjected to prolonged loading at elevated temperatures. A very special type of intercrystalline failure does occur in steel at ordinary temperatures under the simultaneous action of stress and of certain corrosive agents. This phenomenon, called caustic embrittlement, is not responsible for the low temperature brittleness of steel as discussed in this book and therefore will not be discussed further. Another type of intercrystalline separation has also been observed in certain steels. Such failure is probably not actually of grain boundary type because it appears to go through or adjacent to a brittle phase formed at the grain boundaries by certain heat treatments. This seems to occur in some temper embrittled low alloy steels, but since such embrittlement does not occur in structural carbon steel, it will not be considered herein.

Only two modes of fracture are of importance to the present discussion; the fracture in both passes through the crystals. These are the *shear* and *cleavage* modes. The crystallographic nature of these failures can best be described with reference to the crystal structure of iron. Fig. 2.1 shows the unit cell of the body centered cubic

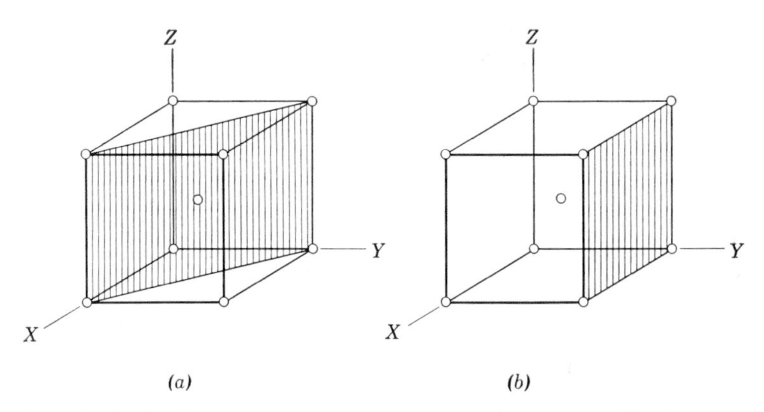

Fig. 2.1 Sketch of unit cell of body centered cubic iron showing (a) (110) slip plane, (b) (010) cleavage plane.

lattice, consisting of an atom located at each corner of the cube and another at its center. It is well known that slip, or plastic flow, takes place by the shearing of certain crystallographic planes over one another. The important feature of slip is that translation always occurs in the direction having the minimum interatomic distance and usually on the planes having the greatest atomic density. There are three known types of slip planes in iron, all having common slip directions —the cube diagonals. These planes are described by the symbolic designations of the Miller indices * as the {110}, the {112,} and the {123} planes. One of the {110} planes, the (110) plane, is shown in Fig. 2.1(*a*). There are, of course, five other planes of the {110} type as well as several other planes of the {112} and {123} types, which are all potential slip planes in the body centered cubic lattice.

Shear type fractures are promoted by the action of shear stresses and may be compared to the separation of cards in a deck when one part of the deck slides over the other until the translation separates the deck into two stacks. This type of fracture occurs on slip or shear planes, e.g., the (110) plane shown in Fig. 2.1(*a*).

The cleavage mode of fracture, on the other hand, is caused by normal (tensile) stresses and is typified by the fracture of mica when sheets are peeled apart. This type occurs in iron on a different set of crystallographic planes, the {100} family, of which the (010) plane is shown in Fig. 2.1(*b*). A great deal more remains to be said about these two types of fracture. The important fact, however, is that the two types do occur; and since different crystallographic planes are involved, the nature of individual fractures can be determined by metallographic examination.

The two basic types of separation produce fractures that differ radically in appearance (see Figs. 2.2(*a*) and 2.2(*b*)). Occasionally different parts of the same piece of steel fail in different ways, resulting in a fracture with a mixed appearance. The part failing by shear appears *gray and silky,* whereas the part failing by cleavage appears *bright and granular.* An example of this mixed type of fracture is shown

* The Miller indices are universally used as a system of notation for the faces of a crystal and for the planes within a crystal or a space lattice. They specify orientation without giving the position in space. Miller indices are based on intercepts of a plane with the three crystal axes. The intercepts are measured in terms of the unit cell dimensions. Miller indices are determined as follows: (1) Find intercepts on three axes, (2) Take reciprocals of these numbers, (3) Reduce to three smallest integers having same ratio, (4) Enclose in parentheses, e.g., (100). Parentheses indicate a single plane or set of parallel planes. Braces signify all equivalent planes, e.g., $\{100\} = (100) + (010) + (001) + (\bar{1}00) + (0\bar{1}0) + (00\bar{1})$, where the dash above the number indicates a minus number.

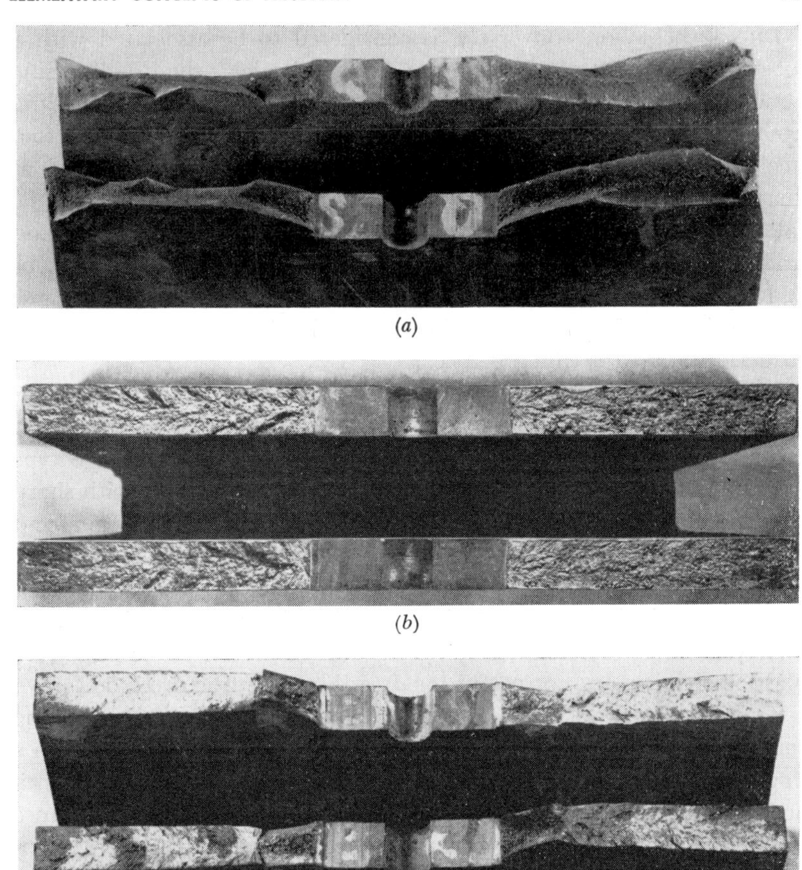

(a)

(b)

(c)

Fig. 2.2 Photographs of fractured steel specimens showing the fracture appearance for the following modes of fracture: (a) Shear, (b) cleavage, (c) mixed shear and cleavage.

in Fig. 2.2(*c*). As mentioned previously, cleavage type fractures have been called cleavage, brittle, crystalline, or granular, and shear type fractures have been described as shear, ductile, silky, or fibrous. Certain of these words, however, have come to have specific meanings and hence should be reserved for the use intended. For example, brittle behavior literally means that separation occurred without plastic flow. This extreme condition, which rarely if ever occurs with steel, is, nevertheless, closely approached. But even with the most brittle specimens, small amounts of plastic flow have been detected at the fracture surface by means of X-ray diffraction.

Ductile behavior, conversely, is considered to be associated with a substantial amount of plastic flow. Obviously then, the dividing line between ductile and brittle behavior is an arbitrary one, depending upon the judgment of the observer. For example, a hardened tool steel that elongated 2 per cent before fracture would be classed as ductile, whereas the same behavior in annealed mild steel would be called brittle. Since there is no fixed boundary between ductile and brittle behavior, there is always room for differences in opinion, or at least for a discussion between two observers examining the same fractured part. In general, a specimen having less than a few per cent reduction in area is called brittle.

While *the crystallographic mode of fracture,* i.e., cleavage or shear, is specific in meaning, the terms "brittle" and "ductile" are not. A shear type fracture may appear to be brittle, while a cleavage type fracture may be ductile. For example, cylindrical test bars with sharp deep notches may not change dimensions by more than a per cent or so when broken, yet the fracture might be by the shear mode. Also, many fractures occurring by cleavage are preceded by large amounts of plastic flow, and these must, therefore, be classed as ductile. Thus it may be seen that the terms describing the degree of ductility, or plastic behavior, are not useful for describing the fracture mode.

The fracture appearance naturally varies somewhat with testing conditions, particularly when the two modes of fracture are mixed in a single surface. Nevertheless, only two basic types have been identified, and the use of a multiplicity of terms to describe the appearance of fracture surfaces is somewhat confusing. Consequently, *the appearance of fracture* will generally be described by the two terms "fibrous" and "granular." Other terms used in the literature for this purpose sometimes offer the advantage of increased clarity and hence will find occasional use.

The following table proposed by Low and used by Gensamer [1] summarizes the terms commonly used in connection with discussions of fractures.

Behavior Described	Terms Used	
Crystallographic mode	Shear	Cleavage
Appearance of fracture	Fibrous	Granular
Energy or strain to fracture	Ductile	Brittle

Granular appearance is associated with cleavage fractures, and fibrous appearance is characteristic of shear. However, fractures are frequently mixed, showing varying amounts of fibrous and granular fracture. The appearance of the fracture does not necessarily reveal the exact percentage of shear or cleavage; this can be determined accurately only by a tedious metallographic examination; therefore, "per cent fibrous" appearance is commonly reported instead of per cent shear mode when behavior is being evaluated by the appearance of the fracture surfaces.

It is important to consider the conditions that favor the occurrence of each fracture type. These conditions have been studied in great detail and therefore can be described rather specifically. Of major importance for a given material are the state of stress and the temperature. Other factors, such as strain rate and strain history, are important and must also be considered. Unfortunately, fracture is a complex phenomenon and cannot be described in a quantitative manner by a simple "law." However, a rather good qualitatively correct picture of fracture has been developed, and it is the purpose of this chapter to present in as simple a manner as possible the concepts involved. A more advanced treatment is available in Chapter III.

PLASTIC FLOW AND FRACTURE UNDER UNIAXIAL LOADING

The plastic flow and fracture properties of metals are normally evaluated by the ordinary tension test.[2] The utility of this test lies in its simplicity and in the reproducibility of the results obtained. It is an accurate means for determining the flow characteristic of metals, particularly in the region of uniform strain. After the ultimate load is reached and further strain becomes concentrated in the local region of the neck, the condition of stress is no longer that of simple tension. Necking introduces a component of triaxial tensile stress which is superimposed on the average longitudinal stress. This will be discussed in detail later, but it should be borne in mind that the fracture stress is in reality something different from the load at failure divided by the final cross sectional area. This discrepancy is probably the simplest of the many complications that make fracture characteristics difficult to evaluate quantitatively. In the preliminary treatment of the fracture problem, such complications will be ignored. A discussion of the effect of the triaxial stress component will be reserved for the later section.

The applicability of the tension test to the present problem can be appreciated if the analysis of this test is followed. A sketch showing a typical engineering stress-strain curve, or load-elongation curve, for a mild steel is presented in Fig. 2.3. The stresses are calculated from the axial load and original cross sectional area, as indicated by equation (1) below, and the strains are calculated from the length at any stress and the original gage length as defined by equation (2).

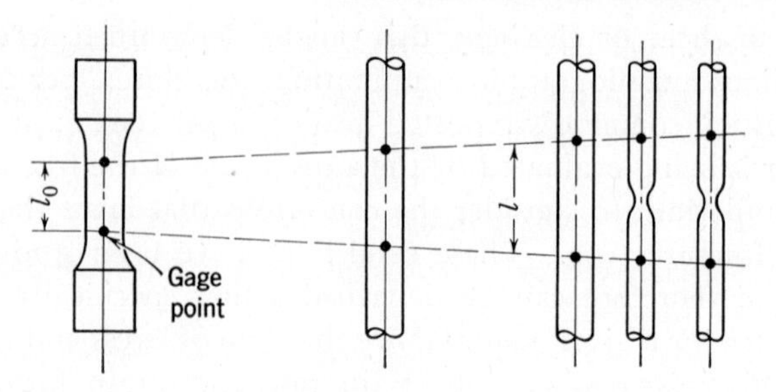

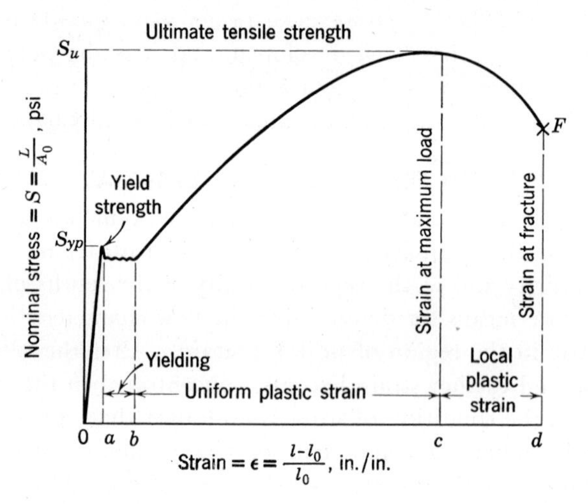

Fig. 2.3 Typical engineering stress-strain curve for mild steel.

$$\text{Stress} = S = \frac{L}{A_0} \tag{1}$$

$$\text{Strain} = \epsilon = \frac{l - l_0}{l_0} \tag{2}$$

where L is the load, A_0 is the original cross sectional area, l_0 is the original gage length (frequently 2 in.) and l is the distance between gage marks at any strain. The stress-strain relation is essentially linear up to the yield point stress and follows Hooke's law; i.e., the stress increases in proportion to the strain. Therefore:

$$\frac{S}{\epsilon} = E \tag{3}$$

where E is Young's modulus of elasticity, which is about 30×10^6 psi for steel. Loads below the yield point will produce practically no permanent set when the specimen is unloaded. The small deviations from this ideal behavior are inconsequential for the present study. As the yield point stress of mild steel is reached during loading, the specimen undergoes a permanent extension, usually accompanied by a temporary dropping of the load. Determination of the yield point does not require sensitive gages because of the discontinuity in the stress-strain curve. As the test progresses beyond the yield, the load rises at a decreasing rate until finally a maximum value of load is reached. The stress obtained when this load is divided by the original area is called the ultimate tensile strength of the material. The strain at the ultimate strength is uniform over the entire gage length; the amount is indicated by the letter "c" in Fig. 2.3. This strain is now almost entirely plastic, the elastic part being equal to about one per cent of the total. When the straining is continued beyond the ultimate load, the specimen no longer extends uniformly over its entire length but flows only in a restricted volume. The diameter in this actively straining region continues to decrease, causing a neck to form in the specimen. Eventually the flow process is terminated by the formation of a crack near the specimen axis, which grows progressively until the section separates. The stress at fracture is difficult to measure experimentally because of the rapid dropoff in load that occurs as the fracture strain is approached. Frequently the specimen fails gradually, tearing slowly across the section. Since the fracture usually originates inside rather than at the surface, it is extremely difficult to determine when the crack first forms. Data for the final reduction in area and elongation are obtained by placing the two fracture surfaces in firm contact and measuring the final dimensions of the specimen.

Many materials, e.g., cold-rolled steel, hardened steel, aluminum, copper, and brass, do not exhibit the yield point phenomenon. Hence, the yield condition for these materials must be defined in a different manner. In these cases yielding is defined in an arbitrary way; the "yield strength" is generally determined by drawing a line parallel to the elastic modulus line but intersecting the abscissa at a value of 0.002 strain. The stress corresponding to the intersection of this line with the stress-strain curve is called the 0.2% yield strength. Other values of offset, e.g., 0.005 strain, are sometimes chosen for this determination. Hence, when quoting values it is essential to state the strain offset at which the yield strength was determined.

Returning to the stress-strain curve for mild steel, the strain increment between maximum load and fracture load appears to be a relatively small portion of the total strain. This is misleading because the actual strain occurring in this portion of the test is confined to a very small region, whereas the calculated strain is based upon the original length (e.g., 2 in.). A much better picture of the local strain can be obtained if the deformation is measured over a very short gage length. The effect of using different gage lengths on the recorded value of strain is illustrated in Fig. 2.4. It is evident that the value of strain obtained from a given test after necking begins is highly dependent upon the gage length selected; hence it is essential to use a standard length, such as one of those recommended by ASTM,[3] and to state the gage length employed.

The per cent elongation at fracture, e.g., when measured over a 2-in. initial gage length, is known as the per cent elongation in 2 in.

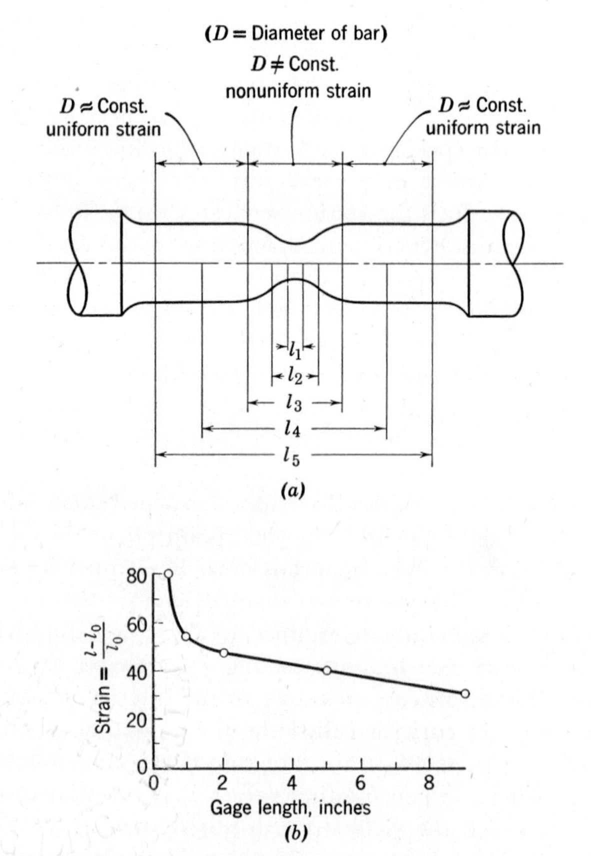

Fig. 2.4 Effect of different gage lengths on recorded value of strain.

This quantity obviously does not represent the maximum ductility that might be achieved if the straining were carried out by a process that did not permit necking, such as rolling, drawing, or extruding. The capacity of a material to undergo strain without fracturing is more truly represented by the strain in a very short gage length at the minimum section of the neck. This strain can be defined in the following manner:

$$\epsilon' = \frac{l - l_0}{l_0} \tag{4}$$

where l_0 and l are infinitesimal gage lengths in the necked portion before and after deformation and ϵ' is the strain over this short gage length. This has been called the "mean strain," but this term is not particularly descriptive. The "zero gage length strain" would be a more definitive description of the quantity under consideration. The use of infinitesimal gage lengths for the actual measurement of elongation is, of course, impractical. Fortunately, however, there is a simple means for determining the zero gage length strain. Inasmuch as the volume of a metal during plastic flow changes only a few hundredths of one per cent, the volume may be assumed to be constant. Hence

$$\left(\frac{l}{l_0}\right)_{l \to 0} = \frac{D_0^2}{D^2} = \frac{A_0}{A} \tag{5}$$

where D_0 is the original diameter and D is the minimum diameter in the necked section after fracture. Correspondingly, A_0 and A are the initial and final cross sectional areas. Then the reduction in area, $R.A.$, becomes

$$R.A. = \frac{A_0 - A}{A_0} \tag{6}$$

and the zero gage length elongation, ϵ', is defined by

$$\epsilon' = \frac{R.A.}{1 - R.A.} \tag{7}$$

As an example, when the reduction in area is 35 per cent, the zero gage length elongation is 54 per cent as compared with an elongation in 2 in. of 24 per cent. It appears that the reduction in area and zero gage length elongation more nearly represent the inherent ductility of a material.

For the purpose of mathematical manipulation, especially for additions of plastic strain, Ludwik [4] in 1909 defined a strain, which has become generally accepted by metallurgists and engineers. This strain, variously known as "natural strain," "true strain," and "logarithmic strain," is defined by

$$\varepsilon = \int_{l_0}^{l} \frac{dl}{l} = \ln \frac{l}{l_0} \tag{8}$$

where ε is the true strain and ln indicates the natural logarithm. Up to the elongation at which necking begins, the strain is uniform, hence l_0 can have any value. After necking begins, however, the infinitesimal gage length at the minimum diameter must be used for calculating values of ε. Up to the maximum load, the true strain and engineering strain are related by

$$\varepsilon = \ln (\epsilon + 1) \tag{9}$$

Similarly, after necking

$$\varepsilon = \ln \frac{A_0}{A} = 2 \ln \frac{D_0}{D} = \ln (\epsilon' + 1) \tag{10}$$

Thus in the example given previously where the reduction in area was 35 per cent, the true strain becomes 43 per cent as compared with 24 per cent for the elongation in 2 in. and 54 per cent for the zero gage length strain. Of these strains, the true strain is most frequently used for theoretical work.

The stress plotted in Fig. 2.3, like the strain, is only a nominal value because the continuously changing cross sectional area has not been taken into account in the stress calculations. The actual or "true stress," σ, on the specimen at any strain is given by

$$\sigma = \frac{P}{A} \tag{11}$$

where P is load and A is the actual area, which, after necking begins, is the minimum area of the neck. Fig. 2.5 shows a typical true-stress true-strain curve for mild steel. It is apparent from this figure that the true strain up to the maximum load is only a small portion of the total true strain. Also, it becomes evident that the stress actually increases continuously with increasing strain. The true-stress true-strain curve is commonly referred to as a flow curve. The use of the word "flow" in connection with a material that does not flow under constant load is somewhat at variance with the usual meaning of the word, which implies a dynamic process. However, for lack of better terms, "flow curve" and "flow stress" have become generally accepted by investigators in the field.

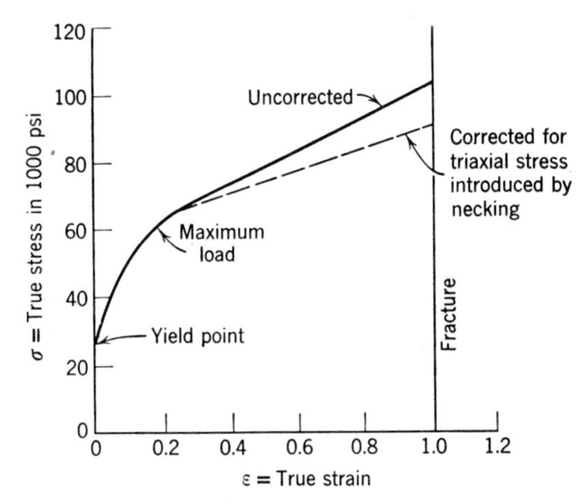

Fig. 2.5 Typical true-stress true-strain curve for mild steel.

Each point on the curve represents a definite state of tensile deformation. If during the test the load is released, the elastic strain will be recovered and the unloading line will be very nearly parallel to the original modulus line. Upon reloading, the tensile specimen behaves elastically as during the original loading. Plastic flow, however, begins at a slightly lower stress than that reached prior to unloading, as illustrated in Fig. 2.6. There is also a slight hysteresis during unloading and loading in addition to the lowering of the flow stress. The reason for the departure from the modulus line has been discussed

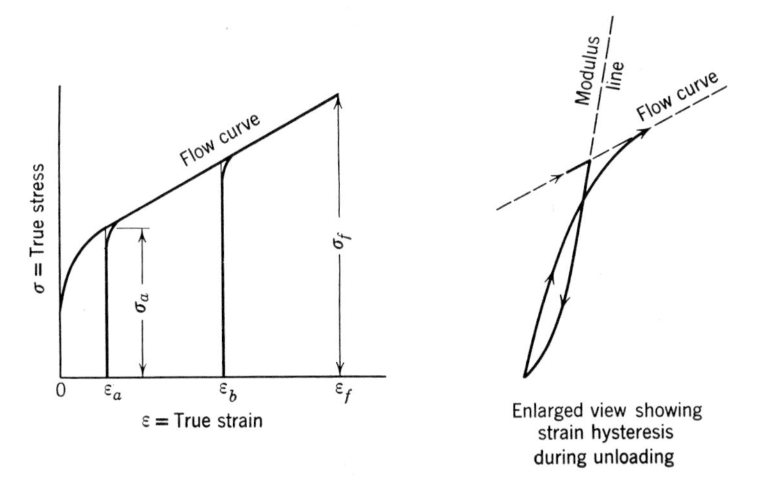

Fig. 2.6 The effect of loading and unloading during tensile testing on the shape of the true-stress true-strain curve.

by Nadai.[5] This nonideal behavior is unimportant in the present study and will not be discussed further here. It will be assumed, therefore, that in an interrupted test the material behaves perfectly elastically during unloading and loading, with flow beginning only after the stress has again reached the maximum value attained before unloading.

From the foregoing discussion, it appears that the flow curve is in reality a locus of state points, each one representing the stress required to cause plastic flow at the corresponding strain. A mild steel specimen strained in tension by the amount ε_a, as indicated in Fig. 2.6, will yield when loaded to a stress σ_a and will fracture at ε_f and σ_f whether unloaded during straining or not.

It is generally believed, as originally suggested by Ludwik,[6] that fracture will occur when the flow stress curve intersects a fracture stress curve. Although this simple concept has some objections that will be discussed later, it does permit a simple treatment and qualitatively correct picture of the fracture phenomenon. From a modified Ludwik concept it is possible to obtain a clear understanding of a wide variety of both laboratory and service failures.

A schematic representation of a fracture stress curve intersecting a flow stress curve is presented in Fig. 2.7. This simple view of fracture is incomplete because it is now known that there are not *one* but *two* fracture curves, one for the shear mode and the other for cleavage. Hence it has been necessary to modify Ludwik's concept by introducing a second fracture curve as shown in Fig. 2.8. In a simple tension test when the cleavage fracture strength curve falls above the shear fracture strength curve, failures will be by the shear mode. Failure by the cleavage mode will occur when the fracture stress curves fall

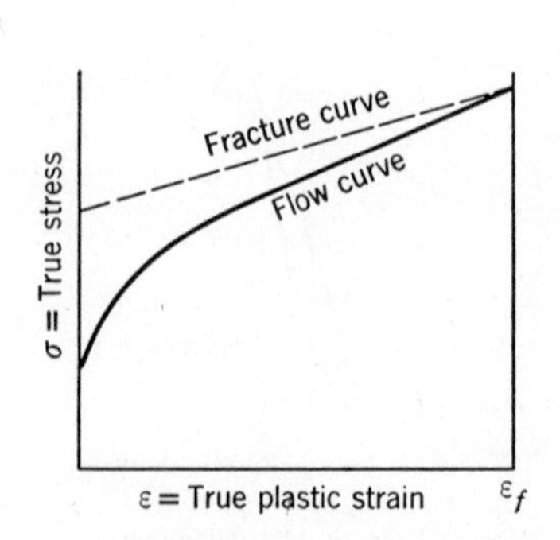

Fig. 2.7 Schematic representation of a fracture stress curve intersecting a flow stress curve.

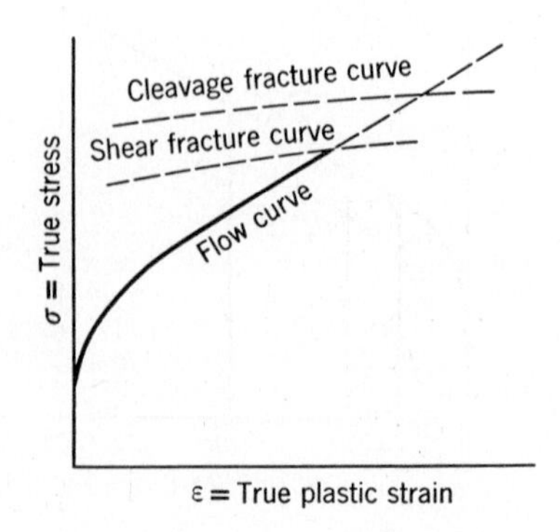

Fig. 2.8 Schematic representation of both cleavage and shear fracture curves intersecting a flow stress curve.

in the reverse order. The relative positions of these two curves depend upon many factors. For example, a hardened steel may have both the flow and the shear fracture stress curves raised relative to the cleavage fracture curve. As an example of an extreme case, when the yield strength of a hardened tool steel equals the cleavage fracture strength, brittle behavior is inevitable.

Several possible cases are illustrated schematically in Fig. 2.9. Sketch (*a*) of this figure shows that the amount of plastic flow prior to shear fracture may be large if the flow curve and the shear fracture stress curve are widely separated in the low strain range; sketch (*b*) reveals that the total strain at shear fracture is low when the flow and fracture curves intersect at a low strain. Similarly, cleavage type fractures may be preceded by a great deal of plastic flow, as indicated

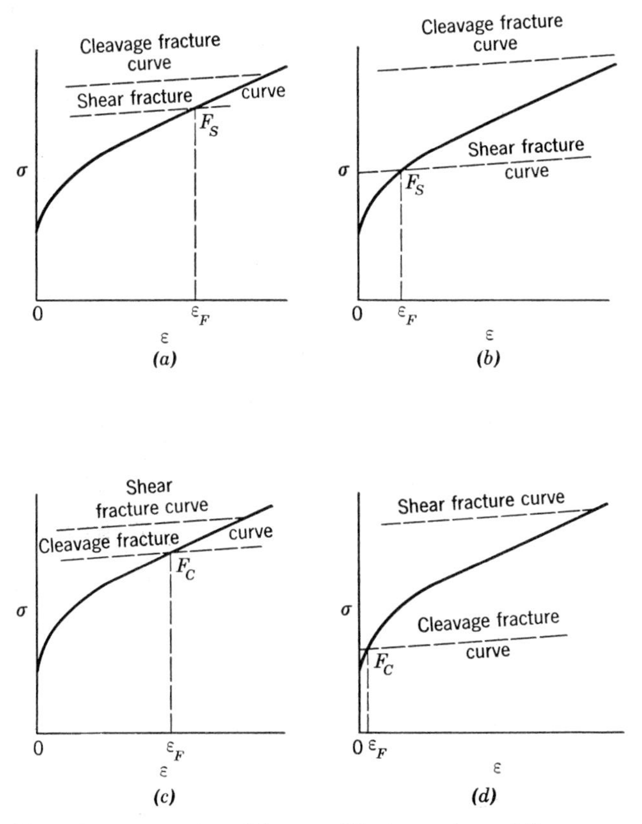

Fig. 2.9 Schematic representation of four possible intersections of flow stress curve with cleavage and shear fracture curves. F_S indicates a shear fracture, and F_C a cleavage fracture.

in (*c*), or they may occur with little or no flow, as shown in (*d*). There are many examples of each kind of failure, not only in steels but in nonmetallic materials as well. For example, concrete cylinders will be brittle when compression loaded, yet the fracture will occur along planes of maximum shear stress. Also, mine openings in hard rock fail along planes of maximum shear stress rather than on planes subjected to the maximum tension. However, under certain conditions, namely, when there is a high component of hydrostatic pressure or a high temperature, marble [7] and even sapphire may be induced to undergo substantial flow without fracturing. Metallic materials fail in all the prescribed ways.

Unfortunately, it is extremely difficult to obtain fracture stress curves experimentally. The cleavage fracture strength curve of most steels can be obtained only at temperatures below that of liquid nitrogen because failures in simple tension tests at higher temperatures are by the shear mode only. This is illustrated by Fig. 2.10, where results obtained on a 1020 steel by Eldin and Collins [8] have been replotted. The cleavage strength is increased substantially by cold work and actually falls above the shear fracture strength curve shown for the higher temperatures in this figure. Values for cleavage at higher temperatures must be obtained by extrapolation.

The slope of the shear-fracture strength vs. strain curve can be determined fairly well at high strains by first rolling or extruding the metal to high equivalent strains and then testing. There is some uncertainty about the shape of the shear fracture curve at low strains,

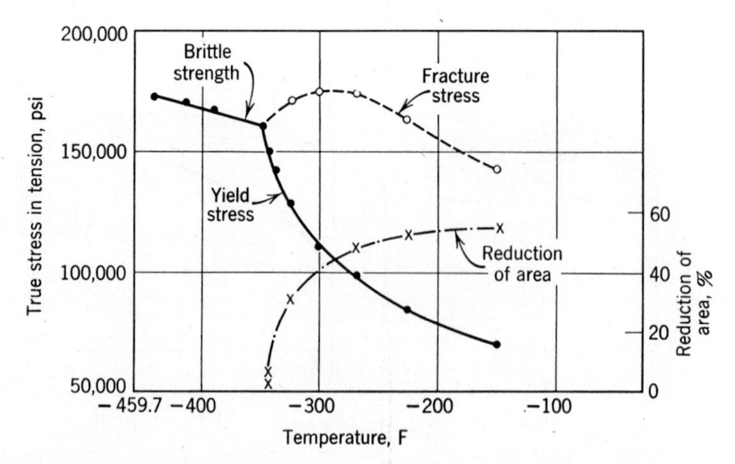

Fig. 2.10 The effect of testing temperature on fracture stress, yield stress, and reduction in area of an SAE 1020 steel. (Data replotted from Eldin and Collins.[8])

however, because there is no direct means for determining its position. The complications involved are discussed in more detail in Chapter III.

INFLUENCE OF STRAIN RATE

The rate of loading has a profound effect upon the properties of structural carbon steel. To illustrate this, results from some work by Manjoine [9] are shown in Figs. 2.11 and 2.12. In the first of these figures, stress-strain curves obtained at strain rates ranging from 9.5×10^{-7} per second to 300 per second are shown. Both the yield

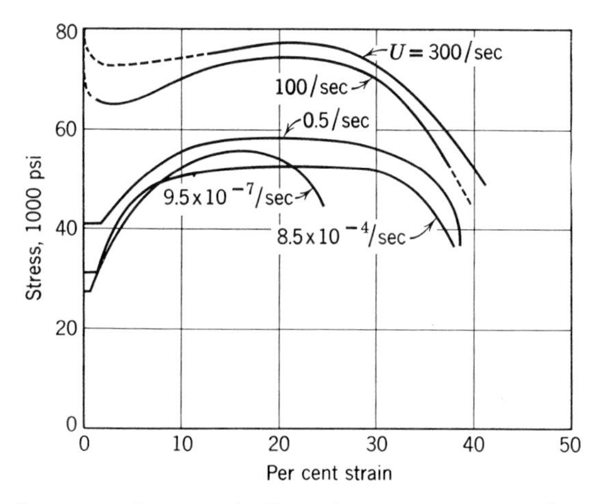

Fig. 2.11 Tensile stress-strain curves of mild steel at room temperature for various rates of strain. (Data from Manjoine.[9])

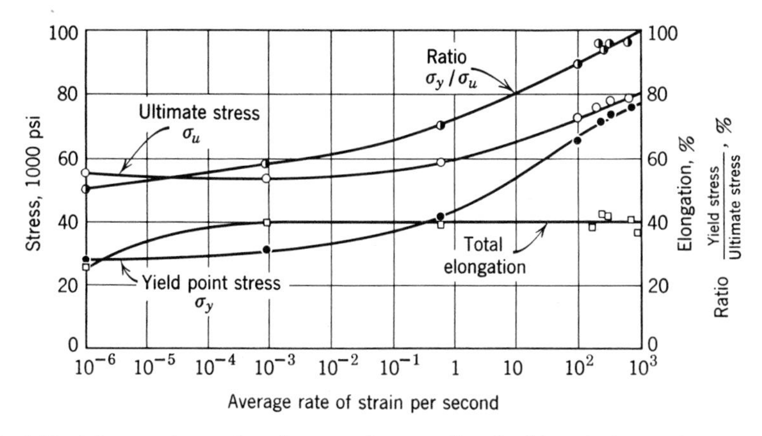

Fig. 2.12 Influence of rate of strain on tensile properties of mild steel at room temperature. (Data from Manjoine.[9])

strength and the ultimate strength are markedly increased, but the yield strength rises at a faster rate. As shown in Fig. 2.12, the ratio of yield strength to ultimate strength is increased from 0.5 to nearly 1.0 when the strain rate is raised from 10^{-6} to 300 per second. The high sensitivity to strain rate is partly responsible for the brittle behavior of steel. Many brittle fractures have been started by impact loading.

The effect of increasing strain rate on the relative positions of the flow and fracture curves is shown schematically in Fig. 2.13. The

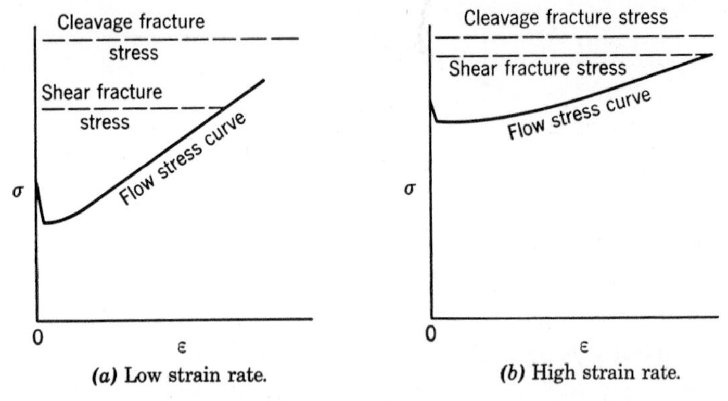

(a) Low strain rate. (b) High strain rate.

Fig. 2.13 Schematic representation of effect of increasing strain rate on the relative positions of flow and fracture curves.

sketch shown as (*a*) of this figure represents the conditions normally associated with low strain rates, and sketch (*b*) represents what appears to happen at high strain rates. The stresses in Figs. 2.11 and 2.12 are nominal stresses based on the original area; those of Fig. 2.13 are true stresses. True strains, rather than values of elongations, are indicated in Fig. 2.13.

Many attempts have been made to establish a "mechanical equation of state" for the plastic flow of metals.[10] If such an equation existed, the stress would be uniquely determined by the strain ε, the strain rate $\dot{\varepsilon}$, and the absolute temperature T, as indicated by equation (12),

$$\sigma = f(\varepsilon, \dot{\varepsilon}, T) \tag{12}$$

Unfortunately, this simple equation is inadequate to define the complex behavior of metal. There are, however, certain relations between strain rate and yield strength and between strain rate and temperature that appear to be valid over quite wide ranges of strain rate.

When the strain rate is increased, both the lower yield point and the flow curve are raised, but the yield point rises at a faster rate. The following expression [11] represents the relation between lower yield point, σ_y, and strain rate, $\dot{\varepsilon}$.

$$\sigma_y = K(\dot{\varepsilon})^n \tag{13}$$

K and n are constants.

The flow stress also increases when the strain rate is increased, but the effect is smaller than for the lower yield strength. The true stress at fracture is also raised by the higher strain rates, but good quantitative data are lacking.

There seems to be an equivalence between strain rate and temperature,[12] at least over certain ranges of temperature and strain rate. This equivalence has been formulated mathematically as follows:

$$\sigma_\varepsilon = f(\dot{\varepsilon}e^{Q/RT}) \tag{14}$$

where σ_ε is the stress at a given strain ε, $\dot{\varepsilon}$ is the strain rate, R is the gas constant, T is the absolute temperature, Q an experimental constant, and e is the base of natural logarithms. The stress required for plastic flow thus depends upon the parameter P

$$P = \dot{\varepsilon}e^{Q/RT} \tag{15}$$

and not upon either the strain rate or the temperature independently. A given stress may thus correspond to a high strain rate at a high temperate or a low strain rate at a low temperature. This relation has been tested over a wide range of temperature but only over a small range of strain rates. The data obtained by Zener and Hollomon [12] confirming the validity of this relation are reproduced in Fig. 2.14.

There is an apparent equivalence between strain rate and temperature below which a steel becomes brittle in a given test. Wittmann and Stepanov [13] performed impact tests on unnotched steel specimens and found that the temperature of brittle behavior was related to the impact velocity as anticipated by equation (15). Their results are reproduced in Fig. 2.15.

In notched specimens the strain rate is higher than for unnotched bars because of the stress (and therefore strain) concentration at the base of the notch. The maximum strain rate at the notch apex is equal to the stress concentration factor multiplied by the strain rate present in an unnotched bar tested in the same manner. This increased strain rate has the effect of raising the temperature below which brittle behavior occurs. The sharper and deeper the notch,

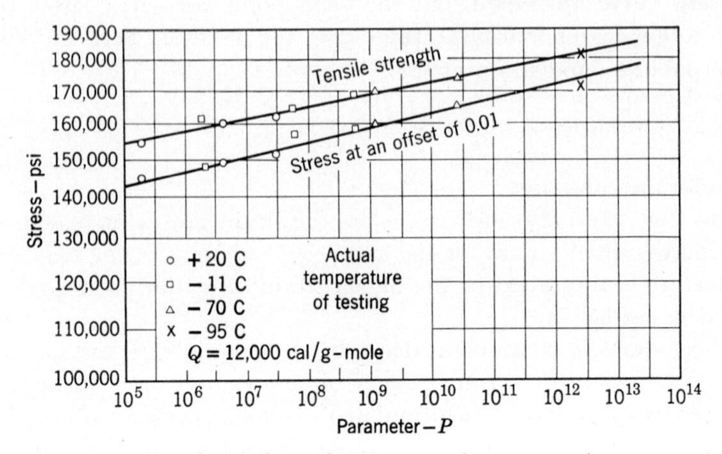

Fig. 2.14 Demonstration of equivalence of strain rate and temperature for a cast steel. The parameter, P, is a function of strain rate and temperature as indicated by the following equation: $P = \dot{\varepsilon}e^{Q/RT}$, where $\dot{\varepsilon}$ is the strain rate, e the base of the natural logarithms, Q is a constant that depends on the steel, R is the gas constant, and T is the absolute temperature.

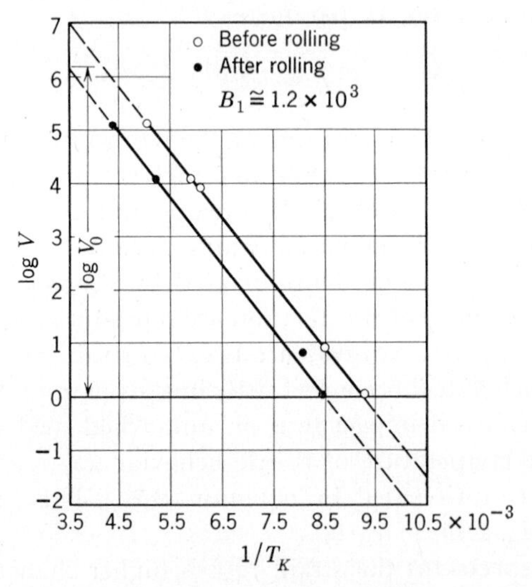

Fig. 2.15 Relationship between ductility-transition temperature T_K and deformation rate (given by the impact velocity V) for a 0.2% carbon steel. The specimens were unnotched bars and were subjected to bending. (Data from Wittmann and Stepanov.[13])

the higher the temperature of brittle behavior due to the strain rate effect (in addition, this temperature is raised because of the change in stress state). There is an enormous difference between the strain rate in a standard tensile test and a notched bar impact test. The strain rate at the notch apex in a V-notch Charpy specimen has been estimated to be [14] about 10^3 per second; this is about ten million times the strain rate used in a tensile test.

INFLUENCE OF TEMPERATURE

It is now appropriate to consider the influence of temperature upon the shape of the flow stress curve and on the nature of the fracture. Fig. 2.16 shows the effect of testing temperature on the properties of a pearlitic steel, as reported by Zener and Hollomon.[12] They found that the flow stress for a given strain increased with decreasing testing temperature. The fracture stress increased also, but the ductility to fracture decreased. The dotted line gives the approximate fracture condition as observed in these tests. (The data shown in Fig. 2.16 do

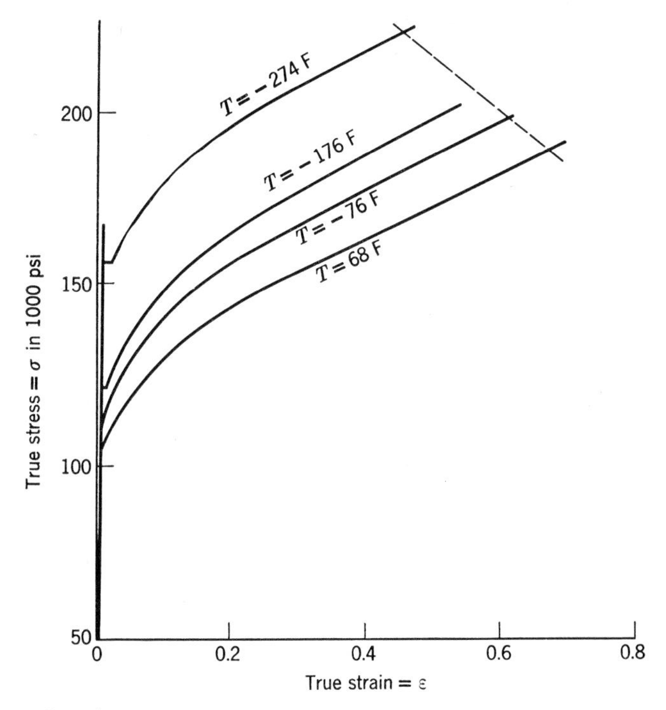

Fig. 2.16 Effect of testing temperature on the tensile properties of a pearlitic steel. (Data from Zener and Hollomon.[12])

not necessarily represent the general case.) Fig. 2.17 shows data for two hot-rolled mild steels; the yield stress and fracture stress (true stress at fracture) are plotted against temperature. The reduction-of-area data have also been plotted for comparison. Note that for both of these steels the shear fracture stress increases continuously with de-

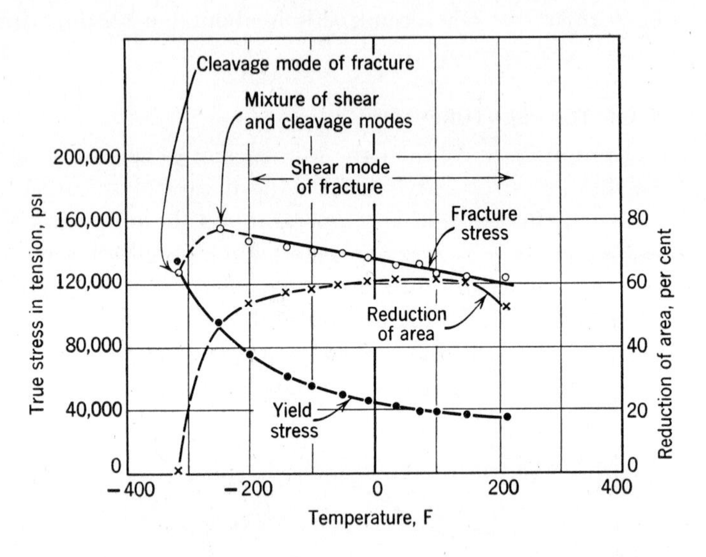

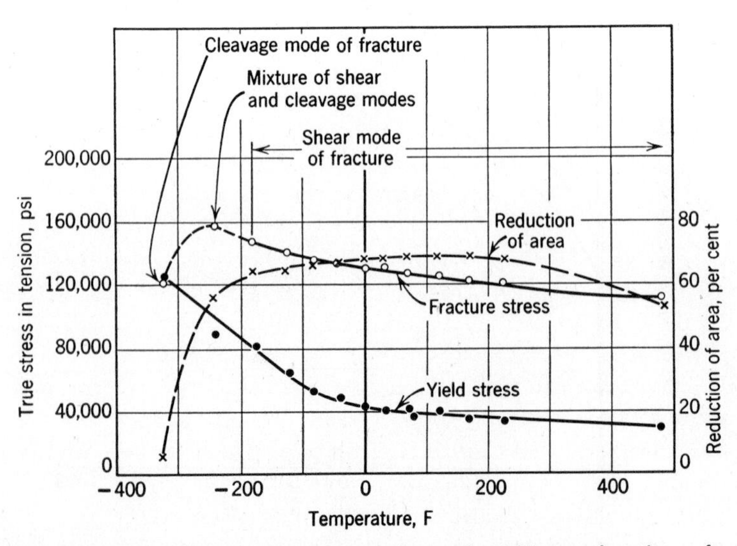

Fig. 2.17 The effect of testing temperature on the tensile yield strength and true fracture stress for two hot-rolled semikilled 0.2% carbon steels.

creasing temperature but the reduction of area (hence natural strain) at fracture remains substantially constant until the mode of failure changes from shear to cleavage. This occurs in the neighborhood of −250 F, which is approximately the transition temperature of these steels for the simple tension test. Examples of the flow and fracture stress curves from which these data were obtained are shown in Fig.

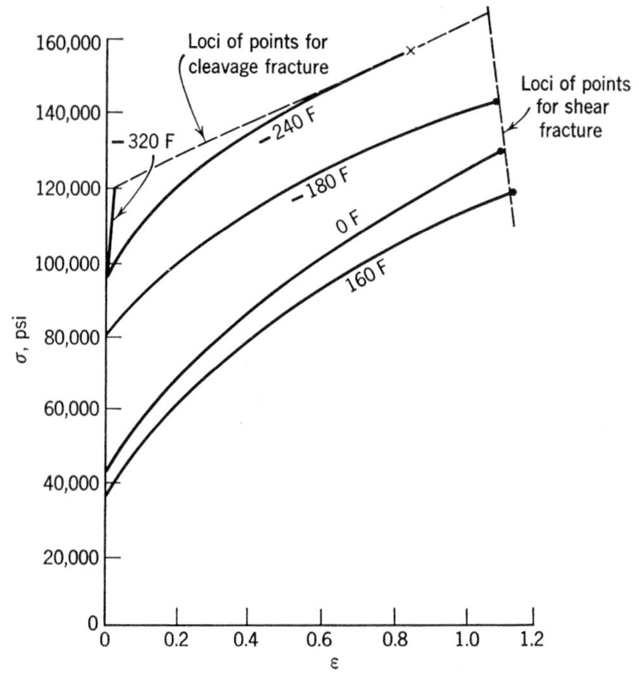

Fig. 2.18 Stress-strain curves at various temperatures showing flow and fracture stresses for a hot-rolled semikilled 0.2% carbon steel.

2.18. The locus of shear fracture points is a vertical line in this case, whereas the locus of cleavage fracture points is a line inclined at a moderate angle to the horizontal. The explanation for the upward slope will be presented later.

The change in the mode of fracture from shear to cleavage may be considered to be caused by the intersection of the flow curve with the cleavage fracture curve. When this happens at a low strain, the energy required to cause fracture is very small. If, however, this happens at a fairly large strain, the energy may be quite high. A representative curve of energy to fracture vs. temperature is shown in Fig. 2.19. The sharp decrease in energy at the transition temperature

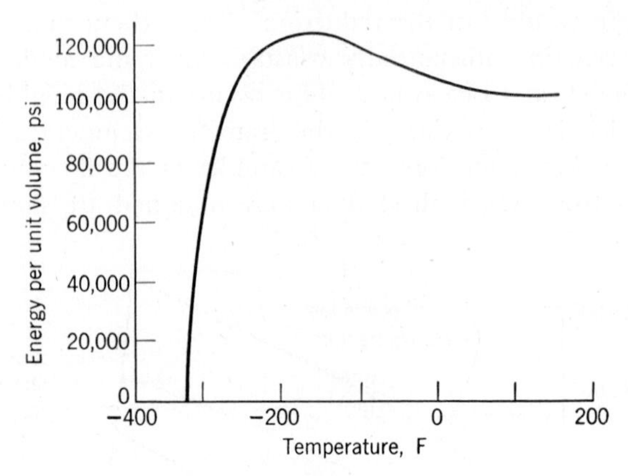

Fig. 2.19 Representative curve of energy absorbed to fracture vs. testing temperature for simple tensile specimens of hot-rolled semikilled 0.2% carbon steel.

occurs because of the relatively low energy associated with brittle behavior.

FLOW AND FRACTURE UNDER COMBINED STRESS

This section is devoted to the concepts of multiaxial or combined stresses and to the influence that such stresses have upon the flow and fracture of steel. Some examples will be drawn from data for nonferrous metals and alloys because of the inadequate experimental evidence available for steel.

A firm grasp of the concepts of combined stresses is essential for the understanding of the effect of multiaxial stress systems upon the brittle behavior of steel. Combined stresses may be analyzed by considering the stresses acting at a point in a solid loaded body. The state of stress for static equilibrium is fully described by the six components thereof, three of which are normal stresses, the other three shear stresses. These components may be referred to any set of coordinate axes whether Cartesian, cylindrical, or a special set that may be more convenient for the problem being considered. Rotation of the reference axes using the point in question as a pivot point will not alter the state of stress, although the equations representing this state will be changed by the rotation. This fact is utilized in rotating rectangular or cylindrical coordinate axes into certain directions along which the shear stresses vanish. Only one position of the coordinate axes will meet this restriction; when this condition is satisfied the axes are called the principal axes. The normal stresses acting parallel to the principal axes are called principal stresses. They are usually identified by the symbols σ_1, σ_2, and σ_3, where the subscripts 1, 2, and 3 often refer to the algebraically largest, intermediate, and smallest stresses, respectively. As will be apparent from symmetry, however, these subscripts can be used interchangeably.

Consideration of principal stresses instead of the more general case of six stress components greatly simplifies the discussion of flow and fracture and hence will be used hereafter. In practice the directions of principal stress are generally known or can easily be determined.

A further advantage of expressing the state of stress at a point in terms of the principal stresses is that the maximum shear stress occurs on a plane making 45° angles with the planes of maximum and minimum normal stresses. The maximum shear stress, τ_{max}, is related to the principal stresses by the following equation:

$$\tau_{max} = \frac{\sigma_1 - \sigma_3}{2} \tag{16}$$

For the case of uniaxial tension, the principal stresses are σ_1, which is the tensile stress, and zero. Hence, the maximum shear stress is always equal to one half of the tensile stress in this simple case. For biaxial stress conditions, e.g., in thin walled spherical or cylindrical pressure vessels, the two tensile stresses are σ_1 and σ_2, with σ_3 being zero (or nearly so). Here again the maximum shear stress is equal to one half of the maximum principal stress. For triaxial stresses, the maximum shear stress is given by equation (16). The great significance of triaxial stresses is that the maximum shear stress approaches zero as the three principal stresses approach equality. Since plastic flow can occur only when shear stresses are present, it is evident that no plastic flow is possible when hydrostatic compression or equal triaxial tension stresses are present. The significance of this was pointed out in Chapter I and is further emphasized in Chapters IV and V. Furthermore, fracture should be impossible in a system subjected to hydrostatic compression because neither shear nor tension stresses would be present to cause fracture. With equal triaxial tension stresses cleavage failure could occur but shear fractures could not. In accordance with these speculations, experimental evidence indicates that, as the principal tensile stresses become more nearly equal, the probability of a brittle cleavage fracture increases. It has also been found that materials subjected to hydrostatic compression loading do not fracture.

Similarly, it may be reasoned that the type of fracture should be substantially unaffected when the stress system is changed from uniaxial to biaxial tension. Again the experimental evidence seems to be in general accord with this prediction, although there are minor deviations from the ideal simple behavior. Biaxial stresses can raise the yield strength of a metal by as much as 15 per cent and may therefore induce brittle behavior at somewhat higher temperatures than those found for the case of simple tension.

An appropriate place to start the discussion of plastic flow under multiaxial stresses is to consider the stress at which flow begins. A number of criteria for yielding have been proposed at various times,[5,15] but only two of them will be considered here. These two are based upon (*a*) the maximum shear stress and (*b*) the maximum shear distortion energy. Tresca introduced the shear stress criterion for plastic flow in 1868; however, it is commonly attributed to Guest, who reintroduced this concept in 1900. According to this criterion, plastic flow will begin when the maximum shear stress reaches a critical value. This criterion can be written symbolically as

$$\tau_{cr} = \frac{\sigma_1 - \sigma_3}{2} = \text{Constant} \tag{17}$$

If σ_{ys} is the yield stress in uniaxial tension, then $2\tau_{cr} = \sigma_{ys}$. Thus the shear stress at which plastic flow begins is one half of the value of the tensile yield stress. The flow condition given by equation (17) can be presented as a surface in a three-dimensional stress system, as shown in Fig. 2.20. This surface is an infinitely long hexagonal prism inclined at equal angles to the three principal stress axes. This surface is known as the maximum shear stress yield surface.

According to Fig. 2.20 if the state of stress were represented by a vector starting at the origin and extending in any direction, the deformation would be entirely elastic if the vector terminated within the prism. Yielding would begin when the vector just reached the surface, and plastic flow would occur for larger vectorial values. It can be seen that as the three principal stresses approach equality the stress vector must become longer in order to pierce the yield surface; for hydrostatic compression or for equal triaxial tension, yielding would not occur even with infinitely large stresses.

Similarly, if shear fracture occurred when the maximum shear stress reached a critical value, there would be an equivalent surface in three-dimensional stress space. An equation like (17) could be used as a criterion for shear fracture.

The surface shown in Fig. 2.20 represents the yield surface for the virgin materials only. After plastic flow has occurred and the metal

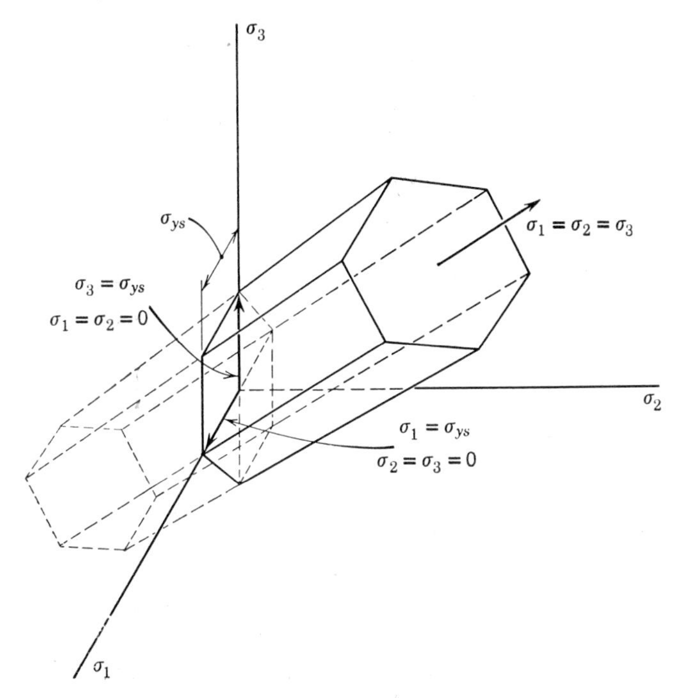

Fig. 2.20 Sketch showing the hexagonal prism in three-dimensional stress space that represents the surface of yielding based on the maximum shear stress criterion.

has work hardened, a new and enlarged envelope represents the new yield surface. Deformation continues until the yield and fracture surfaces finally coincide; then fracture occurs.

Nature, however, apparently does not permit materials to behave in this simple ideal way. Experiments have shown that such a picture is only a rough first approximation to the actual behavior.

Actually, the maximum shear stress "law" for flow and fracture has not been substantiated by experimental evidence. Efforts to obtain more satisfactory criteria have met with success for flow but not for fracture. The von Mises criterion [15] for yielding (also known as the elastic shear distortion energy theory) is in good agreement with experimental results. This theory postulates that plastic flow begins when the shear strain energy reaches a critical value, as indicated below

$$K \approx \sqrt{(\sigma_1 - \sigma_2)^2 + (\sigma_2 - \sigma_3)^2 + (\sigma_1 - \sigma_3)^2} \tag{18}$$

where K is a constant. The same expression has been used in the generalized theory of plasticity by such workers as Nadai [5] and Dorn et al.[16] Each, however, has seen fit to use a different constant of proportionality and to apply a different name to the expression, such as octahedral or effective shear stress. When equation (18) is rewritten in terms of the effective stress it becomes

$$\bar{\sigma} = \sqrt{\frac{(\sigma_1 - \sigma_2)^2 + (\sigma_1 - \sigma_3)^2 + (\sigma_2 - \sigma_3)^2}{2}} = \text{Constant} \qquad (19)$$

Various meanings have been applied to this type of equation, but a very satisfactory interpretation is to consider it as the simplest expression for the root mean square average shear stress. Thus it may be seen that the difference between the two criteria is that equations (18) and (19) average the three maximum shear stresses, whereas equation (17) considers only the largest of the three major shear stresses.

If the uniaxial tension test is analyzed by means of equation (19), it becomes evident that the proportionality constant has been chosen so that $\bar{\sigma} = \sigma_{ys}$ for this simple case. Just as equation (17) described a space surface, the yield condition defined by equation (19) also represents a surface in three-dimensional stress space. If located in relation to its principal stress axes, it is an infinitely long right circular cylinder with its axis at equal angles to the principal stress axes. This cylinder is shown in Fig. 2.21. It would just inscribe the hexagon

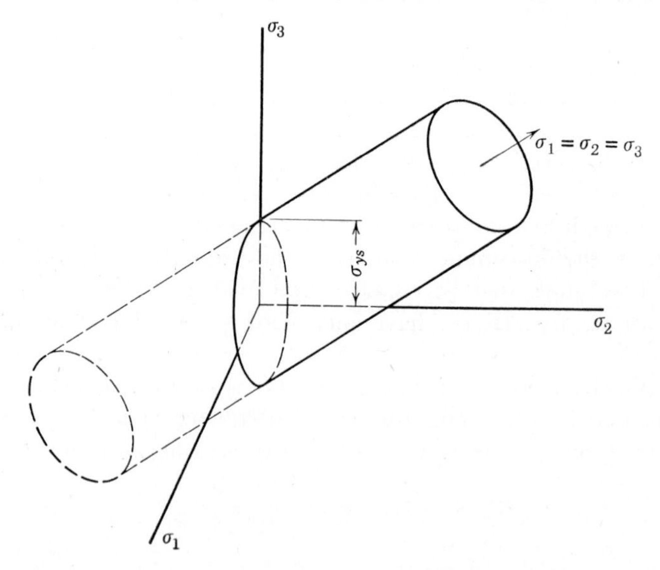

Fig. 2.21 Sketch showing the cylindrical surface in three-dimensional stress space that represents the surface of yielding based on the shear distortion energy criterion.

shown in Fig. 2.20. As was the case with the maximum shear stress surface, the cylinder expands during plastic flow, thereby assuming larger radii as the metal work hardens and the yield is increased. Experiments have shown that equations (18) and (19) define the yield surface quite well.

The equivalent criterion for fracture would imply that shear fracture would occur when the yield surface touched the fracture surface defined by a critical value of shear stress. Unfortunately, the shape of the fracture surface is complex; the exact shape is unknown at present and hence cannot be sketched with the precision of the yield surface. The simple but highly idealized fracture surface can be illustrated by a hexagonal prism similar in shape to that in Fig. 2.20, but with the dimension σ_{ys} replaced by σ_F, representing the fracture stress in simple tension or compression. The shear fracture stress surface is thus an infinitely long hexagonal prism whose axis makes equal angles with the three principal stress axes. This prism surrounds the yield surface.

Fig. 2.22 represents the loci of all points in three-dimensional stress space that would correspond to the state of normal stress required to cause the cleavage mode of fracture. It consists of three perpendicular planes each a unit distance σ_F from the origin along the positive direction of a principal stress axis. This surface terminates at the intersections of these planes but extends an infinite distance in the negative stress directions.

It is somewhat easier to visualize flow and fracture conditions from two-dimensional plots, which are sections through the three-dimensional figures. The simple examples are planes perpendicular to one

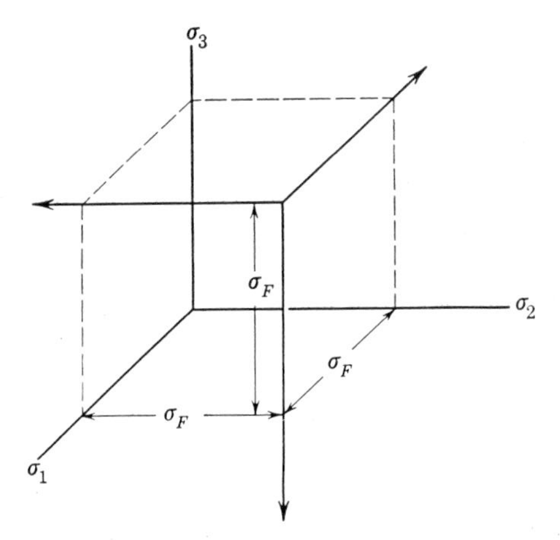

Fig. 2.22 Idealized cleavage fracture surface in three-dimensional stress space.

of the principal stress axes. Such a plane will represent the case where one of the principal stresses is constant and the other two are allowed to vary independently. When this plane passes through the origin, one of the stresses is zero. This is illustrated in Fig. 2.23, in which the intersections of the flow and fracture surfaces with the

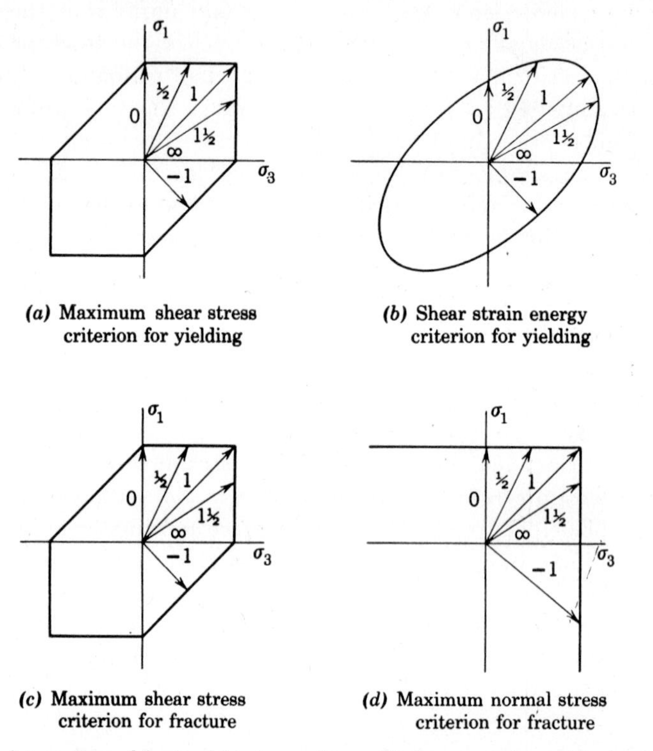

Fig. 2.23 Intersections of flow and fracture surfaces with the σ_1–σ_3 plane. Numbers indicate ratios of σ_3 to σ_1.

σ_1-σ_3 plane are shown. The lines in these plots represent the loci of stress conditions that will cause yielding or fracture. In Figs. 2.23(*a*) and 2.23(*b*) the stress paths for various ratios of biaxial stress ranging from $\sigma_3/\sigma_1 = 0$ to -1 are shown as arrows. Where the arrow touches the yield line, yielding occurs.

A similar case is shown in Figs. 2.23(*c*) and 2.23(*d*) for shear fracture. Note that uniaxial tension is indicated by a ratio of zero or infinity in the first quadrant and that torsion is defined by a ratio of -1. Thus if shear and cleavage fractures require about equal tensile stresses, it would be impossible to distinguish the nature of the fracture from biaxial tests conducted with stress ratios ranging from zero to infinity.

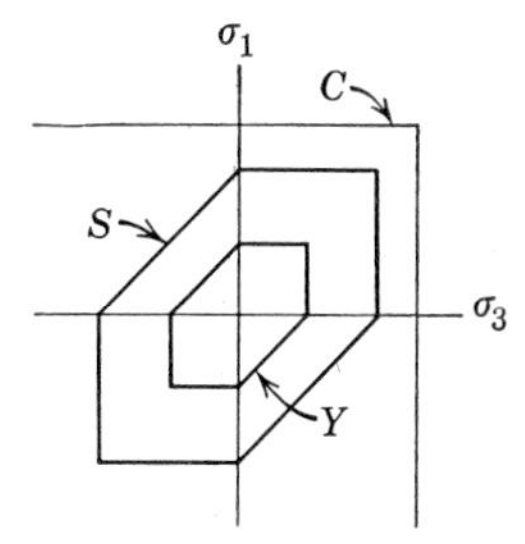

(a) Normal stress for fracture greater than shear stress; yield stress lower than fracture stresses

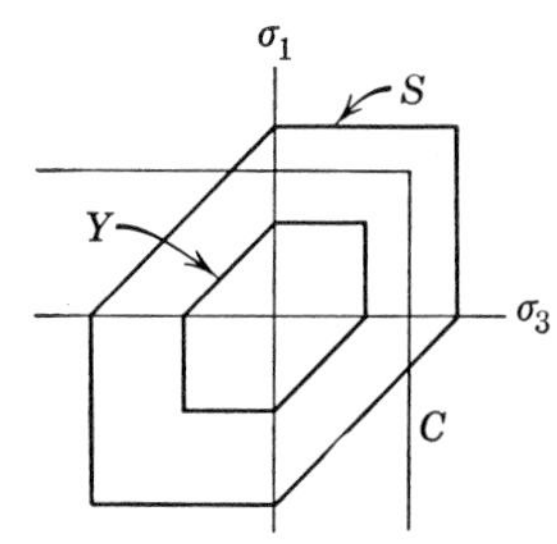

(b) Normal stress for fracture less than shear stress in first quadrant; yield stress lower than fracture stresses

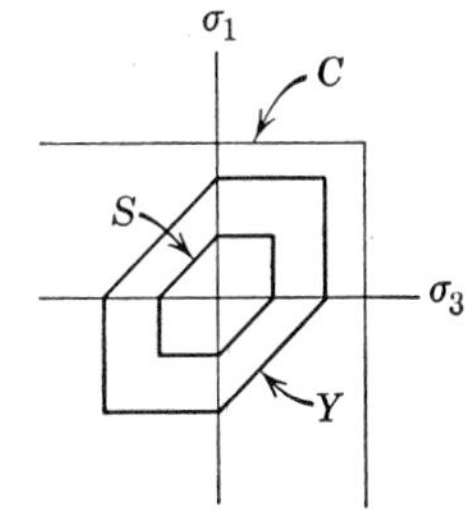

(c) Shear fracture stress below yield and normal fracture stresses

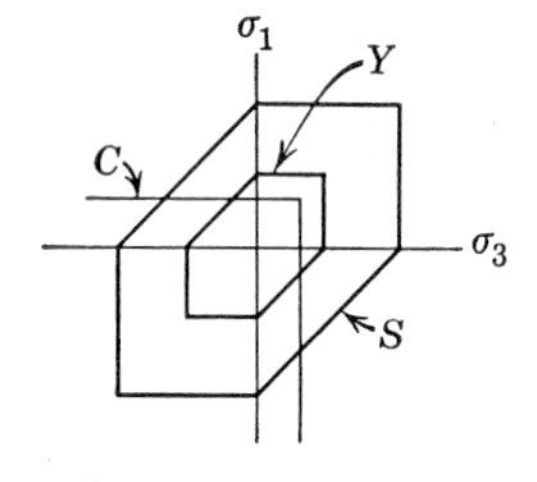

(d) Normal fracture stress below yield and shear fracture stresses in first quadrant

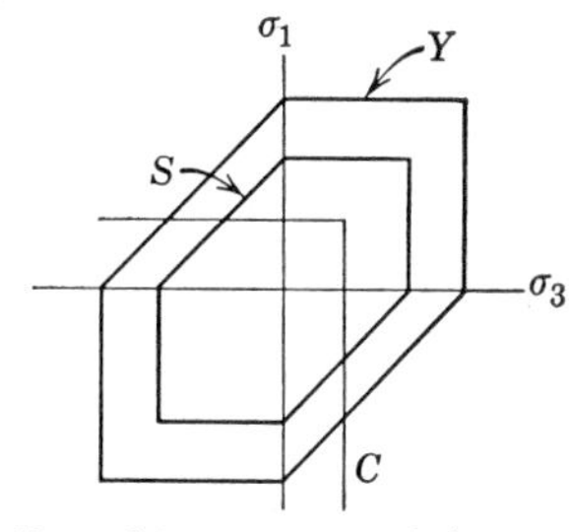

(e) Normal fracture stress below yield stress in first quadrant; shear fracture stress below yield stress

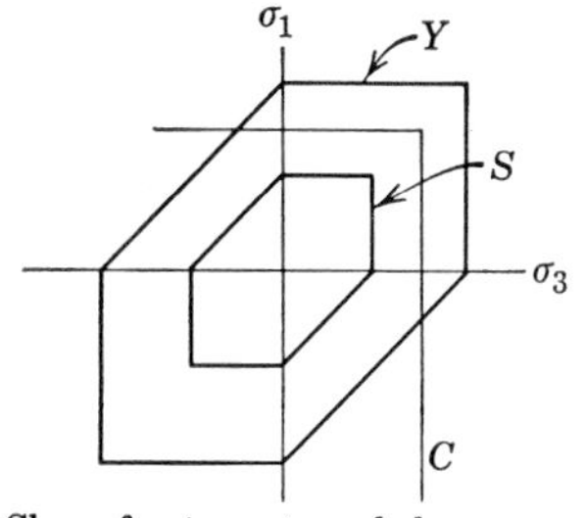

(f) Shear fracture stress below normal fracture and yield stresses

C = Stress for cleavage mode of fracture
S = Stress for shear mode of fracture
Y = Stress for yielding

Fig. 2.24 Composite plots showing possible relative positions of traces of flow and fracture surfaces on the σ_1–σ_3 plane.

A torsion test, however, would be a critical one because the magnitudes of the stresses required for fracture would vary by a factor of 2. The shear strain energy criterion for yielding and the maximum normal stress criterion for fracture are also sketched in the figure.

Fig. 2.24 shows several possible relative positions of traces of yield and fracture surfaces. For simplicity, only the traces dictated by the maximum shear stress criterion for yielding have been shown. There are, of course, six possible arrangements of the three lines, as illustrated in (*a*) through (*f*) of this figure. When the cleavage strength is high relative to the yield stress and shear strength, as is the case for (*a*) and (*c*), only shear fractures can occur under any kind of biaxial stressing. When the shear fracture stress is high relative to the cleavage strength, as shown in (*b*), (*d*), and (*e*), cleavage fractures will occur under biaxial tensile loading. However, for (*b*) the metal will behave in a ductile manner under biaxial tensile loading even though it fails by the cleavage mode; the behavior of materials having properties as shown in figure (*d*) and (*e*) will be brittle under biaxial tension. For torsion loading, however, both (*b*) and (*d*) would exhibit some ductility. Brittle behavior would always be found in the case of (*e*) because the yield surface always falls outside of the shear fracture surface. Both cleavage and shear mode of fractures would be found in this case, depending upon the stress ratio.

Fig. 2.25 illustrates the effect of a third component of stress on the relative positions of the yield and fracture curves. Mild steel at room

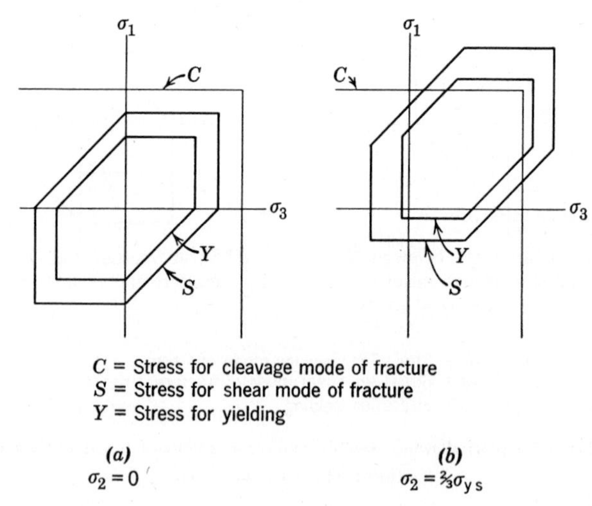

Fig. 2.25 Sketch showing the effect of a third component of stress on the relative positions of the yield and fracture curves.

temperature behaves as indicated by (*a*) in this figure. Note that for uniaxial or biaxial stressing, regardless of the stress ratio, the material would be ductile because the yield lines are always within the fracture lines when $\sigma_2 = 0$. Furthermore, fracture would always be by the shear mode because the shear fracture lines are always within the area enclosed by the normal or cleavage fracture lines. Observe, however, the drastic difference that develops when the third stress component is increased from zero to a value in tension equal to two thirds of the tensile yield strength. This alteration in stress places the normal fracture stress lines within the yield and shear fracture line throughout most of the first quadrant. The main function of a sharp deep notch in promoting brittle cleavage fractures is to alter the stress condition to something like that shown in Fig. 2.25(*b*), where the ratios σ_2/σ_3 and σ_2/σ_1 approach unity.

Chapter III is devoted to discussions of deviations from the idealized fracture behavior of materials, which have just been presented. It is not necessary to master this material to have an adequate grasp of the concepts of brittle behavior of mild steel—the ideal picture is sufficient for a general appreciation of the problem. The more advanced discussion is offered for the benefit of those who wish to acquire a more intimate grasp of the subject.

SUMMARY

Three basic types of fractures have been observed, namely, (1) grain boundary fractures, (2) cleavage fractures across the grains, and (3) shear fractures across the grains. In iron the grain boundary fractures are rare at ordinary or low temperatures and are of little importance in connection with the discussions contained herein. Shear fractures are associated with ductile behavior, and brittle behavior is characterized by the cleavage mode of fracture. Cleavage fractures follow the cube faces of the ferrite crystals; shear fractures do not. Consequently, either of the two modes of fracture can be identified by a microscopic examination. The shear mode of fracture is associated with a gray and silky appearance of the fracture surface, whereas the cleavage mode causes the surface to be bright and granular.

The generally used values of stress (load divided by original cross sectional area) and strain (change in length divided by the original gage length) are inadequate for flow and fracture studies. True stress (load divided by actual area) and true strain (natural logarithm of final length divided by original length) must be used to define the actual state of stress and strain. When combined stresses are involved, more complex expressions are needed to define the behavior of a stressed metal.

The effect of lowering the test temperature on the properties of medium carbon structural steel is to increase the yield point, increase the shear fracture stress, and increase the cleavage fracture stress. An increase in strain rate has the same effect as lowering the temperature. Biaxial tensile loading has a minor effect upon the brittle behavior of steel, but triaxial tensile loading has a profound effect, inducing brittle behavior even at ordinary temperatures.

REFERENCES

1. M. Gensamer, "General Survey of the Problem of Fatigue and Fracture," *Fatigue and Fracture of Metals,* p. 3. Massachusetts Institute of Technology: Technology Press, 1952.
2. *Metals Handbook,* pp. 105–109. Cleveland: American Society for Metals, 1948.
3. *Selected ASTM Standards for Students in Engineering, Engineering Materials Standards,* pp. 10–20. Philadelphia: American Society for Testing Materials, 1941.
4. P. Ludwik, *Elemente der Technologischen Mechanik.* Berlin: Julius Springer, 1909.
5. A. Nadai, *Theory of Flow and Fracture of Solids,* pp. 17–29. New York: McGraw-Hill Book Co., 1950.
6. P. Ludwik, "Die Bedeutung des Gleit- und Reisswiderstandes für die Werkstoffprüfung," *Z. Ver. deut. Ing., 71*:2, 1532–1538 (1927).
7. P. W. Bridgman, *Studies in Large Plastic Flow and Fracture,* pp. 118–130. New York: McGraw-Hill Book Co., 1952.
8. A. S. Eldin and S. C. Collins, "Fracture and Yield Stress of 1020 Steel at Low Temperature," *J. Appl. Phys., 22,* 1296, 1297 (1951).
9. M. J. Manjoine, "Influence of Rate of Strain and Temperature on Yield Stresses of Mild Steel," *J. Appl. Mechanics, 11,* no. 4 (December 1944).
10. J. H. Hollomon, "The Mechanical Equation of State," *Trans. Am. Inst. Mining Met. Engrs.: Inst. Metals Div., 171,* 535–545 (1947).
11. J. H. Hollomon and L. D. Jaffe, *Ferrous Metallurgical Design,* p. 112. New York: John Wiley & Sons, 1947.
12. C. Zener and J. H. Hollomon, "Effect of Strain Rate upon Plastic Flow of Steel," *J. Appl. Phys., 15,* 22–32 (1944).
13. F. Wittmann and W. Stepanov, "On the Influence of the Deformation Rate on the Coldbrittleness of Steel," *J. Tech. Phys. (U.S.S.R.), 9*:2, 1070–1085 (1939).
14. J. H. Hollomon, "The Notched-Bar Impact Test," *Trans. Am. Inst. Mining Met. Engrs., 158,* 298–327 (1944).
15. R. von Mises, "Mechanik der festen Körper in plastischdeformablen Zustand," *Nachr. Ges. Wiss. Göttingen, Math-physik. Kl.,* pp. 582–592. Berlin: (1913).
16. J. J. Jelinek, A. Latter, E. G. Thomsen, and J. E. Dorn, "Plastic Flow in Metals," *Office of Production Research and Development,* Rept. W-200, p. 65 (released 1945).

CHAPTER

III

Theories of Fracture

The preceding chapter dealt with the elementary concepts of fracture, whereas the material to follow is a brief review of current theories of fracture and pertinent experimental results. The theories will be examined in the light of available data in an attempt to check the validity of each hypothesis.

As the presentation proceeds, it will soon become clear that no theory adequately explains the complex behavior of metal under stress. Fracture theory is still in an extremely unsatisfactory state, despite the fact that many people have devoted a great deal of time and thought to this problem. The conclusions reached in the remaining portion of the chapter are: (1) that fracture is a more complex phenomenon than any existing theory postulates, (2) that the laws governing fracture are not yet known quantitatively, and (3) that fracture characteristics are nevertheless well understood in a qualitative way.

When metallic materials are tested to destruction under ordinary conditions of tensile loading, the measured strength is always found to be less than the maximum theoretical value by a factor ranging from 100 to 1000. The discrepancy between measured and calculated strengths has been a subject of discussion among scientists for many years. A simple approximate calculation of theoretical fracture strength can be made if it is assumed that failure will occur when the atoms are displaced by one half atomic distance, i.e., an elastic strain of 50 per cent. Then the tensile stress for cleavage fracture would be

$$\sigma_{CF} = 0.5E \tag{1}$$

where σ_{CF} is the cleavage fracture strength and E is the tensile modulus of elasticity. The theoretical shear strength has been calculated in a more refined manner as being of the order of one tenth of the shear modulus. Polanyi [1] suggested that a correction must be made in these calculations because the process of fracturing involves the creation of two new surfaces; a part of the work expended in breaking a crystal appears as surface energy. The equation derived by Polanyi expressing this portion of fracture energy is

$$\sigma_{CF} d = 2F \tag{2}$$

where F is the energy per unit of area required for the creation of a new surface and d is the atomic spacing. The factor "2" appears on the right hand side of the equation because two surfaces are formed during breaking. The theoretical strengths calculated for various metals by means of equations (1) and (2) are listed in Table 3.1.[2] It may be noted that the values from Polanyi's equation are lower than those for equation (1) but even these are 10 to 800 times the observed

TABLE 3.1

THEORETICAL VALUES OF RUPTURE STRESS (AFTER SEITZ [2])

Substance	From Equation (2) psi	$0.5E$ psi	Observed Strength psi
Al	530,000	4,250,000	
Ag	936,000	5,700,000	
Au	1,110,000	5,700,000	
Bi	350,000	....	450
Cd	590,000	5,000,000	
Fe	1,700,000	14,200,000	200,000 *
Cu	1,260,000	8,550,000	
Ga	380,000	....	
Hg	355,000	....	
K	234,000	....	
Na	173,000	....	
Pb	370,000	1,130,000	
Pt	178,000	11,300,000	
Sb	354,000	....	930
Se	89,000	....	
Sn	506,000	2,840,000	
Zn	825,000	7,100,000	250
AgCl	132,000	....	14,000
NaCl	119,000	....	14,000

* Added by author.

strengths. The values of surface tension used in equation (2) for computing the strength are those of the liquid metals because there are no values available for the surface energies of most solids.

The lack of agreement between theory and experiment has been responsible for the speculation that real crystals are not perfect. A theoretical analysis by Inglis [3] showed that in the elastic range a large stress concentration exists at the end of a small crack. The work of Inglis led Griffith [4] to postulate that microcracks were responsible for the observed low values of strength. According to this theory microcracks are present in all real materials, but these will grow only when the free energy of the system is continually reduced by the growth of the cracks. In order to calculate the free energy, Griffith considered two types of energy, the surface energy of the crack and the elastic strain energy of the system. The surface energy increases and the strain energy decreases as a crack grows. Calculations show that for a given normal stress, if the crack is to grow it must exceed a critical length, which is inversely proportional to the square of the normal stress. Griffith made extensive experiments with glass plate in which he introduced cracks and found that the results obtained were in agreement with the theory. He found also that the proportionality constant between the critical normal stress and the reciprocal of the square root of the crack length was approximately equal to the value calculated from measured surface tension and elastic constants of the material. The simple theory of Griffith, while adequate for a truly brittle material such as glass, does not provide reasonable answers for metals. In addition to the surface energy, there is always some energy associated with plastic flow even in the most brittle metals. The plastic flow energy is usually 100 to 1000 times as great as the surface energy.

This microcrack theory, while originally developed for amorphous materials, has recently been extended to polycrystalline metals. Kuntze [5] and later Hollomon [6] and co-workers discussed the effect of orientation of microcracks on the fracture strength of metals. According to this hypothesis, such defects, while randomly oriented initially, may assume a preferred orientation during plastic flow. This causes the fracture strength to be anisotropic, fracture at low stresses being more likely in certain directions. From the point of view of this theory, nonmetallic inclusions, such as those normally found in commercial metals, may be regarded as microcracks. Thus no special theory need be invented to account for the presence of such defects in ordinary metals. Whatever the source of microcrack type defects, the effect of plastic deformation is to produce mechanical fibering of inclusions and/or alignment of cracks. If fracture is due to normal stress, then rolling or drawing should improve the tensile strength in the longitudinal direction because these deformation processes tend to align the defects parallel to this direction. Although such imperfections tend to become aligned in a favorable direction for longitudinal strength, they assume a less favorable position for transverse strength. Another prediction permitted by the theory is that a rolled bar twisted by a torsional load would have the defects rotated into helical configurations. With torsion loading the maximum principal stress acts on a plane at 45° to the plane of maximum shear stress. Thus when the defects have rotated to the 45° position they reside on the plane of maximum normal stress. This causes a marked weakening of the material and could cause fracture at a low stress. It has been observed that for some mild steels the fracture strength in torsion is lower than in tension. This was presumed to support the theory. The theory is unsatisfactory nevertheless because it is based upon the assumption that only tensile fractures occur, whereas it is now well known that most fractures are by the shear mode.

Other experimental results are not in accord with this theory. These results as well as others can be explained in a different but very satisfactory manner if the two types of fracture are recognized. For example, when Thomsen [7] and co-workers tested a series of alloys in torsion, they found that all of the fractures were smooth on a macroscopic scale and that the fracture surfaces were always perpendicular to the specimen axis regardless of the extent of the deformation.[8] Aluminum alloys as well as mild steels fractured on the plane of maximum shear stress and hence the results were not in accord with the microcrack critical-normal-stress hypothesis.

Other experimental results, including those from biaxial stress tests, will be presented later to illustrate further the dual nature of fracture. A study of available data leads to the inevitable conclusion that *any theory that considers only one type of fracture can never satisfactorily explain all experimental results.* All theories thus far proposed suffer from this shortcoming.

In spite of the limitations of the Griffith theory of fracture of brittle materials, several other interesting modifications have been proposed. A few of these will be discussed in some detail because of their potential importance in connection with brittle behavior of steel.

Weibull [9] used Griffith's concepts for explaining the strength of small wires. As in the case of previous exponents of this theory, Weibull visualized an originally random distribution of cracks and assumed that no new cracks were formed during plastic flow. He further assumed, as did Griffith, that surface cracks were mainly responsible for fracture. If the rod from which the wire was drawn contained a fixed number of cracks, the number per inch of length would depend upon the diameter; the smaller the wire size, the fewer would be the number of defects per unit of length. Thus, according to the theory, the smaller the wire, the lower the probability of fracture at any stress.

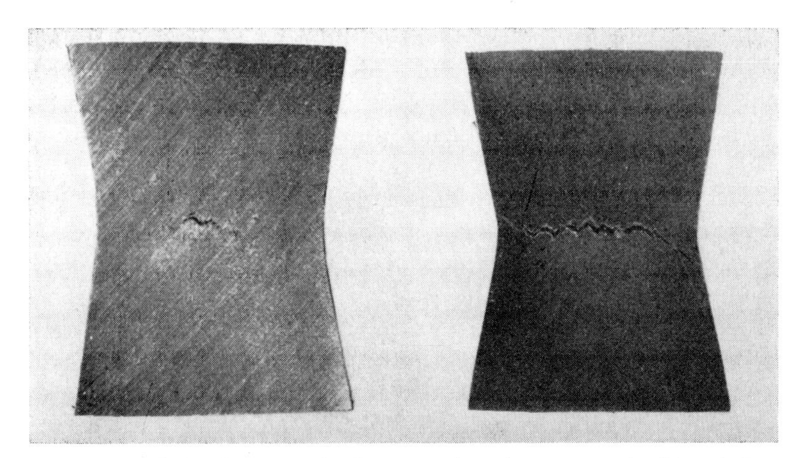

Fig. 3.1 Macrographs of a longitudinally sectioned tensile specimen of mild steel showing that origin of fracture is in the center: (*a*) just prior to fracture, (*b*) after fracture.

Weibull's adaptation of Griffith's theory, while useful for explaining the increased strength of glass as the fiber diameter is reduced, does not appear to be applicable to ductile metals. For example, it is well known that tensile test specimens of ductile metals fracture first near the center of the cross section, as is shown in Fig. 3.1, rather than at the surface. Also, it is doubtful that the number and distribution of "original cracks" would always be the same regardless, say, of the method of manufacturing mild steel, yet the measured strength of a given type of steel varies over a much smaller range than does the strength of glass. Neither of these considerations can be explained by the proposed modifications of Griffith's theory.

Zener[10] also assumed that the relatively low strength of metals is associated with the presence of cracks. However, he postulated that *the cracks formed during plastic flow* and thus were not pre-existent. Zener believed that the cataclysmic manner in which slip moved through a crystal caused the material within the slip band to behave viscously during this transient condition. The high strain rates occurring in these localized regions presumably destroyed the perfection of the crystal structure locally. He postulated that relaxation of the shear stress within the slip band during propagation of the shear front produced a high stress concentration ahead of the advancing slip band. The more the shear stress was relaxed behind the advancing spearhead of slip, the greater was the stress concentration ahead of it. If this stress concentration reached a critical value, a crack would form in the crystal. On the other hand, if the slip band traveled across a grain without producing a crack, one of two things might happen when the wavefront of slip reached the boundary; first, another slip band could be initiated in the adjacent grain, or secondly, if the stress concentration were high enough, a crack might form. The latter possibility seems highly probable when the adjacent crystal is a hard brittle phase.

Zener also believed that the accumulation of dislocations might lead to crack formation. Dislocations are one of the types of defects assumed or known to exist in crystals. The edge or line type of dislocation, consisting of a missing half plane in a lattice, was a concept introduced by Taylor [11] and by Orowan [12] to explain the plastic behavior of metals. This lattice defect is illustrated in Fig. 3.2(*a*), which shows a section through the lattice at right angles to the missing half plane and perpendicular to the slip plane. This type of defect constitutes a potential fracture source as indicated in (*b*) of the same figure. The coalescence of a number of such defects, as shown in (*c*) and (*d*), could provide a fracture nucleus. The free energy of the system would be lowered if the crack could close. However, at the present time it is not possible to say whether such crack nuclei could form and grow during plastic deformation. If they did form, fracture might take place through these regions. It is interesting to note that the condition for fracture by this mechanism is very dependent upon the extent of prior plastic flow. From the evidence available, Zener concluded that the concept introduced by Ludwik [13] could not be correct. Ludwik had reasoned that fracture is determined by the intersection of a flow stress with a fracture stress curve. Zener's theory, on the other hand, has the shortcoming that it considers only one mode of fracture, i.e., that resulting from plastic flow. It is apparently true that fractures in mild steel, no matter how brittle they appear from external measurements, always seem to be accompanied by some flow. X-ray diffraction pictures have been taken of a few fracture surfaces of brittle steel specimens. They have shown that the material in the neighborhood of the break, at least back for a few thousand atoms

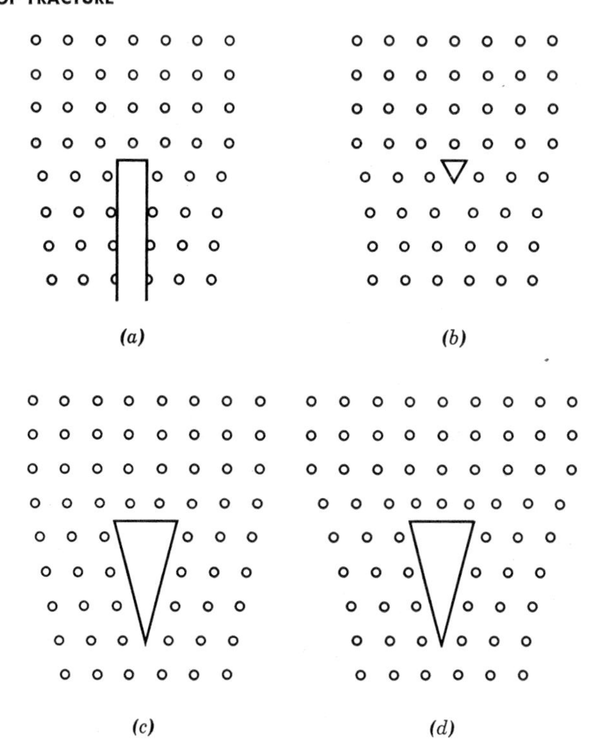

Fig. 3.2 Schematic diagrams showing possible fracture nucleus due to accumulation of dislocations in crystal. Circles represent atom positions. (*a*) single dislocation (missing half plane), (*b*) potential fracture source due to a single dislocation, (*c*, *d*) coalescence of several dislocations to form a crack nucleus.

from the fracture surface, has undergone severe plastic distortion.[14] It is equally true that many minerals cleave without prior flow, and the possibility that metallic crystals can cleave without flow cannot be ruled out. Thus it appears that none of the existing theories is capable of explaining all of the experimental results.

There has been an interesting modification of the Griffith theory suggested by Orowan,[15] which seems to be of interest in connection with the brittle behavior of steel. He has pointed out that mild steel, even in its most brittle state, undergoes some plastic flow prior to fracture and that the energy involved in this deformation is perhaps 1000 times as large as the energy required to create two new surfaces. Thus a plastic strain energy term must be included in the theory.

In the Griffith theory of cracking in brittle solids, the energy required to create two new surfaces is given by

$$W_s \approx C^2\omega \tag{3}$$

where W_s = energy of new surfaces.
C = diameter of internal crack or twice the length of a surface crack.
ω = surface energy per unit of area.

The elastic strain energy stored in the loaded material is given by

$$W_e \approx \frac{C^3\sigma^2}{E} \tag{4}$$

where W_e = elastic strain energy released by formation of crack (in a spherical volume and of diameter C).
C = diameter of crack.
σ = mean stress in metal prior to crack growth.

When W_e equals or exceeds W_s a crack can grow. Equating these terms yields

$$\sigma \approx \sqrt{\frac{E\omega}{C}} \tag{5}$$

From equation (5) it can be seen that the stress required to make a crack grow is inversely proportional to the square root of the crack length.

Orowan has pointed out that equation (5) is unsuitable for steel and that it should be modified as follows to include the plastic strain energy, p, associated with fracturing:

$$\sigma \approx \sqrt{\frac{E(\omega + p)}{C}} \tag{6}$$

Since the plastic strain energy is of the order of 1000 times the surface energy, it follows that if the ratio $\sigma/\sqrt{E}$ is the same for glass and steel, then cracks which will grow must be about 1000 times longer in steel than in glass. Thus dangerous cracks in steel must be of the order of 0.1 in. as compared with 0.0001 in. for glass.

It should be kept in mind that the plastic energy term, p, is temperature dependent. This is a very important point. When the temperature is above the transition range, p will be large and, as seen from equation (6), the stress level, σ, to make a crack grow will be correspondingly large. Below the transition range, however, where the metal is brittle, p will be small and the stress to cause crack growth will therefore be reduced. At intermediate stress levels, it is apparent that failure can be made to occur just by lowering the temperature until it is below the temperature at which brittleness occurs. A fracture, once started, can progress with increasing velocity until it approaches the theoretical maximum of about 10,000 ft per sec, the velocity of a transverse elastic wave in steel. (Velocities as high as 6000 ft per sec have actually been measured.[16,17]) The reason for the accelerated progression of the crack is evident from equation (6), which shows that as the crack length increases, the stress required to keep it growing decreases rapidly. An interesting discussion on fracture propagation has been presented by Irwin.[18]

Several service failures have occurred during periods of low temperature, even though the structures had been operated satisfactorily at higher temperatures and sometimes even at higher stresses during the warmer periods. It is evident that the Orowan theory is extremely helpful in explaining some of the service failures. Furthermore, the theory is amenable to experimental verification but attempts to obtain quantitative data for the temperature dependence of p have as yet been unsuccessful.

EXPERIMENTAL RESULTS

The statement was made in the preceding chapters that there are two modes of fracture, *shear* and *cleavage*. The experimental evidence supporting this statement will now be examined.

Parker et al.[19] have shown that the trace of the fracture surface is parallel to the trace of the slip planes in the individual crystals of polycrystalline mild steel when the fracture is due to the shear stress and that the fracture follows cleavage planes when it is caused by the normal stress. The crystallographic nature of shear and cleavage fractures was shown in Fig. 2.1.

In reviewing briefly, it will be recalled that Figs. 2.15 and 2.16 illustrate the fracture strength of mild steel as a function of temperature. Note that there is a discontinuity in the curves at low temperatures which is caused by a change in the mode of fracture from shear to cleavage. As shown in Fig. 2.17, the energy for fracture undergoes a precipitous drop when the change in fracture mechanism occurs. Fig. 3.3 is a photograph showing the appearance of cylindrical tensile specimens of mild steel broken at various temperatures. Typical cup-cone fractures were obtained at the higher temperatures, and flat brittle breaks were found at the lowest temperatures. A macroscopic examination of longitudinal sections of these and similar series of specimens

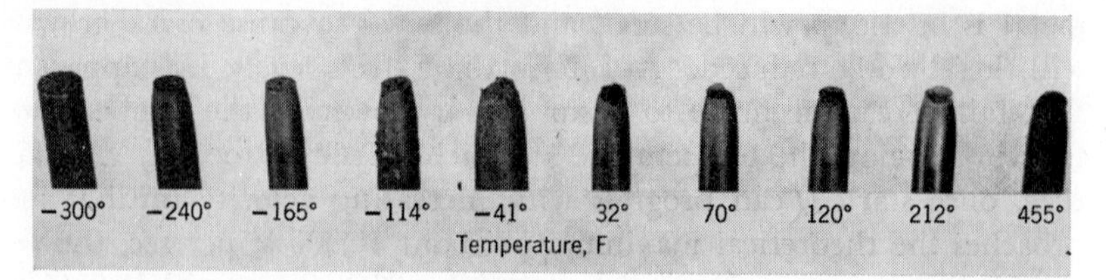

Fig. 3.3 Photograph showing the appearance of cylindrical tensile specimens of mild steel broken at various temperatures.

revealed that the higher temperature fractures followed planes of maximum shear stress, whereas the low temperature ones followed planes of maximum normal stress.

It has long been thought [20] that the crack which first formed at the center of the necked section of a tensile specimen of a ductile metal was due to the normal stress. A photograph illustrating such a fracture is shown in Fig. 3.1. A close examination of the trace of the fracture plane on the longitudinal section reveals, however, that the break generally follows a saw-toothed path, with the surfaces of the "teeth" being planes of maximum shear stress rather than those of maximum normal stress. Low temperature failures, on the other hand, can be seen when examined on a macroscopic scale to follow the plane of maximum normal stress. There has been a considerable amount of confusion introduced into the literature by the assumption made by Ludwik [21] long ago that the initial internal fracture, as shown in Fig. 3.1, was due to the normal stress. This seemed justified at the time because a casual examination of the broken surface indicated that the flat part of the cup-cone followed the plane of maximum normal stress. The saw-toothed nature of the fracture apparently was ignored for many years, and Ludwik's original hypothesis was quoted by most authors in this field as being truly representative of the existing conditions. In substantiation of this view, Bridgman,[22] by making certain simplifying assumptions, was able to compute magnitudes and distributions of the three principal stresses in the necked section of a tensile test specimen. His analysis indicated that the stress system could be considered as a uniform axial tensile stress with a superimposed hydrostatic tension. The magnitude of the hydrostatic stress ranged from zero at the outer surface to a maximum at the specimen axis. According to the calculations and as a direct result of the assumptions made, the maximum shear stress was constant across the section (with equal probability of shear fracture starting anywhere); however, the normal stress was found to be a maximum at the center. Thus the high normal stresses might be expected to initiate fracture at the center. Bridgman's analysis, although adding quantitative information, did nothing to change the prevailing concept that fracture originates at the axis of the necked tensile specimen because the normal stress is a maximum there. Since macroscopic as well as microscopic examinations showed that shear fractures originate near the specimen axis, further work seemed necessary.

Examination of many broken tensile specimens revealed that on a macroscopic scale the fracture followed planes of maximum shear stress. In order to do this, however, the fracture must zigzag back and forth between equivalent shear planes as cracking progresses across the section. Since the hills and valleys thus produced are tiny, the visual impression is that the central area of the cup-cone is "flat." The assumption that this is a region of normal stress failure is consequently a natural one. However, there is an alternative and perfectly satisfactory explanation for the flat portion that is consistent with the macroscopic observations. The saw-toothed appearance can be accounted for by the fact that no fracture on any 45° plane could extend far from the minimum diameter of the necked section without running into regions of lower stress. Since all planes at 45° to the specimen axis are subjected to the same maximum shear stress, fracture due to this stress should follow a surface that oscillates in a saw-toothed manner across the minimum section. Zigzagging would continue until the crack approached the surface, where final separation would occur on a single 45° surface—the "lip" of the cup-cone fracture.

In addition to the macroscopic evidence for the shear nature of ductile fractures, there is substantiation for this concept from the results of microscopic examinations. Longitudinal sections of fractures obtained in mild steel at both low and normal temperatures, such as the ones shown in Fig. 3.3, were polished and examined microscopically. Nickel was plated on the fracture surface to prevent damage to the edges caused by rounding off during polishing; this procedure made a critical examination possible. Cubic etch pits were developed in the ferrite crystals on the polished longitudinal section by using an etchant consisting of 25 per cent nitric acid and 75 per cent water. Traces of these etch pits were used to indicate the relative orientations of the ferrite grains through which the fracture passed. Photographs showing typical results from such an investigation are presented in Fig. 3.4. Examination of many mild steel tensile specimens that had been pulled to failure showed clearly that at room temperature the fractures invariably followed the slip or shear planes in the ferrite crystals, but at low temperatures these planes were avoided and the break followed the cleavage planes (see Fig. 2.1). There still remained the prob-

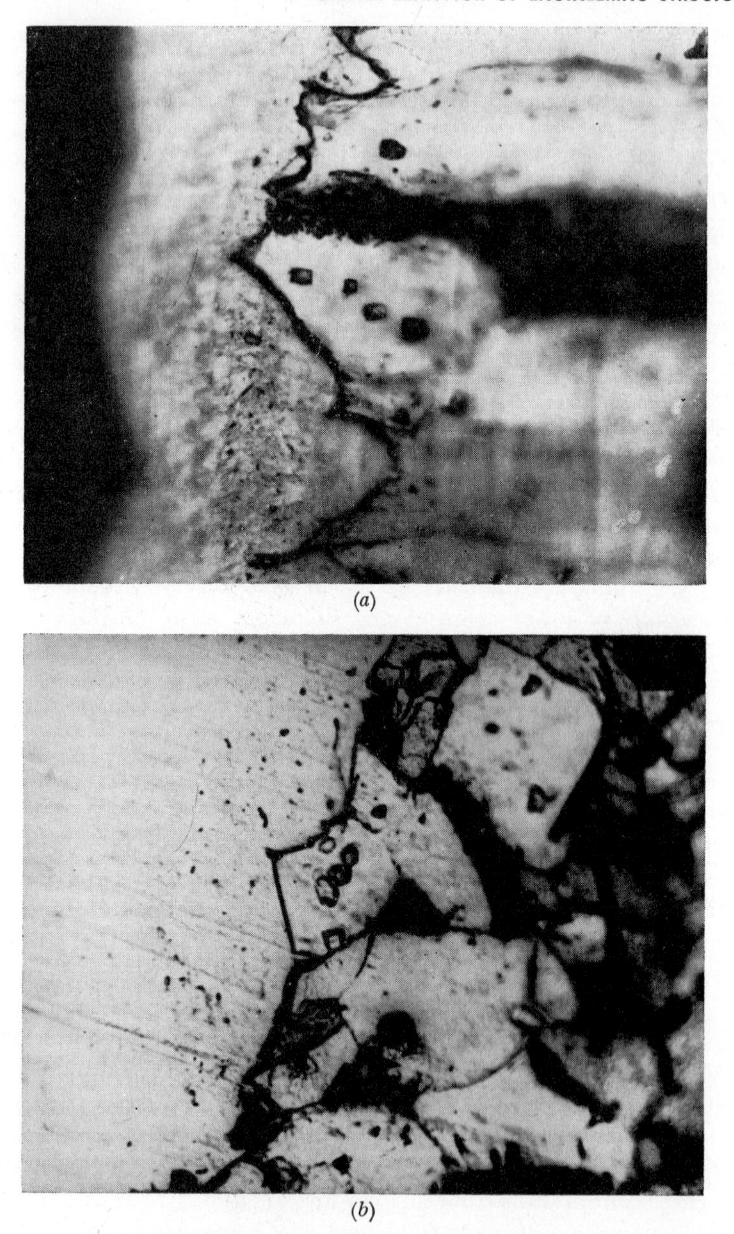

(*a*)

(*b*)

Fig. 3.4 Photographs showing cubic etch pits in ferrite crystals. (*a*) Room temperature shear fracture shows trace of fracture surface not parallel to trace of cubic etch pit. (*b*) Low temperature cleavage fracture shows trace of fracture surface parallel to trace of etch pit.

lem of explaining why shear fractures originated at the center of the minimum section; this observation was not in accord with Bridgman's analysis [22] nor with current concepts. Parker, Davis, and Flanigan [23] used a combination of experiment and theory in an attempt to resolve this problem. Using a number of 2-in. diameter annealed mild steel tensile specimens, they elongated them to different values of strain and they analyzed the stress system in each bar. This was accomplished by unloading each specimen, placing it in a lathe and relaxing the residual stresses in the necked region by boring out successive layers from the interior of the bar. The stresses throughout the section were computed from the surface strains measured during the boring operation and from the stress changes that occurred during unloading. Resistance wire strain gages were employed for these measurements. The stress distribution obtained just prior to fracture is shown in Fig. 3.5. Note that *the shear stress as well as the normal stress reaches a maximum value at the center of the section.* Hence it is to be expected that any tensile fracture involving necking, whether shear or cleavage, should originate near the specimen axis.

Biaxial stress tests have also been of great value in clarifying the

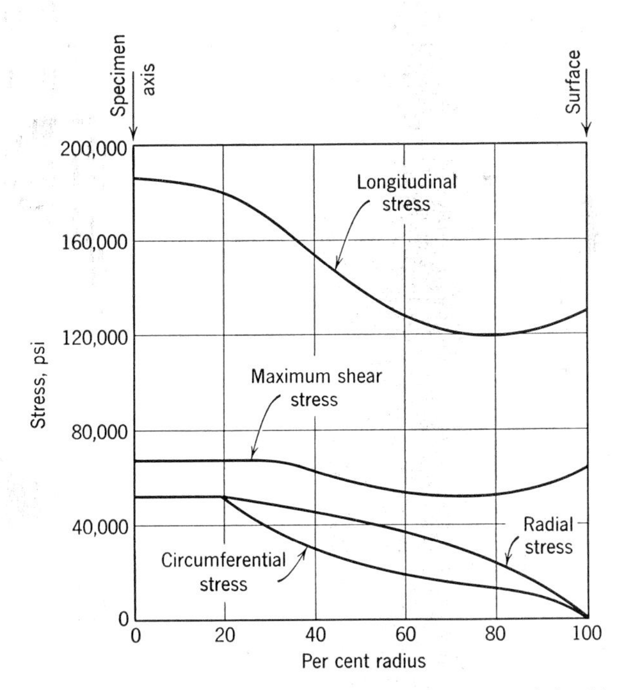

Fig. 3.5 The stress distribution in the neck of a 2-in. diameter annealed mild steel tensile specimen just preceding fracture.

fracture problem. Traces of the yield and fracture surfaces have been determined experimentally for a number of metals. The yield stresses were found to follow closely the elliptical trace of the maximum shear strain energy criterion.[24] Although much less is known about fracture, enough tests have been made to establish the basic pattern of behavior. Since the yield stress data have been adequately treated elsewhere,[25] the following discussion will be confined to the results from fracture studies.

Tubular specimens are generally employed for biaxial stress investigations because of the ease with which the ratio of principal stresses can be varied and controlled. The longitudinal stress is provided by an axial tensile (or compressive) load, which supplements the axial component supplied by the internal pressure used to regulate the circumferential stress. The radial stress is generally assumed to be insignificant but may in some cases be large enough to have an appreciable effect.

Siebel and Maier [26] determined the behavior of tubular specimens of various steels under biaxial tension conditions. Typical test results for a mild steel are shown in Fig. 3.6; σ_l in this case is the net axial stress, and σ_t is the tangential or hoop stress. The loads were applied in such a way that the stress ratio during a single test was supposedly maintained constant until fracture occurred; each test was conducted

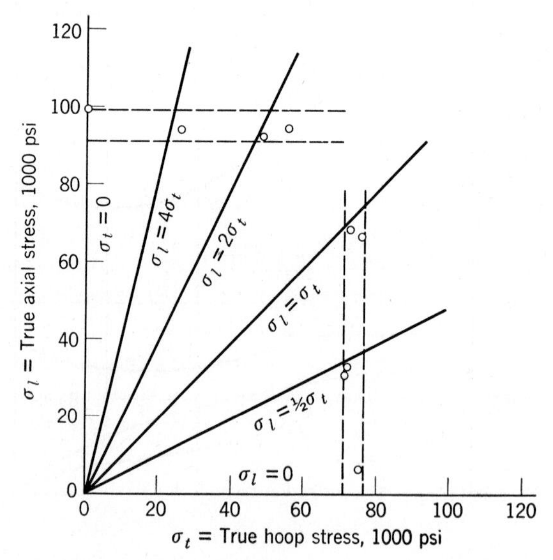

Fig. 3.6 Fracture stresses of tubular mild steel specimens ruptured under essentially biaxial tension loading. (Data from Siebel and Maier.[26])

with a different stress ratio. Since σ_3 (or σ_r), the radial stress, was essentially zero, it appeared from the results that fracture depended only on the largest principal stress, σ_1, and was independent of σ_2. This was interpreted as meaning that fracture occurred when the normal stress exceeded a critical value, σ_F. This interpretation, while accepted by many, appears to be unwarranted because, as pointed out previously, it is impossible from tests in the first quadrant (stress ratios ranging from 0 to ∞) to differentiate between a critical normal stress for fracture and a critical shear stress. Reference to Fig. 2.23(*c*) and (*d*) will clarify this point. Siebel and Maier's data thus cannot be used to prove that fracture was due to the normal stress as such. On the other hand, tests in the fourth quadrant, where the shear fracture line makes an angle of 45° with the coordinate axes and the normal fracture stress line is perpendicular to the horizontal axis, are capable of differentiating between the two modes of fracture.

There is another complication involved in tests on tubes that makes the interpretation of results questionable. Ductile materials either bulge, neck, or do both during the later stages of testing. This behavior alters the stress condition at the fracture location in an uncontrollable manner. Hence the stress ratio at fracture differs from that reported; necking tends to introduce a ratio of stress of 2:1 regardless of the loading conditions employed. Tube tests on materials that do not bulge or neck are not subject to this shortcoming.

Thomsen and Dorn [27] have shown clearly that magnesium alloys fail by shear at room temperature. Their results are presented in Fig. 3.7, from which it may be seen that tests in the fourth quadrant prove that a maximum shear stress criterion is closely followed when these alloys are fractured with biaxial stress. The dotted line indicates the theoretical fracture strength. The negative slope of the upper portion of the fracture curve is caused by the internal pressure, which generates a radial stress ranging from zero for $\sigma_t/\sigma_l = 0$ to a maximum when $\sigma_t = \sigma_l$. Since the radial stress is not insignificant, nor even constant, for all stress ratios, tests on tubes cannot be considered as a true biaxial stress test. They do, however, approach ideality closely enough for practical purposes. The reason for the cusp in the vertical portion of the curve is not clear, but it may be assumed to have been caused by the anisotropy of properties in the magnesium extrusions used for these tests.

Further confirmation of the shear nature of the fractures was found in the angle made by the macroscopic plane of the fracture with the planes of principal stress. Fig. 3.7 reveals that the planes of fractures followed planes of maximum shear stress, i.e., planes at 45° to

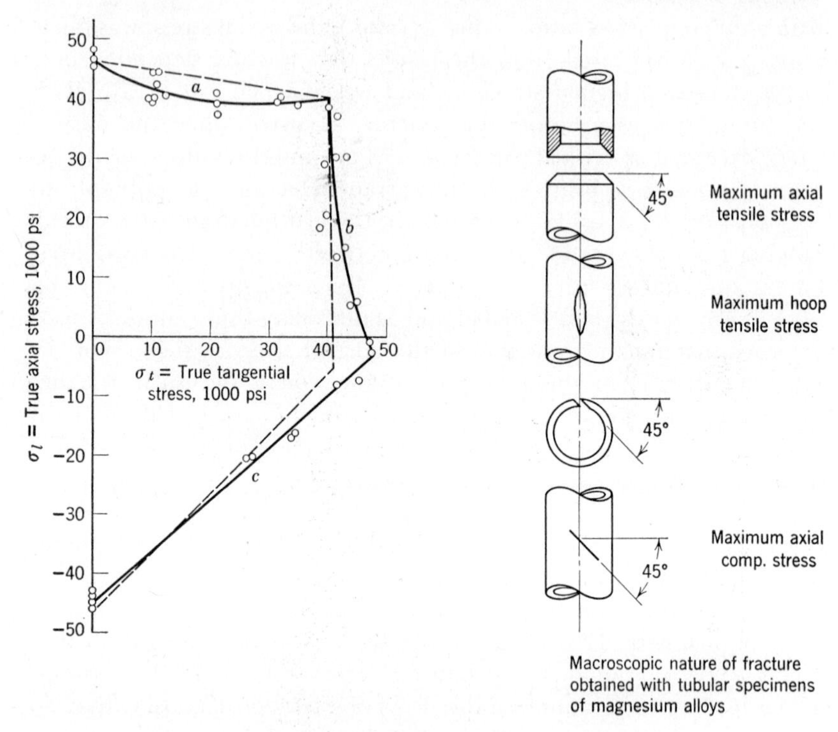

Fig. 3.7 Fracture stresses of tubular magnesium alloy (J-1) specimens ruptured under essentially biaxial loading. (Data from Thomsen and Dorn.[27])

the directions of the principal stresses. Similar results on 24S-T81 aluminum alloy obtained by Thomsen et al.[28] again showed that the maximum shear stress criterion was approximately followed (Fig. 3.8). Here again this alloy appeared to be somewhat anisotropic, because the magnitudes of the shear fracture stress varied somewhat in the longitudinal and tangential directions.

Other experiments on cast iron tubes reported by Grassi and Cornet [29] indicate that the normal stress law of fracture may apply to some materials. As shown in Fig. 3.9, cast iron appears to follow a normal stress criterion for fracture in the first quadrant and the upper part of the fourth. The fracture under compression loading, however, appears to obey a shear stress law.

Tests on tubular specimens of mild steel have been made by Davis,[30] Troxell, Parker, Davis, and Boodberg,[31] Griffis, Morikawa, and Fraenkel,[32] and others. At ordinary temperatures the fractures were found to originate on planes of maximum shear stress. In some cases the mode of fracture changed to cleavage and followed planes of maxi-

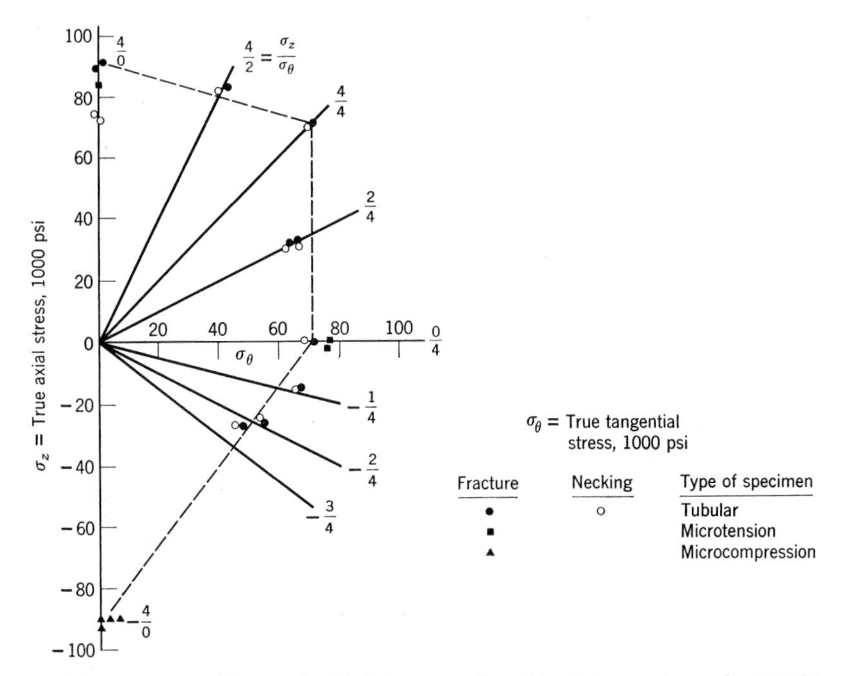

Fig. 3.8 Fracture conditions under biaxial stress studies with tubular specimens, for 24S-T81 aluminum alloys. (Data from Thomsen et al.[28])

mum tensile stress but only *after the crack had formed and grown sufficiently to introduce a third component of tensile stress in the radial direction* by the notch action previously described.

Uniaxial and biaxial stress data are sufficiently definitive to establish that a number of ductile metals can and do fracture by shear at ordinary temperature; some data, however, support the normal stress criterion. A survey of the available facts reveals that biaxial stress test data are in accord with the results from uniaxial tension tests discussed previously. Furthermore, in almost all cases the flow and fracture behavior of a metal under biaxial stressing can be predicted accurately from simple tensile test results. This is true, of course, because biaxial stressing does not alter the critical stress ratio of maximum normal stress to maximum shear stress. Experimental evidence from uniaxial and biaxial stress tests leaves little room for doubt about the dual nature of fracture. The possible existence of a simple law (or laws) of fracture was thoroughly explored by Bridgman.[33] He has probably done more than any other investigator to reveal the complex nature of fracture. His work included a painstaking exploration of the effect of superimposed hydrostatic pressure on the fracture char-

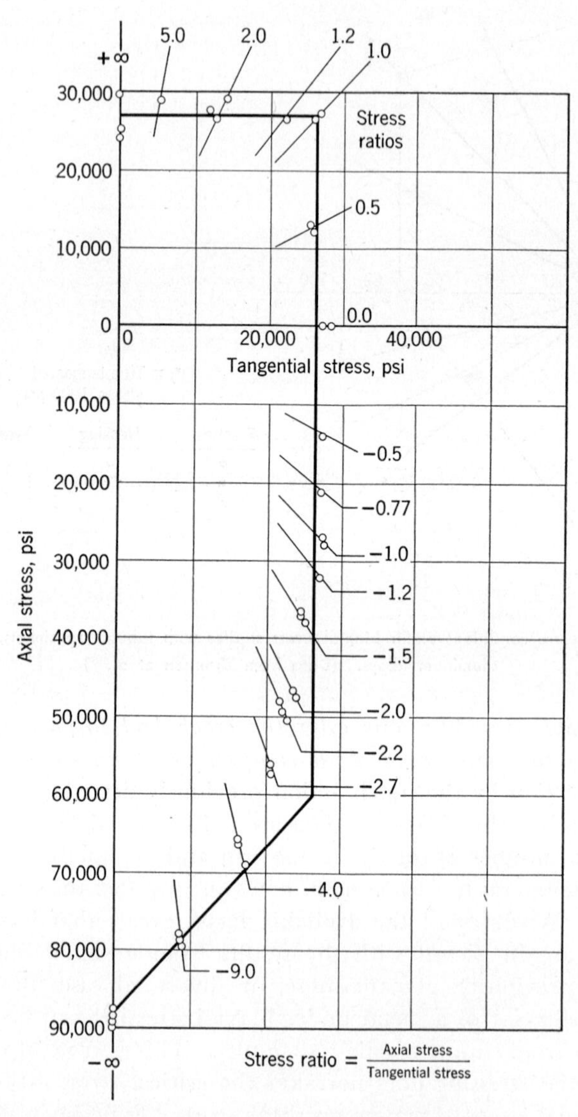

Fig. 3.9 Fracture stresses of tubular specimens of gray cast iron under essentially biaxial loading. (Data from Grassi and Cornet.[29])

acteristics of many materials. The most striking result he obtained with mild steel was the tremendous increase in ductility promoted by hydrostatic pressure. The amount of plastic deformation that could be tolerated without fracture was increased as much as 300-fold by pressures in the range between 300,000 and 450,000 psi. Fig. 3.10, due to Bridgman,[34] illustrates this effect. One specimen was broken in tension at atmospheric pressure while the second, under a hydro-

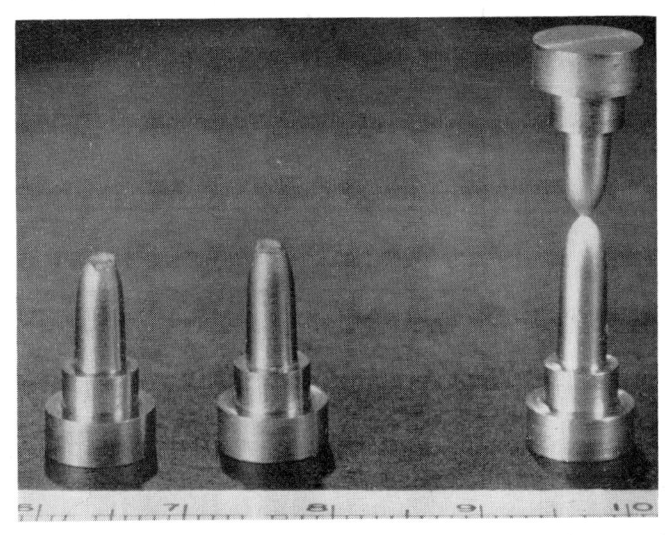

Fig. 3.10 Photograph of mild steel tensile specimens broken under different conditions of hydrostatic pressure. Specimen at left was broken under atmospheric pressure; specimen at right was broken under a hydrostatic pressure of 350,000 psi. (Bridgman.[34])

static pressure of 350,000 psi, was pulled without failure to a higher stress at a much greater strain. The fact that the strength and ductility are both greatly increased by hydrostatic pressure, while the ratio of maximum normal stress to maximum shear stress remains constant, demonstrates clearly that there can be no simple criterion for fracture. Other investigators have also found that the fracture stress is markedly affected by prior strain history.[35,36] As an example, Fig. 3.11 shows the effect of prestraining at various higher temperatures on the cleavage fracture stress of hot-rolled mild steel tested at −300 F. The fracture stress undergoes a remarkably large increase due to plastic flow but the temperature of prestraining seems to have little if any effect.

Bridgman[33,34] conducted tests on steels under combinations of tension plus various hydrostatic pressures. Fig. 3.12 shows a summary

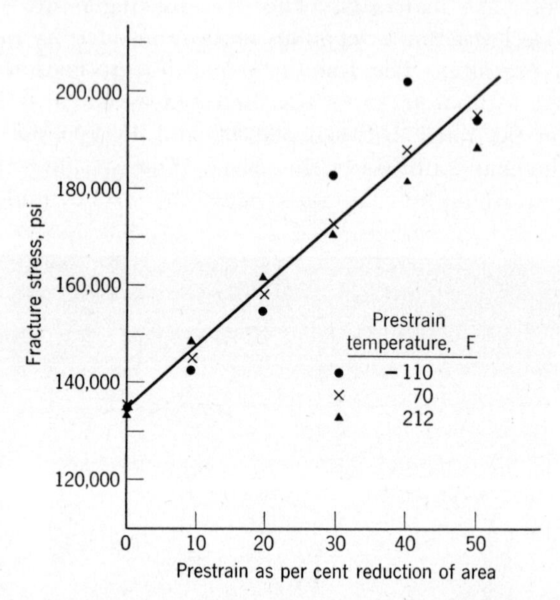

Fig. 3.11 Effect of prestraining at various temperatures on the cleavage fracture stress of hot-rolled mild steel. All specimens broken at −300 F.

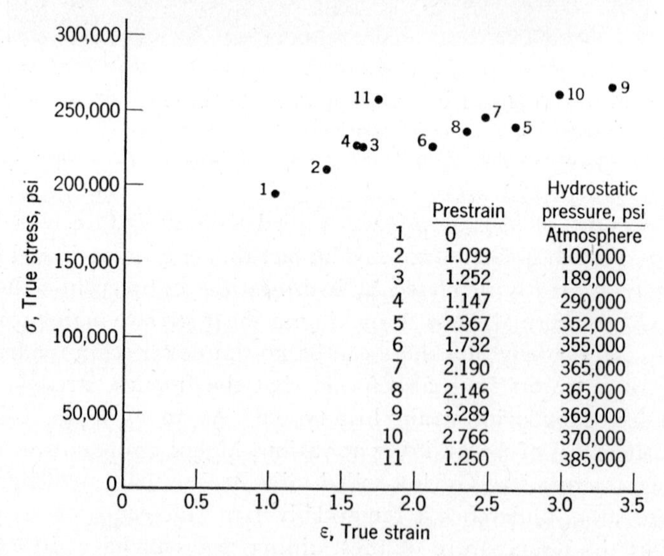

Fig. 3.12 Summary of fracture stresses for steel tensile specimens subjected to combinations of tension and hydrostatic pressures. (Bridgman.[33])

of his results. The appearance of the fracture changes with increasing values of hydrostatic pressure, as shown in Fig. 3.13. At low pressures conventional cup-cone fractures occurred. Bridgman attributed the flat part of the cup-cone to tensile-type failures, but as previously discussed, even this portion of the break may be by the shear mode. At high pressures the flat part of the cup-cone disappears and the fracture closely follows planes of maximum shear stress. Note, however, that when this occurs, the necked section is so small in area that the fracture may follow a single 45° plane nearly across the specimen and still be within the most highly stressed region of the neck. In (*d*) of Fig. 3.13 the saw-toothed nature of the broken surface is reduced to only three changes in slope, while in (*e*) and (*f*) only one change in slope is present. The evidence is strong that the nature of the failure is unaltered by the presence of the hydrostatic pressure, even though Bridgman concluded that the two types of fractures were present. Further confirmation of the belief that only one occurred is available from the data in Fig. 3.12. A change in the mode of fracture is generally associated with a discontinuity in either the ductility or fracture strength, as shown in Fig. 2.17. No such discontinuity is present in the results shown in Fig. 3.12.

There is ample evidence showing that both shear and cleavage fracture strengths are dependent upon the prior strain history of the material. The magnitude of the strain effect varies widely for different materials and for different strain histories. The data just discussed show strikingly large effects; other test results show little change in fracture stress with increasing strain to fracture. For example, Lynch, Ripling, and Sachs [37] have demonstrated that the fracture stress for 24ST aluminum is increased very little when the prestraining is done by drawing or extruding.

Bridgman [33] has made a very enlightening summary of fracture data for a heat treated SAE 1045 steel which shows that there is no simple criterion for fracture. As indicated previously, an analysis of the stress at the axis of a tension specimen shows that it may be considered as consisting of three independent stress systems: (*a*) the hydrostatic pressure in the ambient liquid, (*b*) a tensile stress uniform across the minimum section, and (*c*) a hydrostatic tension, consisting of three equal components of tensile stress, which increases from zero at the surface to a maximum at the axis. The principal stress axes of all three systems are coincident. Referring to Figs. 3.14 and 3.15, P indicates the hydrostatic pressure component and is plotted as positive instead of negative; HT denotes the hydrostatic tension at the axis; F is the "flow stress" or (*b*) as described above; $Z = F + HT - P$, the net com-

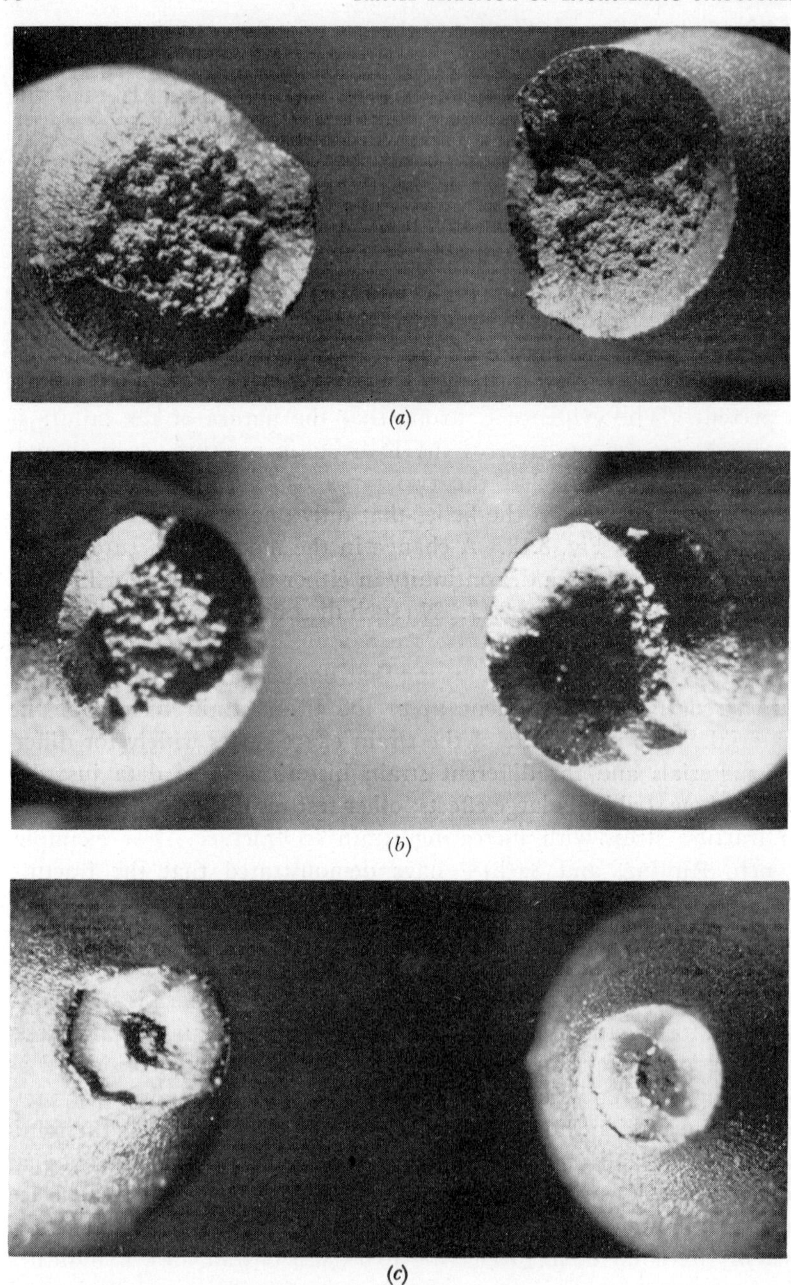

(a)

(b)

(c)

Fig. 3.13 Photographs showing the progressive change in the character of the fracture for tensile specimens of steel broken under various hydrostatic pressures. (a) Broken at atmospheric pressure. (b) Broken under 34,000 psi hydrostatic pressure. (c) Broken under 145,000

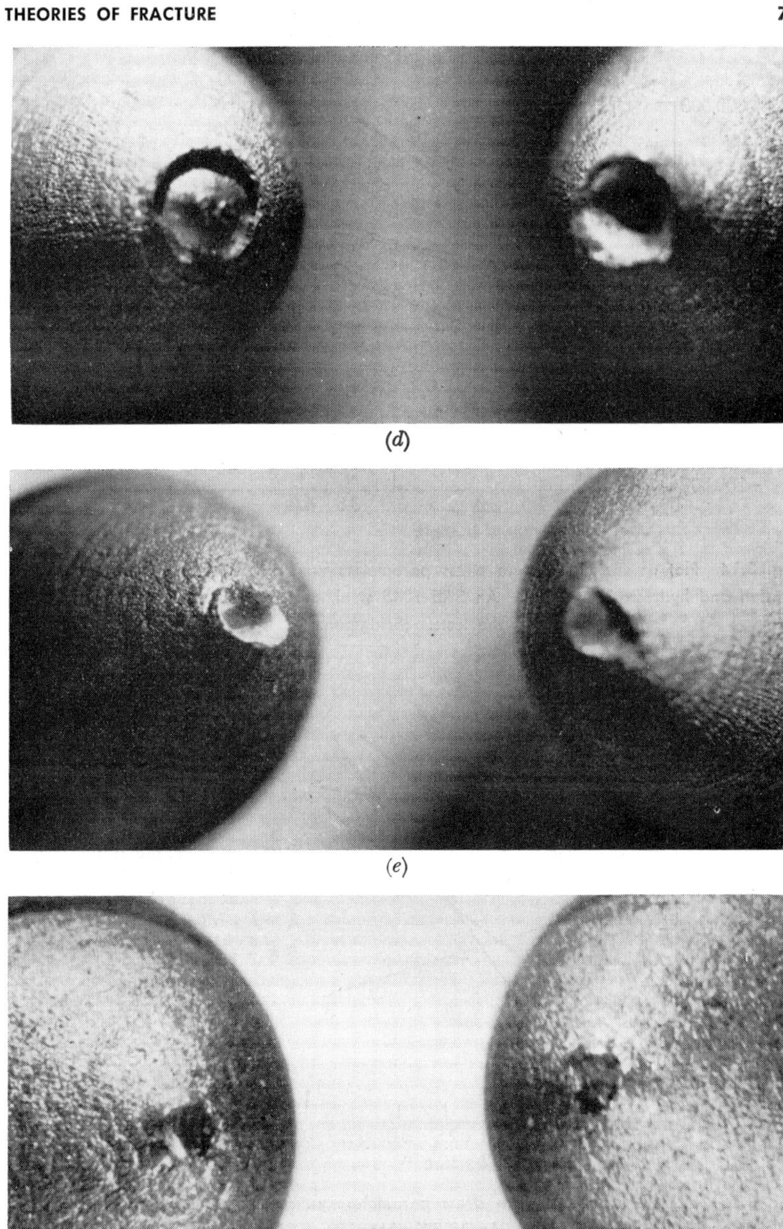

(d)

(e)

(f)

psi hydrostatic pressure. (d) Broken under 186,000 psi hydrostatic pressure. (e) Broken under 268,000 psi hydrostatic pressure. (f) Broken under 387,000 psi hydrostatic pressure. (Bridgman.[34]) (a) and (b) ×10; (c), (d), and (e) ×12; (f) ×18.

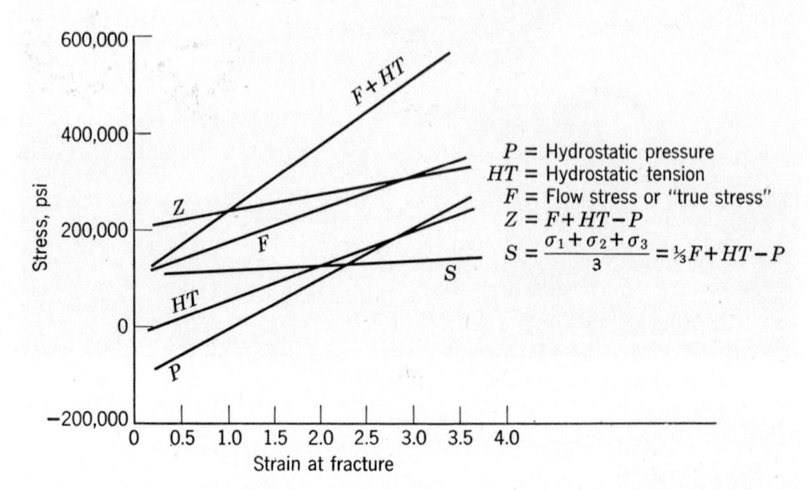

Fig. 3.14 Plot of various fracture stress parameters vs. strain for various combinations of tension and hydrostatic pressure. An SAE 1045 steel, austempered at 1100 F, was used for the tests. (Bridgman.[33])

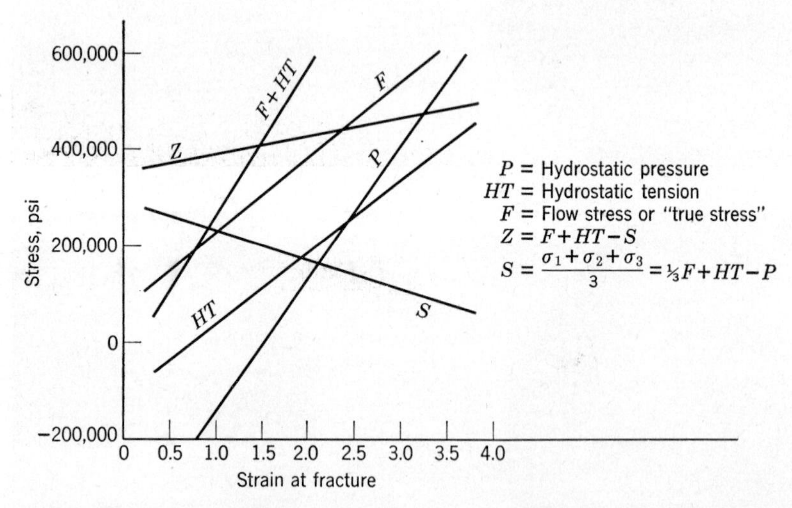

Fig. 3.15 Plot of various fracture stress parameters vs. strain for various combinations of tension and hydrostatic pressure. An 18.5% chromium, 8.95% nickel steel was used for the tests. (Bridgman.[33])

ponent of tensile stress; and $S = \frac{1}{3}F + HT - P$, one third of the sum of the three principal stresses. The nomenclature in the figures is due to Bridgman. A valid criterion for fracture would be indicated by a horizontal line in the two figures. However, it may be seen that neither the maximum normal stress nor the maximum shear stress is a valid criterion for fracture. The other criteria are equally unsatisfactory.

Thus it must be concluded that the simple picture of fracture presented in Chapter II, although good enough for practical purposes, cannot be quantitatively correct.

Although it seems that the phenomenon of fracture should be well understood, the evidence shows that it is not. Bridgman [34] has found that when local failure occurs under certain conditions of high pressure, there may actually be self-healing, and straining may be continued for hundreds or thousands of per cent without separation. He concluded that fractures, particularly those of the shear type, are initiated on an atomic scale. The small scale instability that nucleates fracture may grow and become macroscopic in size, or it may disappear by a self-healing process. Thus it is probable that the macroscopically measured values of stresses and strains are unable to define fracture criteria because they represent only gross averages, whereas fracture is dependent upon the action of highly localized stresses.

There have been numerous objections to the concept initiated by Ludwik that there is a fracture stress curve which intersects the flow stress curve at the point where fracture occurs. These objections are valid in that the location of the fracture curve depends strongly upon the stress and strain history. Nevertheless, this simple concept of fracture is helpful in explaining the underlying principles of brittle behavior of engineering structures and hence should be retained.

SUMMARY

Uniaxial and biaxial stress data are sufficiently definitive to establish that a number of ductile metals can and do fracture by shear at ordinary temperatures. Some data, however, support the normal stress fracture criterion. Both shear and cleavage fractures have been identified. In almost all cases the flow and fracture behavior of a metal under biaxial stressing can be predicted accurately from simple tensile test results.

Bridgman [33] has shown that there is no simple law (or laws) of fracture. Both the shear fracture strength and the cleavage fracture strength depend upon the prior strain history of the material. Fractures are initiated on an atomic scale. The macroscopically measured values of stresses and strains are unsuitable for establishing a criterion for fracture because they represent only gross averages. Fracture is dependent upon the action of highly localized stresses.

REFERENCES

1. M. Polanyi, "Über die Natur des Zerreissvorganges," *Z. Physik, 7,* 323–327 (1921).
2. F. Seitz, *Physics of Metals,* pp. 164–167. New York: McGraw-Hill Book Co., 1943.
3. C. E. Inglis, "Stresses in a Plate Due to the Presence of Cracks and Sharp Corners," *Trans. Inst. Naval Architects, 55, 1,* 219 (1913).
4. A. A. Griffith, "The Phenomena of Rupture and Flow in Solids," *Physical Trans., Roy. Soc. (London), 221,* p. 163 (1920).
5. W. Kuntze, "Fragen der technischen Kohäsion," *Z. Metallkunde, 22,* 264–268 (1930).
6. J. H. Hollomon, "Fracture and the Structure of Metals," *Fracturing of Metals,* pp. 262–274. Cleveland: American Society for Metals, 1948.
7. E. G. Thomsen, I. Cornet, I. Lotze, and J. E. Dorn, "Investigation on the Validity of an Ideal Theory of Elasto-Plasticity for Wrought Aluminum Alloys," National Advisory Committee for Aeronautics, T.N. no. 1552, pp. 1–47 (1948).
8. Private communication from E. G. Thomsen.
9. W. Weibull, "A Statistical Theory of the Strength of Materials," *Ing. Vetenskaps Akad., 151,* 1–45 (1939).
10. C. Zener, "The Micro-Mechanism of Fracture," *Fracturing of Metals,* pp. 3–31. Cleveland: American Society for Metals, 1948.
11. G. I. Taylor, "The Mechanism of Plastic Deformation of Crystals," *Proc. Roy. Soc. (London), A, 145,* 363–404 (1934).
12. E. Orowan, "Zur Kristallplastizität. III. Über den Mechanismus des Gleitvorganges," *Z. Physik, 89,* 634–659 (1934).
13. P. Ludwik, *Elemente der Technologischen Mechanik.* Berlin, 1909.
14. D. K. Felbeck and E. Orowan, "Experiments on Brittle Fracture of Steel Plates," *Welding J.,* Res. Suppl., pp. 570-s–575-s (November 1955).
15. E. Orowan, "Fundamentals of Brittle Behavior in Metals," *Fatigue and Fracture of Metals,* p. 154. New York: John Wiley & Sons, 1952.
16. G. Hudson and M. Greenfield, "Speed of Propagation of Brittle Cracks in Steel," *J. Appl. Phys., 18,* 4, 405–407 (1947).
17. H. E. Kennedy, "Some Causes of Brittle Failures in Welded Mild Steel Structures," *Welding J.,* Res. Suppl., pp. 588-s–598-s (November 1945).
18. G. R. Irwin and J. A. Kies, "Fracturing and Fracture Dynamics," *Welding J.,* Res. Suppl., pp. 95-s–100-s (February 1952).
19. E. R. Parker, H. E. Davis, and A. E. Flanigan, "A Study of the Tension Test," *Proc. Am. Soc. Testing Materials, 46,* 1159–1174 (1946).
20. M. Gensamer, *Strength of Metals under Combined Stresses,* pp. 54, 55. Cleveland: American Society for Metals, 1941.
21. P. Ludwik, "Die Bedeutung des Gleit- und Reisswiderstandes für die Werkstoffprüfung," *Z. Ver. deut. Ing., 71*:2, 1532–1538 (1927).
22. P. W. Bridgman, "The Stress Distribution at the Neck of a Tension Specimen," *Trans. Am. Soc. Metals, 32,* 553–574 (1944).
23. E. R. Parker, H. E. Davis, and A. E. Flanigan, "A Study of the Tension Test," *Proc. Am. Soc. Testing Materials, 46,* 1159–1174 (1946).

24. G. I. Taylor and H. Quinney, "The Plastic Distortion of Metals," *Phil. Trans. Roy. Soc. (London) A, 230,* 323–362 (1931).
25. J. Marin, *Strength of Materials,* pp. 229–242. New York: The Macmillan Co., 1949.
26. E. Siebel and A. F. Maier, "Einfluss des Spannungszustandes auf das Formänderungsvermögen der Metallischen Werkstoffe," *Z. Ver. deut. Ing., 77,* 1345–1349 (1933).
27. E. G. Thomsen and J. E. Dorn, "The Effect of Combined Stresses on the Ductility and Rupture Strength of Magnesium Alloy Extrusions," *J. Aeronaut. Sci., 11, 2,* 125–136 (1944).
28. E. G. Thomsen, D. M. Cunningham, and J. E. Dorn, "Fracture of Some Aluminum Alloys under Combined Stress," *Trans. Am. Soc. Mech. Engrs., 69,* 81–87 (1947).
29. R. C. Grassi and I. Cornet, "Fracture of Gray Cast Iron Tubes under Biaxial Stresses," *J. Appl. Mechanics, 16,* 2, 178–182.
30. E. A. Davis, "Yielding and Fracture of Medium Carbon Steel under Combined Stress," *J. Appl. Mechanics, 12,* 1, A13–A24.
31. G. E. Troxell, E. R. Parker, H. E. Davis, and A. Boodberg, "The Effect of Temperature and Welding Conditions on the Strength of Large Welded Tubes," *Welding J.,* Res. Suppl., pp. 34-s–49-s (February 1948).
32. L. V. Griffis, G. K. Morikawa, and S. J. Fraenkel, "Tests on Flow and Fracture of Welded and Unwelded Tubes of Steel," *Welding J.,* Res. Suppl., pp. 161-s–208-s (April 1948).
33. P. W. Bridgman, *Studies in Large Plastic Flow and Fracture,* pp. 39–86, 294–305. New York: McGraw-Hill Book Co., 1952.
34. P. W. Bridgman, "Fracture and Hydrostatic Pressure," *Fracturing of Metals,* pp. 246–261. Cleveland: American Society for Metals, 1948.
35. N. Davidenkov and P. Sakharov, "On the Influence of Cold Working upon the Brittleness of Steel," *Tech. Phys. U.S.S.R., 5,* 743–757 (1938).
36. H. E. Davis, E. R. Parker, and A. Boodberg, "A Study of the Transition from Shear to Cleavage Fracture in Mild Steel," *Proc. Am. Soc. Testing Materials, 47,* 483–499 (1947).
37. J. J. Lynch, E. J. Ripling, and G. Sachs, "Effect of Various Stress Histories on the Flow and Fracture Characteristics of the Aluminum Alloy 24 S-T," *Metals Technology,* pp. 1–24. American Institute of Mining and Metallurgical Engineers: 1948. Technical paper No. 2307.

CHAPTER IV

Test Specimens and Methods

INTRODUCTION

This chapter contains a general description of the specimens and test methods now used for evaluating the tendency of steel to behave in a brittle manner. The more interesting portion of this story, i.e., interpretations and comparisons of test results, is presented in Chapters V and VI. Readers already familiar with the numerous specimens and tests currently employed can glance quickly through the following pages, while those less familiar with the subject will find it advantageous to review the specimen designs and test methods described herein.

Standard dimensions have not been adopted for all types of specimens; many of the types employed for testing will, therefore, be portrayed by sketches showing only the general shape. However, numerous references are given in the text so that the details of specimen design and testing procedure can be obtained; dimensions of some of the nonstandard specimens will be given in Chapters V and VI, wherein test results are reported for various kinds of specimens.

Mechanical testing serves a twofold purpose: first, it provides engineering data for design, and second, it is useful for checking the quality of a material or evaluating a method of fabrication. Several types of unnotched tensile and bend specimens that are in general use have been standardized. Unfortunately, unnotched specimens are not particularly useful for evaluating the tendency of a material to fail in a brittle manner; notched specimens, however, are very useful for this purpose. The Charpy impact specimen is one of the few notched specimens that has been standardized.

The results obtained from notched bars are not readily interpreted in terms of design requirements; even with the Charpy specimen there has not been general agreement on the interpretation or on the significance of test results. Investigators, in order to obtain a better understanding of the notch brittleness problem, have tested many kinds of nonstandard notched specimens. All of these have been useful to a certain extent for evaluating notch toughness, but their relative merits are difficult to evaluate. A better understanding of the behavior of steel in service is needed to provide a sound basis for the selection of a suitable test specimen or specimens; also it is necessary to select a suitable criterion of performance. With the diversity of specimen design, different testing procedures, and differing interpretations that are presently in use, it is difficult to make any meaningful comparisons of the results obtained in the various investigations. Possibly a single standard test will never be adopted, for it is argued that plate thickness, welding conditions, and service conditions vary so much from one application to another that the selection of a single standard would be impossible. It is true, however, that tests which are similar, but not identical, are often made with the common objective of indicating the ability of a material to perform in a particular kind of service without failing in a brittle manner. Although such tests may be similar, variations in specimen geometry, testing procedure, or the selection of different criteria of brittle behavior may preclude accurate comparison or correlation of results. It is to the advantage of all concerned to use, whenever possible, generally accepted specimen designs rather than modifications thereof.

There are several dozen types of specimens and test methods now in common use, the general classifications of which are outlined in Table 4.1. The specimens fall into two basic groups—unwelded and welded—and into the following three subdivisions: (1) cylindrical, (2) square or rectangular cross section, (3) special shapes. Each of these may be loaded (*a*) in tension, (*b*) by bending, or (*c*) with a combination of tension and bending.

Mechanical tests on welded specimens are more difficult to interpret because of the additional variables introduced by the welding. Many of the tests made on welds are not mechanical in nature, e.g., radiographic inspection for soundness and microscopic examination of sections for underbead cracking. Such tests, as well as those of the mechanical type, are commonly called *weldability* tests. These are

TABLE 4.1

OUTLINE SHOWING SPECIMEN TYPES AND METHODS OF LOADING

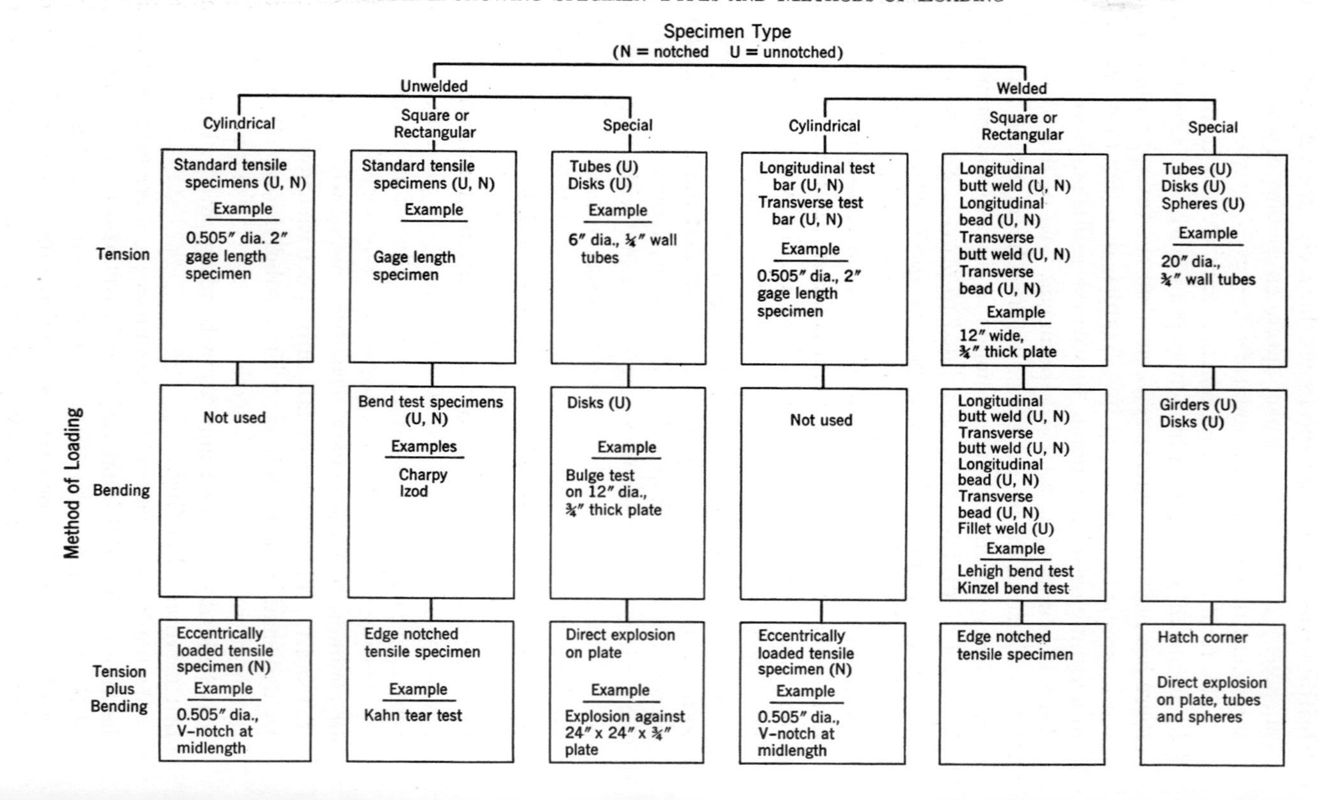

Specimen Type (N = notched U = unnotched)

Method of Loading	Unwelded: Cylindrical	Unwelded: Square or Rectangular	Unwelded: Special	Welded: Cylindrical	Welded: Square or Rectangular	Welded: Special
Tension	Standard tensile specimens (U, N) Example 0.505″ dia. 2″ gage length specimen	Standard tensile specimens (U, N) Example Gage length specimen	Tubes (U) Disks (U) Example 6″ dia., ¼″ wall tubes	Longitudinal test bar (U, N) Transverse test bar (U, N) Example 0.505″ dia., 2″ gage length specimen	Longitudinal butt weld (U, N) Longitudinal bead (U, N) Transverse butt weld (U, N) Transverse bead (U, N) Example 12″ wide, ¾″ thick plate	Tubes (U) Disks (U) Spheres (U) Example 20″ dia., ¾″ wall tubes
Bending	Not used	Bend test specimens (U, N) Examples Charpy Izod	Disks (U) Example Bulge test on 12″ dia., ¾″ thick plate	Not used	Longitudinal butt weld (U, N) Transverse butt weld (U, N) Longitudinal bead (U, N) Transverse bead (U, N) Fillet weld (U) Example Lehigh bend test Kinzel bend test	Girders (U) Disks (U)
Tension plus Bending	Eccentrically loaded tensile specimen (N) Example 0.505″ dia., V-notch at midlength	Edge notched tensile specimen Example Kahn tear test	Direct explosion on plate Example Explosion against 24″ x 24″ x ¾″ plate	Eccentrically loaded tensile specimen (N) Example 0.505″ dia., V-notch at midlength	Edge notched tensile specimen	Hatch corner Direct explosion on plate, tubes and spheres

further classified as *joinability* tests, which are concerned with the soundness of a weld; and *performance* tests, which are used to indicate the mechanical performance of a weldment in service. Determination of weldability has been adequately treated elsewhere[1] and consequently will not be elaborated upon here except insofar as it is related to the brittle fracture problem.

As may be seen in Table 4.1, mechanical tests on welded and unwelded specimens are similar. In the cases of welded specimens which have been notched, however, the location of the notch is critical because each zone in the weld will have different properties. Some of these zones are narrow, whereas others are wide; thus small variations in the location and/or size of the notch can cause large differences in the results obtained. For example, a specimen containing martensite in the heat-affected zone adjacent to the weld would behave in a brittle manner if notched in this region but would ordinarily exhibit tough and ductile characteristics if the notch were located in a nearby portion of the base plate and did not pass through the martensitic zone.

As indicated in the table by the letters "U" and "N," many of the tests are made on both unnotched or notched specimens. Information obtained from a notched specimen test is entirely different from that contributed by its unnotched counterpart. The latter gives values for yield strength, ultimate strength, and ductility—data directly useful for design purposes. Notched specimens, on the other hand, provide information about the propensity of a material to fail in a brittle manner. Hence the primary function of notched bar tests is to measure the tendency of a steel to behave in a brittle manner when a structural discontinuity is present. *This is a property that cannot be evaluated by conventional tests with unnotched specimens.*

TESTS INVOLVING TENSILE LOADING

A brief description of some of the specimens used will be given to acquaint the reader with the more important types. The standard cylindrical tensile specimen is shown in Fig. 4.1, along with its notched counterpart. Although only the dimensions for a 0.505-in. diameter bar are given, there are other standard sizes for this type.[2,3] For the notched specimens the ratio of minimum to maximum diameter, d/D, the root radius, r, and the notch angle, θ, are variables. Both of these types of specimens are normally tested with a slowly applied axial tensile load in an ordinary testing machine. Occasionally, however, they are subjected to impact loading in special machines.[4] Also notched specimens are sometimes loaded eccentrically, thereby pro-

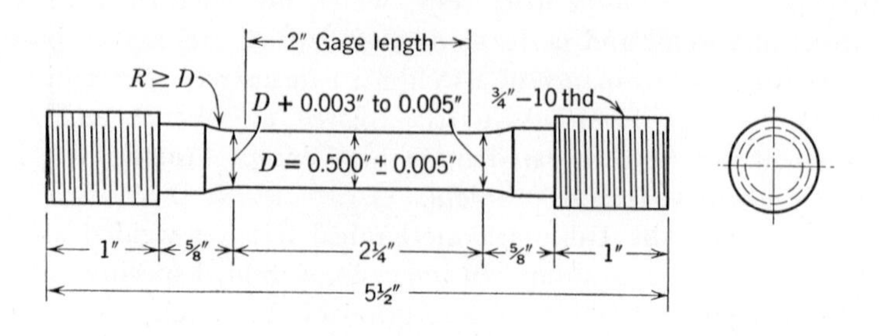

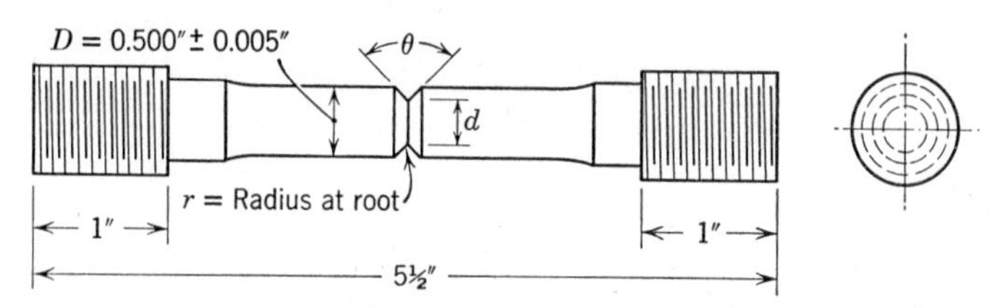

Fig. 4.1 Standard cylindrical tensile specimen and notched counterpart.

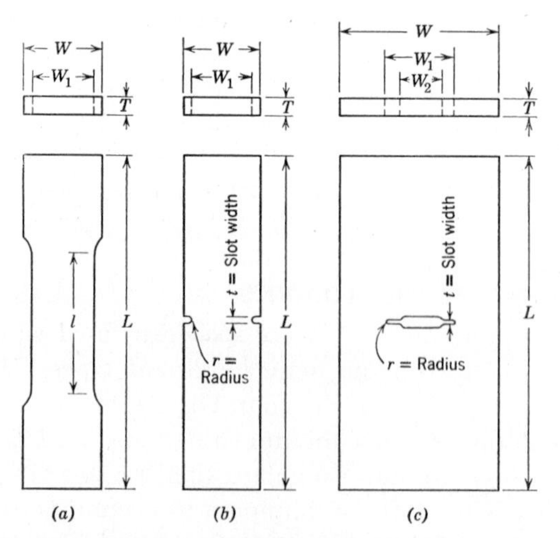

Fig. 4.2 Notched and unnotched specimens of rectangular cross sections. (a) Standard ASTM specimen of rectangular cross section. (b) Nonstandard specimen of rectangular cross section with side notches. (c) Nonstandard specimen of rectangular cross section with center notches.

ducing a combination of tension and bending.[5] The effect of impact loading is to raise the transition temperature by increasing the strain rate, while the effect of eccentric loading is to alter the state of stress at the base of the notch in such a manner that the probability of brittle behavior is enhanced.

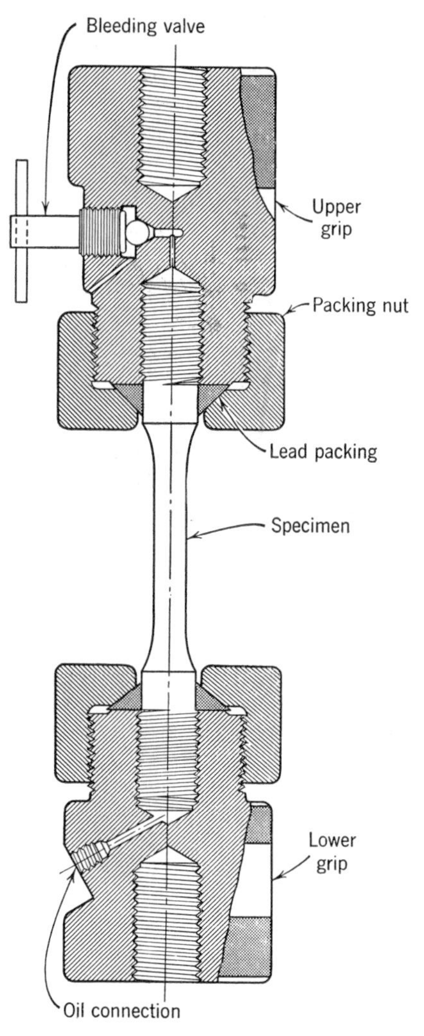

Fig. 4.3 Tubular test specimen for biaxial stress studies.

Fig. 4.2 illustrates specimens having rectangular cross sections. There are standard dimensions given by ASTM[3] for the width, *W*, gage length, *l*, overall length, *L*, and thickness, *T*, of the type shown as (*a*) in this figure. However, the dimensions of most corresponding notched specimens have not been standardized; consequently, a variety of notches have been used, such as hacksaw cuts, drilled holes at the end of sawed or milled slots, and milled notches of various sharpnesses and depths. Specimens having the general shape shown in Fig. 4.2(*c*) have been made in widths up to 9 ft.

A tubular shape, such as that shown in Fig. 4.3, is useful for tests involving biaxial stresses. By using both internal pressure and axial loading, the stress ratio can be varied over a wide range. Both seamless and welded tubes have been subjected to tests of this type at various temperatures.[6,7,8] Seamless tubes are available only up to about 2 ft in diameter. Larger tubes must be made by welding, which modifies the behavior and complicates the analysis of results. Both axial and circumferential welds may be tested in this manner, however, because the ratio of axial to circumferential stress can be regulated by controlling the axial load and the internal pressure.

A few experiments have been made with specimens having unusual shapes, such as spheres [9] loaded internally and disks spun in a vacuum about an axis normal to the plane of the disk.[10] The loads causing failure in spherical specimens produce equal biaxial tension stresses, a stress state approached at the center of the disk-shaped specimen.

Along with the sketches of a sphere and disk in Fig. 4.4 is shown a

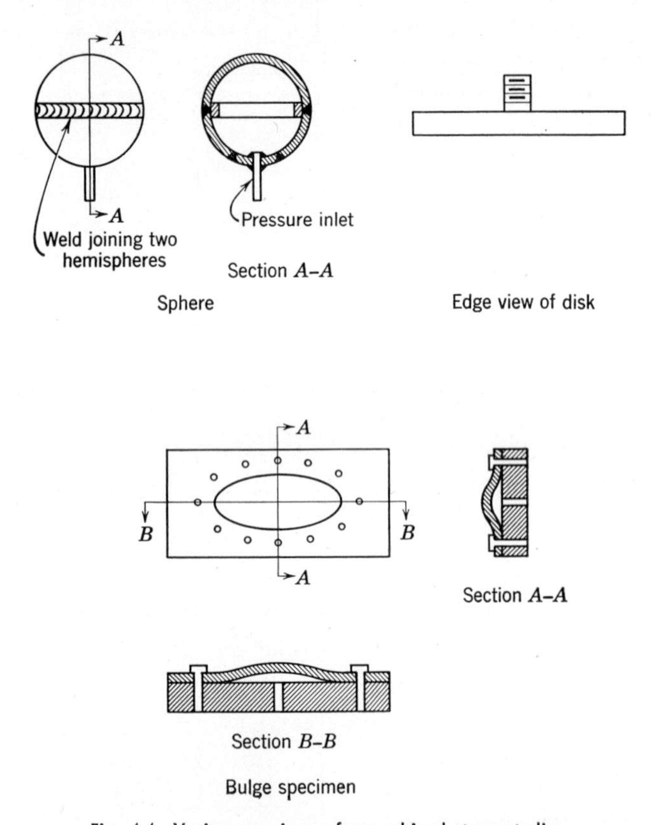

Fig. 4.4 Various specimens for combined stress studies.

bulge test specimen. This type is made from a flat plate that is clamped over a heavy base by a cover. The cover has an opening (which may be circular or elliptical, depending upon the biaxial stress ratio desired), through which the specimen is forced to expand by the fluid pumped between the plate and the base. Bulge specimens, as well as spheres and disks, have found but little use because of the small range of stress ratios obtainable with such specimens and because of the difficulties involved in making specimens or conducting the tests. Bulge tests are particularly useful, however, when explosives are employed for loading.[11]

Theoretical considerations and extensive experimental investigations have shown rather clearly that biaxial tension tests (in the absence of structural discontinuities, which introduce a third component of tensile stress) are of little value in brittle fracture studies. As was pointed out in Chapter III, metals subjected to biaxial tension behave very much as they would under uniaxial tension except that brittle behavior occurs at a somewhat higher temperature than that found with simple tension tests.[12]

Results obtained from welded specimens require a more critical analysis than those from unwelded types because of the multiplicity of variables introduced by the welding. Some of the many kinds of specimens used are sketched in Figs. 4.5 and 4.6. The all-weld metal standard cylindrical tensile specimen, Fig. 4.5(*a*), is commonly used in measurements of the ordinary mechanical properties of weld de-

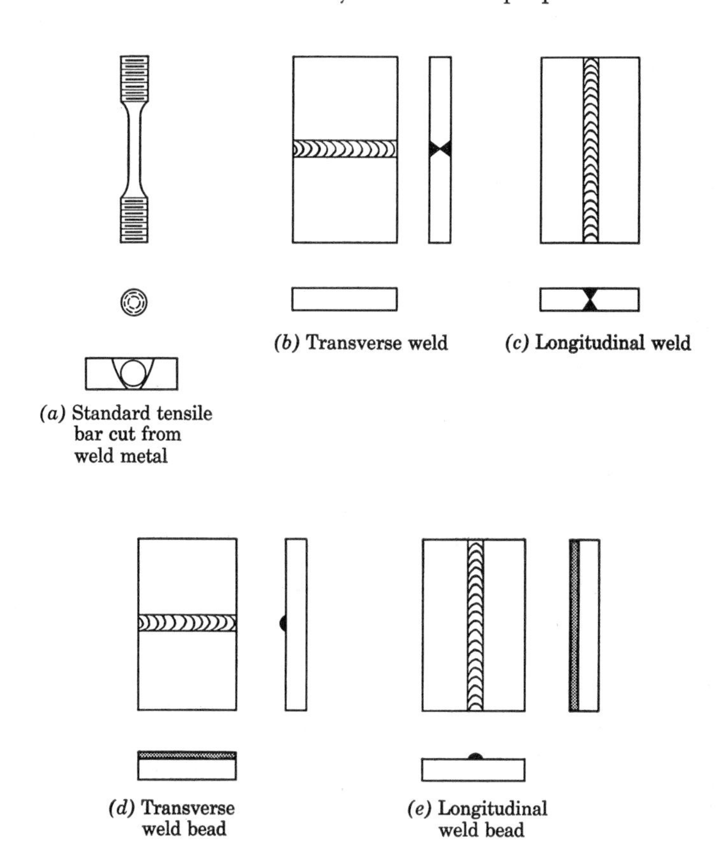

Fig. 4.5 Several types of unnotched welded tensile test specimens.

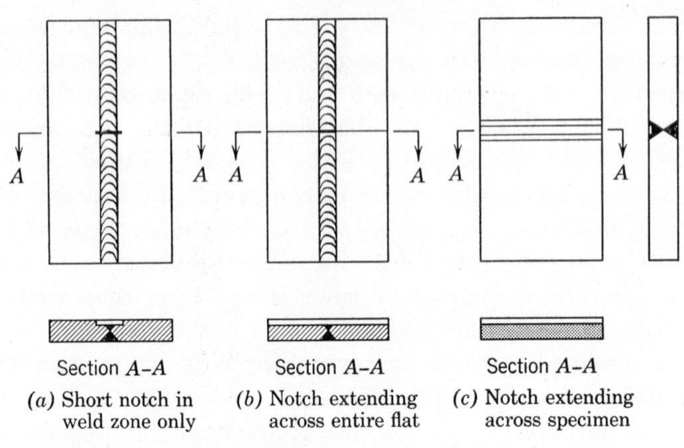

Fig. 4.6 Several types of large notched welded tensile specimens.

posits. However, the results obtained therefrom sometimes fail to provide a true indication of service performance in multipass welds because the overlying passes heat treat and refine the structure of the earlier ones, thereby improving the properties. The last passes deposited do not receive this beneficial reheating and consequently are less ductile than a test bar taken from the re-heated passes would indicate. The longitudinal weld tensile specimen, Fig. 4.5(*c*), is not subject to this criticism because all zones of the weld and base plate are forced to elongate equally when this specimen is pulled. Any brittle region, therefore, will be revealed by the formation of cracks at low strains.

A single bead is sometimes deposited on a test plate to obtain a preliminary evaluation of a welding technique or of an electrode. Such specimens are simpler to make than those involving full penetration butt welds, but they are generally less ductile. This is due in part to the more rapid cooling associated with single bead deposits; in multipass welding the plate is generally heated to a greater extent, and the final passes consequently cool more slowly. Other factors that cause differences in behavior between bead and full weld tests are: (1) the arc is less protected during the deposition of a bead, and so more oxygen and nitrogen are absorbed by the weld metal; and (2) there is greater dilution of the weld metal by the base plate when a single bead is deposited.

The transverse weld test shown in Fig. 4.5(*b*) has no particular merit for brittle fracture studies but is most useful in its ability to evaluate "joint efficiency," i.e., the ratio of tensile load required to break the welded joint to that needed to fracture an unwelded plate. Whenever the weld or heat-affected zone is weaker than the base plate, the joint efficiency is less than 100 per cent. This happens when steels having tensile strengths in excess of about 70,000 psi are welded with mild steel electrodes. On the other hand, when structural carbon steel is welded, the weld, unless defective, will almost invariably be stronger than the base plate.

Notched welded tensile specimens as sketched in Fig. 4.6 are in only limited use because a large tensile machine is required for testing such large specimens. However, similar specimens are frequently tested by bending because bend tests are easy to perform even with a small machine. Notches across the welds (in the longitudinal weld specimens shown as (*a*) and (*b*) in the figure) are of two general types; in one case the notch extends across the weld zone only; in the other the full width of the plate is notched. Specimen (*c*), which has a transverse weld, is notched along the centerline of the weld for the full width of the specimen. Tests conducted on this latter design are of value for revealing the notch brittleness of the weld metal, but they tell nothing about the properties of the heat-affected zone or base plate.

TESTS INVOLVING BENDING

Tests involving bending or a combination of tension and bending are more commonly used in brittle fracture studies than are those employing tension. Specimens subjected to bending loads are similar to those just described for simple tension except that they are generally shorter, a modification made possible because extra length is not required for gripping. Some of the most common shapes are sketched in Figs. 4.7 and 4.8. The first figure shows types of small specimens that have been in use for many years; those illustrated in Fig. 4.8 are of more recent vintage. The latter types were designed to reveal the tendency of welded specimens to fail in a brittle manner. However, the smaller specimens, such as the Charpy or Izod, are sometimes machined from the weld metal, the heat-affected zone, or the base plate to reveal the relative brittleness of these regions.

Of the small specimens Charpy bars are used almost exclusively in the United States, while the Izod type is favored in Great Britain. Both Charpy and Izod specimens are broken by the impact of a heavy swinging pendulum pivoted about a horizontal axis above the specimen.[13] The Charpy specimen is held in a horizontal position by supports at each end. The pendulum applies the load at the midspan and directly opposite the notch. The notched side is thus subjected to a tensile stress as the specimen is forced to bend by the moving pendulum. The Izod specimen is clamped at one end and held in a vertical

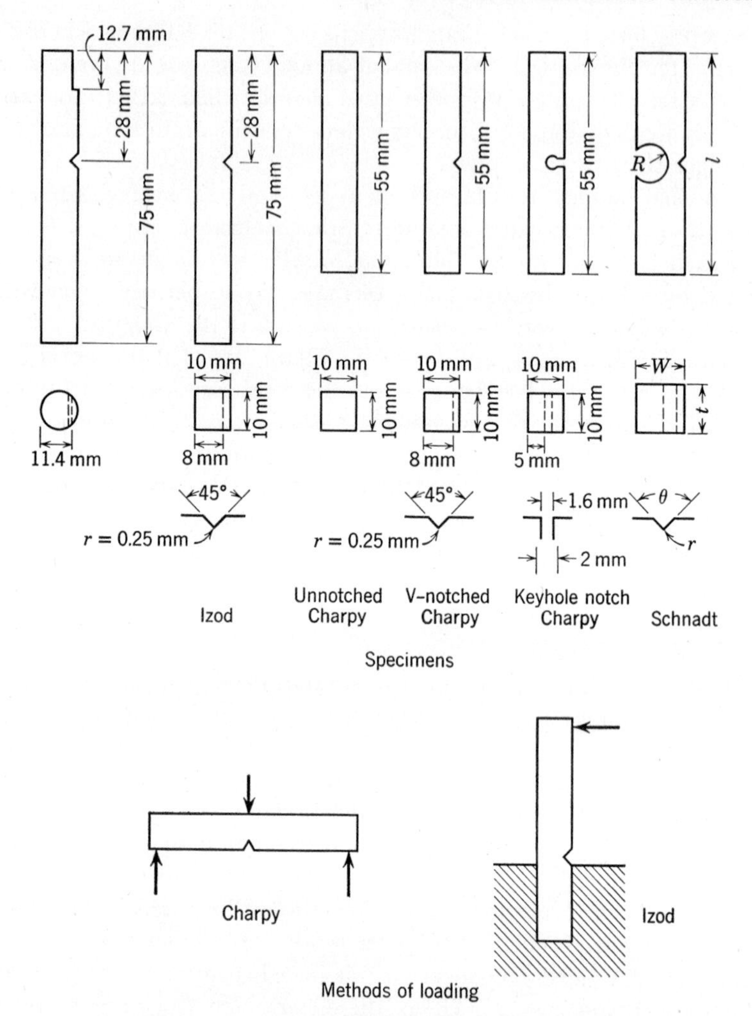

Fig. 4.7 Various types of small bend specimens machined from weld metal, heat-affected zone, or base plate.

plane. It is loaded as a cantilever beam by the pendulum, which strikes the specimen near the free end, and a tensile stress is induced in the material at the base of the notch.

The Schnadt specimen [14] is a recent addition to the small bar group. It is similar to the Charpy type except that the notch geometry is permitted to vary; the Schnadt specimen can be tested in a Charpy impact machine. This specimen contains a close-fitting hardened steel pin inserted in a cylindrical hole on the compression side of the

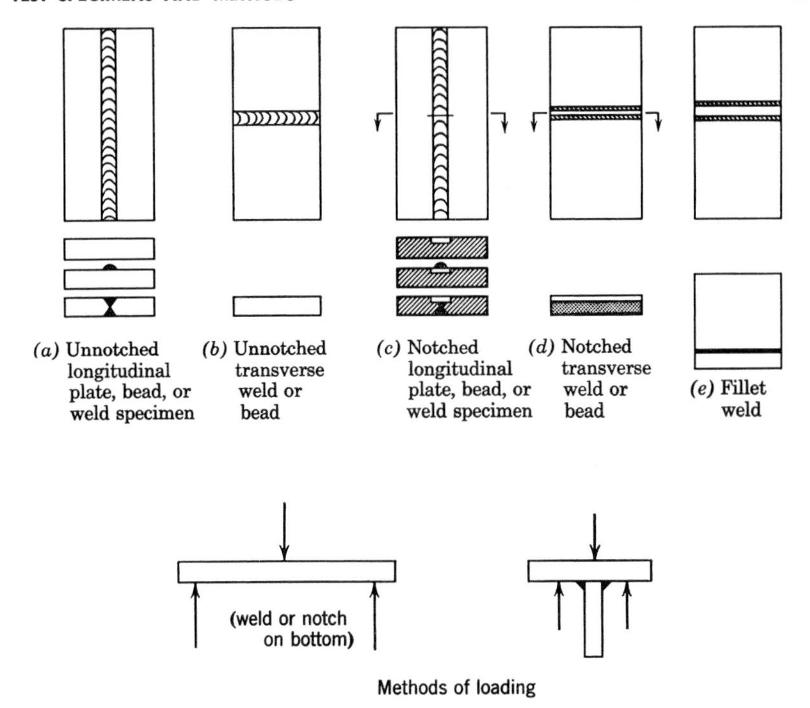

Fig. 4.8 Newer types of welded bend specimens useful for revealing tendency to brittle failure.

specimen. This pin does not yield during the test; hence, the tension zone is forced to contribute the entire plastic strain. According to Weck,[14] Schnadt has postulated that the stress in the metal between the pin and the notch is one of triaxial tension, varying in degree and depending upon the geometry of the notch. He suggested that the stress ratios can be calculated, but there is little evidence to support this contention. The Schnadt specimen seems to have no advantage over the Charpy bars for rating steels according to the order of their transition temperatures, but it does eliminate the energy absorbed on the compression side of the specimen and has the further advantage that it always breaks into two pieces, thus permitting easy examination.

The trend in this country is toward increasing use of V-notched Charpy specimens for evaluating the relative brittleness of steels, but the keyhole notch is still favored by many. The V-notch, being sharper, yields a higher transition temperature than the rounded keyhole notch type. Furthermore, the V-notch is thought to represent actual structural discontinuities better than the keyhole notch. A good correlation has been found between V-notch Charpy properties and service failures of ships; [15] it should be kept in mind, however, that a correlation also exists between V-notch results and results obtained with keyhole specimens.[16] This discussion will be more fully developed in Chapters V and VI.

Welded specimens should be prepared under conditions as nearly like those employed in practice as possible. If this is not done, the test results will have little practical significance. Consequently, the following items must be taken into account when tests are made on notched welded specimens:

1. Wide full-thickness specimens should be used so that welding conditions are equivalent to those in practice.
2. Tests should be made on large enough specimens so that the weld deposit, heat-affected zone, and a portion of the unaffected base plate are included.
3. Specimens should be wide enough so that transverse stresses will develop in a bend test; a width in excess of five times the plate thickness is adequate for any type of specimen, although narrower specimens are satisfactory when sharp notches are used.
4. Tests should be made over a greater range of temperatures than that expected in service.
5. The specimens should contain sharp notches to simulate the worst defects that might be found in an actual structure.

The unnotched longitudinal weld test will not necessarily provide accurate information about the ductility that can be expected from a weld in service because such a laboratory specimen will not likely contain as bad a discontinuity as will be present in service welds. Ordinary commercial welds generally contain worse structural discontinuities in the form of slag inclusions, gas holes, cracks, and incomplete penetration than those present in carefully prepared laboratory specimens. Furthermore, simple test specimens do not contain the structural discontinuities present in structures having complex designs. To obviate these shortcomings, the notched longitudinal weld specimen shown as (*c*) in Fig. 4.8 is frequently used. The notch induces a behavior similar to that expected in the neighborhood of a severe discontinuity, such as a weld crack or an abrupt change in section. Thus the notched specimen gives an indication of the worst performance that can be anticipated, while the unnotched specimen indicates the best that can be expected.

Bending of a wide unnotched plate produces a biaxial stress when the width is much greater than the thickness. This is caused by the tendency of the tension side to contract in width, while the compression side tends to become wider. The net result is that neither side is able to undergo any significant transverse strain. The relations between stress and strain given below show that when the transverse strain is zero the transverse stress is equal to Poisson's ratio times the longitudinal stress (when ϵ_w and σ_t are both zero, $\sigma_w = \mu\sigma_l$)

$$\begin{aligned}\epsilon_l &= \frac{1}{E}[\sigma_l - \mu(\sigma_t + \sigma_w)] \\ \epsilon_w &= \frac{1}{E}[\sigma_w - \mu(\sigma_l + \sigma_t)] \\ \epsilon_t &= \frac{1}{E}[\sigma_t - \mu(\sigma_l + \sigma_w)]\end{aligned} \tag{1}$$

where ϵ_l, ϵ_w, and ϵ_t are, respectively, the strains in the longitudinal, width, and thickness directions.

E = Young's modulus in elastic range, or the reciprocal of a proportionality constant in plastic range.

σ_l, σ_w, and σ_t are, respectively, the stresses in the longitudinal, width, and thickness directions.

μ = Poisson's ratio, about 0.3 in the elastic range for steel.

Thus the maximum transverse stress is about one third of the longitudinal stress in the elastic range. Since the stress in the thickness direction must equal zero and biaxial stresses do not induce brittleness at ordinary temperatures, it is apparent that unnotched plates of materials that exhibit ductility in a tensile test must also be ductile in a bend test; this has been shown by experiment to be true. Biaxial tensile stresses will, however, induce brittleness at temperatures below atmospheric but above the very low temperatures required to induce brittleness in a tensile specimen. Whenever there is a notch present, the behavior is markedly altered even in the atmospheric temperature range because of the triaxial stress system induced by the notch.

Cracks sometimes form at low strain even in sound weld metal. This is particularly noticeable when the weld is located in a region where strain is concentrated, such as in a fillet weld. In general, weld deposits are less ductile than the base plate. When unnotched welded plates are bent with the weld parallel to the major stress direction, cracks generally appear first in the weld metal or heat-affected zone, as shown photographically in Fig. 4.9(*a*). If the temperature is high enough, e.g., 70 F in this case, the cracks merely open but do not extend very far into the more ductile base plate. At lower temperatures, however, the story is quite different. Fig. 4.9(*b*) shows that the crack which formed in the weld metal provided the notch necessary to make the plate fracture by cleavage and with greatly lowered ductility when the test temperature was lowered to 32 F.

Many welds, of course, have excellent ductility. For example, most of the welds made by the submerged arc technique, those made with certain coated electrodes when preheat or postheat is used, and those made with low hydrogen electrodes are frequently nearly as ductile and tough as the metal in the base plate.

(a)

(b)

Fig. 4.9 Photographs of cracks in unnotched welded bend specimens at two test temperatures. (a) Shows crack in weld metal or heat-affected zone, test temperature 70 F. (b) Shows crack in weld metal propagated far into base plate, test temperature 32 F.

The transverse weld tensile specimen almost invariably breaks in the base metal. This behavior has been summarized in the commonly used expression, "The weld is stronger than the base plate." This is a dangerous and misleading concept because many specimens that appear ductile in a transverse weld test are brittle when tested with the weld in the longitudinal direction. When the weld is longitudinal, all elements—the weld, the heat-affected zone, and the base plate—are forced to undergo equal strains. If the heat-affected zone is martensitic, it will crack at a very low strain, and this crack may propagate by cleavage, causing the specimen to fracture in a brittle manner. In the transverse weld specimen, however, the heat-affected zone need not undergo any plastic strain at all. The elastic limit of the hardened heat-affected zone is generally well above the maximum stress that the weld or the base plate can support. Hence all plastic deformation will be forced to occur in the weaker, but ductile, base plate. Thus a specimen with a hard brittle zone may bend through a large angle and appear ductile when the transverse weld specimen is tested but may be brittle when the weld is placed in the longitudinal direction.

Some investigators [11] have employed explosive charges to provide impulse loading to plates and cylinders. Examples of these are shown in Fig. 4.10. The charge may be in direct contact or spaced away from

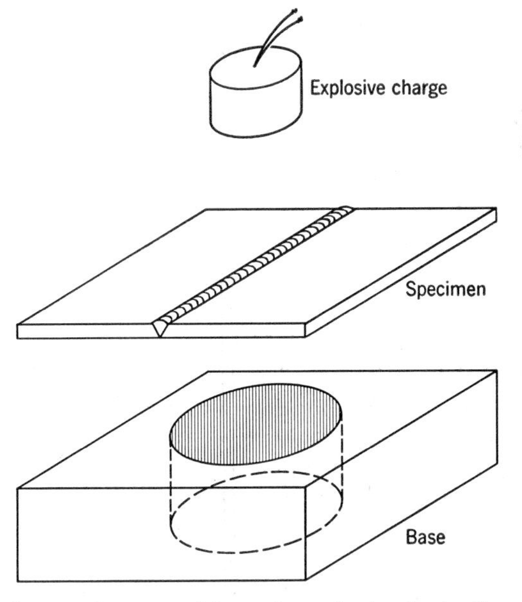

Fig. 4.10 Specimens and setup used for testing under impulse loading with explosive charges.[11]

the specimen surface, depending upon the loading requirement. Direct contact causes local damage, which complicates the interpretation; the "stand-off" charge spaced away from the surface is less severe. Impulse loading creates a triaxial tensile stress and is capable of inducing brittle behavior. The initial impulse travels into the metal as a triaxial compressive stress wave, which is reflected from the opposite surface as triaxial tension. While the compression wave is not harmful insofar as inducing brittleness is concerned, the reflected tensile wave is capable of causing a cleavage fracture and inducing brittle behavior.

TESTS INVOLVING BOTH TENSION AND BENDING

Many of the test specimens in common use are loaded in such a way that the critical area around the notch is subjected to the simultaneous action of tension and bending. This type of loading has one advantage over bending alone in that it is possible to increase the tensile component of the load until the compressive stress, induced in some regions of a specimen by the bending, is eliminated. The existence of tensile stresses everywhere throughout the section creates a more favorable condition for crack propagation. Obviously, if the compressive stresses were high enough, a cleavage crack could not propagate through the compression zone; a cleavage crack could continue if no such zone existed. Thus the main advantage offered by the tension-bending tests seems to be to encourage crack propagation; the initiation of the crack should be substantially the same for bending alone as for tension plus bending. However, this conclusion should not be accepted without reservation because steeper stress gradients exist around notches when bending alone is used. Steeper stress gradients induce larger secondary tensile stresses, so bending is somewhat more likely to induce the formation of a cleavage crack than does combined tension and bending.

Tests involving tension plus bending cover a large range of specimen sizes from eccentrically loaded ½-in. diameter tensile specimens to full-scale welded "hatch-corner" specimens. Small simple specimens are economical to machine but do not necessarily yield results that are representative of the properties of larger sections. On the other hand, the testing of full-scale welded specimens while extremely illuminating is usually prohibitively expensive. Consequently, some investigators have attempted to design specimens that can be made and tested cheaply but that are sufficiently discriminating to indicate the behavior of the material in large sections. This approach is a reasonable one, but as yet attempts to correlate laboratory tests with service failures have met with only moderate success. This subject is developed further in a later chapter.

Some of the simple specimens used for combined loading tests are sketched in Fig. 4.11. The one shown in (*a*) of this figure is a notched tensile specimen that is stressed with a nonaxial load.[5] Eccentric loading is a simple means of applying both tension and bending, the bending moment being governed by the amount of eccentricity.

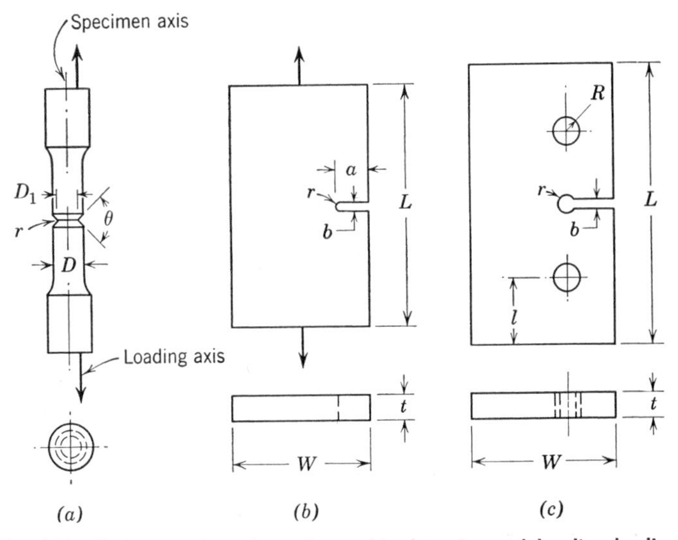

Fig. 4.11 Various specimen forms for combined tension and bending loading.

The plate specimen shown as (*b*) in the figure is of full thickness, but the width is generally limited to 3 or 4 in. by the size of the grips of the testing machine. Convenient lengths range from 18 to 24 in. This type of specimen, while suitable for crude exploratory work, is not very reliable because irregular gripping causes nonuniform loading. The Navy or Kahn tear test shown as (*c*) yields more reproducible results because the load is applied through pins. This test, which has been developed by Kahn and his co-workers,[17,18] has received considerable attention.

An example of a full-scale specimen is sketched in Fig. 4.12. This type was used to evaluate steels in a large complex welded design,[19] and similar specimens were used to evaluate various design modifications.[20,21] Specimens such as these are often 6 ft across and weigh more than a ton; single specimens frequently cost several thousand dollars to make and test. Consequently, the number of such tests

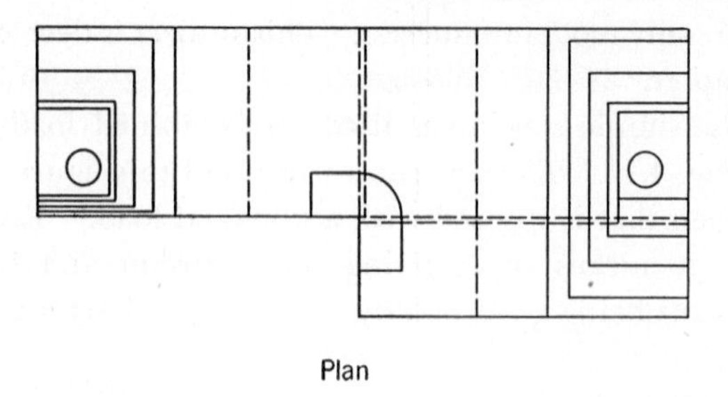

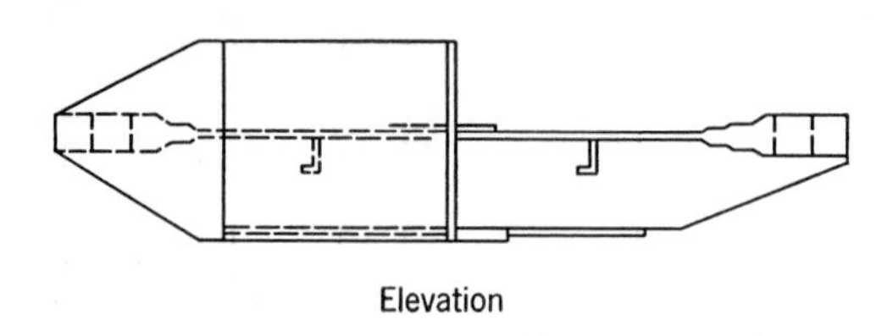

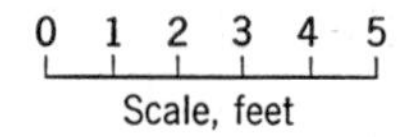

Fig. 4.12 Full-scale specimen (hatch corner) for combined tension and bending loading.[19]

that can be made is very limited, even though the data may be of direct value to the design engineer.

Robertson[22] has designed a specimen that uses a bending load to start a crack and a uniform tensile load to keep it going. The specimen is short and wide; its length is extended by welding on thinner pieces of steel, through which the tensile load is applied to the specimen. The thickness of these extension strips is so adjusted that yield point stress in these members produces the desired tensile stress in the test piece. The plastic flow that occurs in the extension members ensures an even distribution of load over the width of the specimen, and the ratio of thicknesses can be adjusted to provide any desired stress in the test section. This design enabled Robertson to use short test specimens and a simple hydraulic loading device.

In the Robertson specimen a cleavage crack is started at a notch on one edge of the plate by a bullet driven against a special nub by a small explosive charge. The amount of energy available from the explosion is insufficient to make the crack grow more than a very short distance but is large enough to start it. The uniform tensile load tends to keep the crack growing. In Robertson's tests the specimen (shown schematically in Fig. 4.13) contained a temperature gradi-

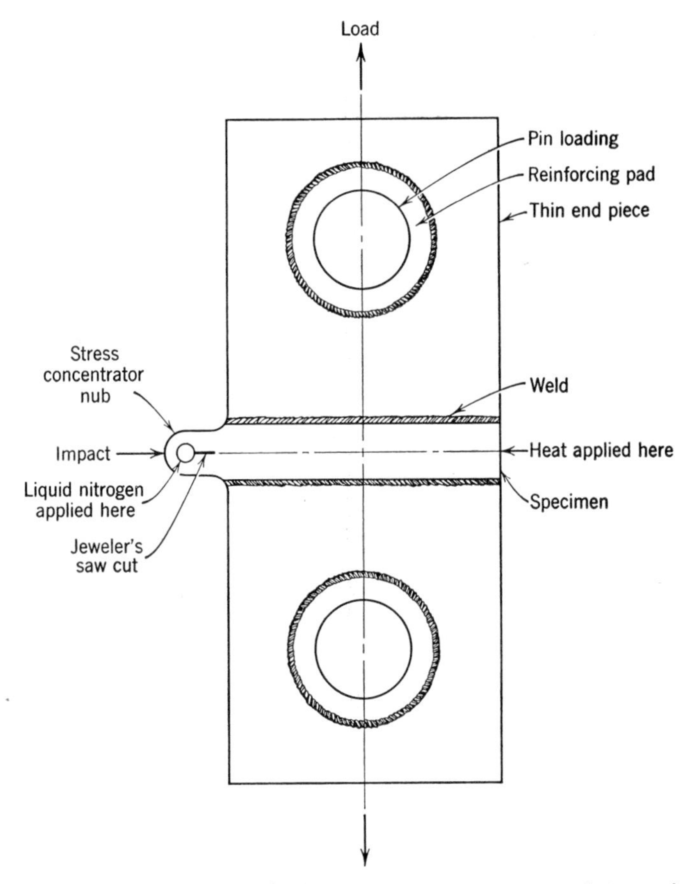

Fig. 4.13 Schematic representation of Robertson's test specimen using explosive crack starter.

ent in the width direction, with the notched side being colder. The crack traveled across the specimen until it reached a zone where the temperature was high enough to permit the material to flow sufficiently to stop the crack. At each stress level he found a temperature above which the crack would not propagate. When the temperature was low enough, the crack would continue to propagate at any stress above 10,000 psi. This test has subsequently been modified by others [23] into a constant temperature test to eliminate the complications introduced by the presence of a temperature gradient.

Even for a single steel or a single specimen, it is possible to employ several different criteria for judging brittle behavior, and each criterion yields a different value of transition temperature. The various criteria, their meanings, and interrelations will be discussed in detail in Chapter V. In Chapter VI the correlations between results from differing specimens made from the same steel will be discussed.

REFERENCES

1. R. D. Stout and W. D. Doty, *Weldability of Steels.* New York: Welding Research Council, 1953.
2. *Metals Handbook,* pp. 86–89. Cleveland: American Society for Metals, 1948.
3. "Mechanical Testing of Steel Products," *1953 Supplement to Book of ASTM Standards, Part I, Ferrous Metals,* p. 336. Philadelphia: American Society for Testing Materials, 1954.
4. D. S. Clark and G. Dätwyler, "Stress-Strain Relations under Tension Impact Loading," *Proc. Am. Soc. Testing Materials, 38,* 98–106 (1938).
5. G. Sachs, J. D. Lubahn, and L. J. Ebert, "Notched Bar Tensile Test Characteristics of Heat Treated Low Alloy Steels," *Trans. Am. Soc. Metals, 33,* 340–395 (1944).
6. J. M. Lessells and C. W. MacGregor, "Combined Stress Experiments on a Nickel-Chrome-Molybdenum Steel," *J. Franklin Inst., 230,* 163–181 (1940).
7. L. V. Griffis, G. K. Morikawa, and S. J. Fraenkel, "Tests on Flow and Fracture of Welded and Unwelded Tubes of Steel," *Welding J.,* Res. Suppl., pp. 161-s–168-s (April 1948).
8. G. E. Troxell, E. R. Parker, H. E. Davis, and A. Boodberg, "The Effect of Temperature and Welding Conditions on the Strength of Large Welded Tubes," *Welding J.,* Res. Suppl., pp. 34-s–49-s (February 1948).
9. J. L. Walmsley, "Spherical Shells Subjected to Internal Pressure and Low Temperatures," *Welding J.,* Res. Suppl., pp. 153-s–167-s (March 1951).
10. C. W. MacGregor and W. D. Tierney, "Developments in High-Speed Rotating Disk Research at M. I. T.," *Welding J.,* Res. Suppl., pp. 303-s–309-s (June 1948).
11. G. S. Mikhalapov, "Structural Strength of the Welded Joint" (Adams Lecture for 1947), *Welding J.,* pp. 193–206 (March 1948).
12. C. W. MacGregor and N. Grossman, "The Effect of Combined Stresses on the Transition Temperature for Brittle Fracture," *Welding J.,* Res. Suppl., pp. 7-s–16-s (June 1948).
13. S. L. Hoyt, "Notched-Bar Impact Tests," *Metals Handbook,* pp. 112–115. Cleveland: American Society for Metals, 1948.
14. R. Weck, "An Account of M. Henri M. Schnadt's Ideas on the Strength of Materials and His Testing Methods," *Trans. Inst. Welding (London), 13,* 41–56 (1950).
15. M. L. Williams, "Brittle Fractures in Ship Plates," *Mechanical Properties of Metals at Low Temperatures,* pp. 180–206. National Bureau of Standards Circ. 520, May 1952.
16. R. W. Vanderbeck and M. Gensamer, "Evaluating Notch Toughness," *Welding J.,* Res. Suppl., pp. 37-s–48-s (January 1950).

17. N. A. Kahn and E. A. Imbembo, "A Method of Evaluating Transition from Shear to Cleavage Failure in Ship Plate and Its Correlation with Large-Scale Plate Tests," *Welding J.*, Res. Suppl., pp. 169-s–182-s (April 1948).
18. N. A. Kahn and E. A. Imbembo, "Notch Sensitivity of Steel Evaluated by Tear Test," *Welding J.*, Res. Suppl., pp. 153-s–165-s (April 1949).
19. E. P. DeGarmo, J. L. Meriam, and R. C. Grassi, "Some Tests of Large Welded Structures," *Welding J.*, Res. Suppl., pp. 257-s–267-s (May 1947).
20. A. Boodberg and E. R. Parker, "Transition Temperature of Structural Steels," *Welding J.*, Res. Suppl., pp. 167-s–177-s (April 1949).
21. E. P. DeGarmo, "Tests of Various Designs of Welded Hatch Corners for Ships," *Welding J.*, Res. Suppl., pp. 50-s–68-s (February 1948).
22. T. S. Robertson, "Brittle Fracture of Mild Steel," *Engineering (London)*, *172*, 445–448 (1951).
23. F. J. Feely, Jr., D. Hrtko, S. R. Kleppe, and M. S. Northup, "Report on Brittle Fracture Studies," *Welding J.*, Res. Suppl., pp. 99-s–111-s (February 1954).

CHAPTER

Methods of Interpreting Test Results

INTRODUCTION

The literature on the brittle behavior of steel is extensive and contains a vast amount of data based upon different types of tests and different methods of evaluation. Few of the many papers presented on the subject have contained general analyses or summaries that would be useful for clarifying and correlating the results. An attempt has been made in this chapter to present the general pattern of results, showing the similarities and dissimilarities that exist and why. The use of test data has been restricted to the amount considered necessary for a clear understanding of the details of behavior.

MEANING OF TRANSITION TEMPERATURE

Notch toughness tests are conducted at various temperatures to determine the temperature range over which an appreciable change takes place in some measured value such as energy absorption, ductility, or fracture appearance. This change frequently occurs rather abruptly, as evidenced by a drop, for example, from relatively high energy absorption to much lower energy absorption at some lower testing temperature. When this type of behavior is observed, it has been found that the change does not occur at a single temperature but rather over a temperature range. In this range the data often show appreciable scatter, with many high values and low values being obtained along with a very few intermediate values. The range in which this scatter occurs is referred to as a transition range, and a typical example of such behavior is shown in Fig. 5.1 for keyhole Charpy impact tests.[1] A transition range is also obtained with numerous other types of specimens such as the Navy tear test,[2] the Schnadt-type notched slow bend test,[3] and the centrally notched wide plate tests.[4] In any particular test specimen a transition range can usually be determined from any one of a number of different measurements having to do with energy absorption, ductility, and fracture appearance. All of

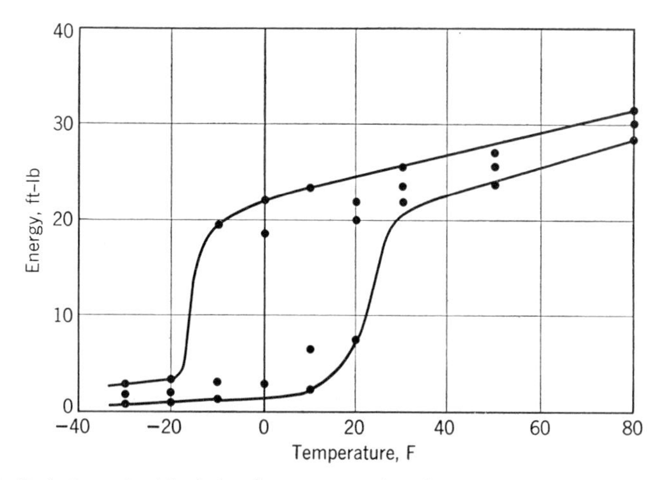

Fig. 5.1 Typical standard keyhole Charpy impact data for medium carbon structural steel.[1]

these measurements, however, will not necessarily give the same transition range even for a given steel and a single type of specimen.

The scatter that is typical of behavior in the transition range has been associated mainly with local variations in the properties of the steel itself.[5] It is possible that with a perfectly uniform steel the transition range could be greatly reduced and with some types of specimens could perhaps be made to occur at a single temperature (provided testing conditions and specimen dimensions were also invariant).

Ranges of temperature are difficult to work with when making comparisons. Moreover, evidence indicates that the width of the transition range is dependent upon the amount of testing near the apparent limits of the range and increases with the number of tests.[5]

It is therefore common practice to select some temperature within this range—for example, at the middle or at some selected level of performance—as the transition temperature and to use this particular temperature for the purpose of rating steels in respect to notch toughness. This seems like a satisfactory procedure since at present there is little hope of relating all the details of behavior in a test to behavior in service. Perhaps the most that can be hoped for is that some single value of temperature in the transition range could be selected that would approximately correlate with the critical temperature for satisfactory performance in service.

Abrupt transitions do not occur with many of the test specimens. An example illustrating such behavior is shown in Fig. 5.2, for the

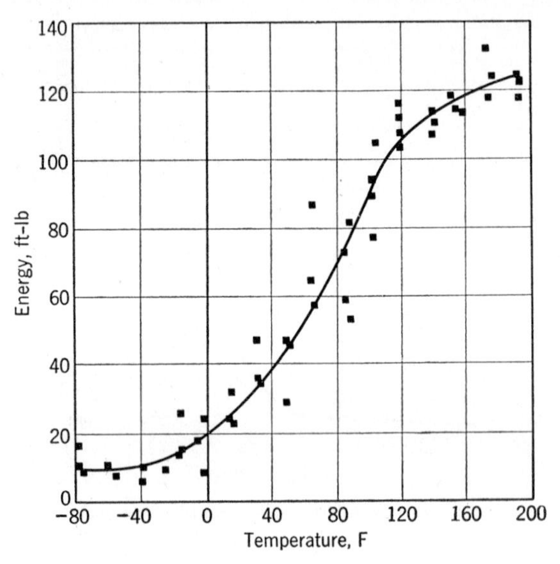

Fig. 5.2 Standard V-notch Charpy impact data for a low carbon, low alloy, hot-rolled steel.[1]

V-notch Charpy impact test. A transition definitely occurs but over a temperature range in which the performance changes rather gradually and uniformly. A critical temperature must therefore be selected at some arbitrary level of performance. This is commonly done, and the selected temperature is referred to as a transition temperature even though a discontinuity in behavior does not take place at a definite temperature as it does with some types of specimens. Both of the methods just described for selecting a transition temperature seem quite satisfactory, but the ultimate criterion of suitability is whether or not a correlation is obtained between the selected transition temperature and service performance.

The transition temperature of a steel will vary with the type of test specimen, with the rate at which the load is applied, and with the criterion of performance used for evaluation. This would not be so disturbing if the various evaluations of transition temperature could be correlated with each other, but unfortunately such is not the case. For example, Charpy impact test results do not correlate with results from centrally notched wide plate tests on the same steels. This is discussed in more detail in Chapter VI.

Stout and McGeady [6] and others have shown that the failure to obtain correlation between test results is in many cases the result of indiscriminate mixing of the criteria used to judge performance. These investigators state that the choice of specimen is far less critical for the correlation of test results than is the choice of the criterion used to establish the transition temperature. They showed that criteria of transition temperature may be divided roughly into two groups. Those in one group depend upon the mode of fracture and hence the fracture appearance. These criteria depend upon the way in which the crack propagates through the specimen and are a measure of what is commonly called a *fracture appearance transition temperature* (sometimes called the *fracture transition*). Those in the second group presumably reflect the relative ability of a steel to flow plastically before extensive cracking occurs. These criteria are concerned with the ductility of the metal at the notch apex and are used to determine what is commonly called a *ductility transition temperature.*

Osborn et al.[7] used Navy tear tests, Schnadt-type notched bend tests, and Lehigh notched bend tests to show how the ductility and fracture transition temperatures differ for each of these specimens. Fig. 5.3 shows some of their data obtained with the tear test specimen. The fracture transition temperature is clearly defined by the criteria of fracture appearance, per cent contraction at midpoint of the specimen, and energy absorbed after maximum load. These criteria indicate that completely brittle behavior would be obtained below 50 F. However, none of these criteria reflect the amount of plastic flow associated with the formation and initial extension of the crack. Other criteria (those of lateral contraction at the base of the notch and elongation across the notch) show that notch ductility is reduced to a low level only at temperatures well below 0°F. The *ductility transition* is thus somewhere below 0°F, the exact temperature being determined by the criterion of minimum ductility selected. If total energy absorbed had been used as a criterion (rather than energy after maximum load), the ductility transition would have been easier to detect.

The change in ductility near the notch apex is often associated with a change in fracture appearance of a very small area just under the notch. As this area changes in appearance from fibrous to granular, the ductility of the metal near the notch decreases rather abruptly and the *ductility transition* is said to occur. This transition is sometimes

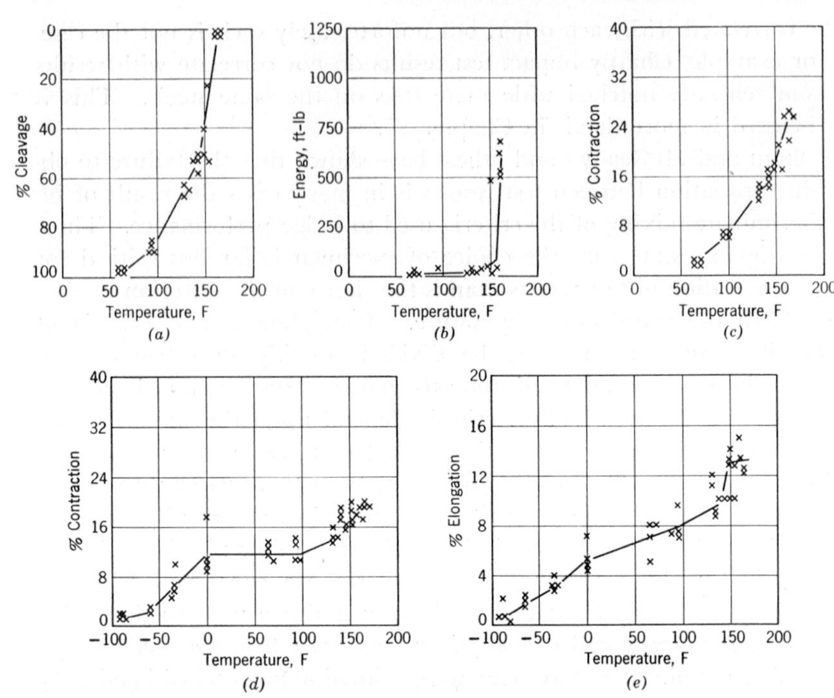

Fig. 5.3 Transition curves for Navy-type tear tests on as-rolled steel (ASTM Specification A-70, $1\frac{1}{4}$-in. thick, 0.18% C plain carbon rimming steel) using various criteria.[7] (*a*) Fracture appearance. (*b*) Energy after maximum load. (*c*) Per cent contraction at midpoint. (*d*) Per cent contraction below notch. (*e*) Per cent elongation $\frac{1}{4}$ in. below notch.

referred to as the transition from "relatively tough" (meaning that some energy can be absorbed by the metal just under the notch) to almost completely brittle behavior. An example of the last remnant of the fibrous appearing fracture is shown in Fig. 5.4. The little shear area at the notch apex is sometimes referred to as a "thumbnail."

The *fracture appearance transition* is the transition associated with the change from a completely fibrous (shear) to a predominantly granular (cleavage) fracture. In some specimens this change takes place abruptly, and the fracture appearance transition is selected as the temperature at which this change occurs. When the fracture appearance changes gradually, the selection of a transition temperature must be made at some arbitrary percentage of fibrous fracture, such as 50 per cent. In both of these cases the fracture appearance transition occurs at a higher level of energy absorption than that associated with the ductility transition. Thus the fracture appearance transition occurs at a higher temperature than the ductility transition. Under

Fig. 5.4 Photograph showing "thumbnail" appearance of shear area at notch apex.

certain conditions, the two transitions may occur at the same temperature, but the fracture appearance transition *never* occurs at a lower temperature than that of the ductility transition. This is a consequence of the observed physical behavior of the specimens and of the manner in which the two transitions have been defined.

Either transition may be measured by any of several criteria, but it is highly desirable to distinguish between these two types of transitional behavior and to avoid comparisons between test results where the criteria of performance are indiscriminately mixed.

Some performance curves, such as the V-notch Charpy curve in Fig. 5.2, do not exhibit any abrupt ductility or fracture appearance transitions. In such cases the criterion for the ductility transition temperature must be arbitrarily chosen and should always be selected so that the transition actually represents the change to almost completely brittle behavior. The ductility transition temperature for the V-notch Charpy curve should therefore be selected near the bottom of the energy-temperature curve, say, at 10 or 15 ft-lb. A fracture appearance transition temperature may be arbitrarily selected where the fracture appearance is 50 per cent fibrous, which is fairly high up on the energy-temperature performance curve—in this case at an energy level of 90 ft-lb.

In the keyhole Charpy test results reproduced in Fig. 5.1, the ductility transition occurs at a mean temperature of 5 F. It is associated with the change in fracture appearance of a small area just under the notch. Just above the ductility transition the fracture is only partly fibrous (e.g., at 30 F in Fig. 5.1 the fracture was 20 per cent fibrous); the amount of fibrous fracture just above the ductility transition depends on the type of steel being tested. The gradual increase in energy above the ductility transition is associated with a gradual change in the fracture appearance of the broken specimens from predominantly granular to entirely fibrous. A fracture appearance transition (for example, when the fracture surface is 50 per cent fibrous) may therefore occur at some higher energy level on this curve.

In the temperature range between the ductility and fracture appearance transitions, the properties vary continuously. It is possible, therefore, to select other criteria of performance, and evaluations of steels are sometimes made at such intermediate performance levels. This is of course permissible, since at present the extent to which these different evaluations in the various tests will correlate with performance in different types of service is not too well known. The kind of evaluation that is being made, however, must always be clearly indicated. This is discussed in more detail in a later chapter. In this chapter major emphasis will be placed upon the transitional aspects of notch-toughness behavior.

EFFECT OF SPECIMEN GEOMETRY

Variations in specimen geometry affect the ductility and fracture appearance transition temperatures quite differently. There is considerable evidence to show that the ductility transition temperature is strongly dependent on the geometry of the notch and on the shape of the specimen, whereas the fracture appearance transition temperature appears to be much less sensitive to geometric factors.

Variation in the notch radius of a specimen will alter the bend angle measured at maximum load, which is sometimes used to evaluate the ductility transition temperature, but the fracture appearance transition temperature remains substantially constant. In Fig. 5.5 are results obtained by Stout and McGeady,[6] who made bend tests on a 0.25% C killed steel and on a 0.21% C rimmed steel. The notch dimensions were altered from 0.04-in. radius at 0.080-in. depth to 0.01-in. radius at 0.125-in. depth. The fracture appearance transition temperature remained almost unchanged, but the ductility transition as measured by bend angle moved noticeably to higher temperatures as the notch severity was increased.

In Fig. 5.6 are results obtained by Thomas and Windenburg [8] on centrally notched plates 12 in. wide. The central slot was 3 in. wide, the ends of which had various notches ranging from ¾-in. diameter down to the notch made by a jeweler's saw cut. In this figure, the energy absorbed to failure in thousands of inch-pounds per square inch of section is plotted for various testing temperatures; the fracture appearance is also indicated. The fracture appearance transition is about 90 to 120 F for notch diameters of ½ in. and less and is about 45 F for the ¾-in. diameter notch. The fracture appearance transition was found to be rather insensitive to these large changes in notch

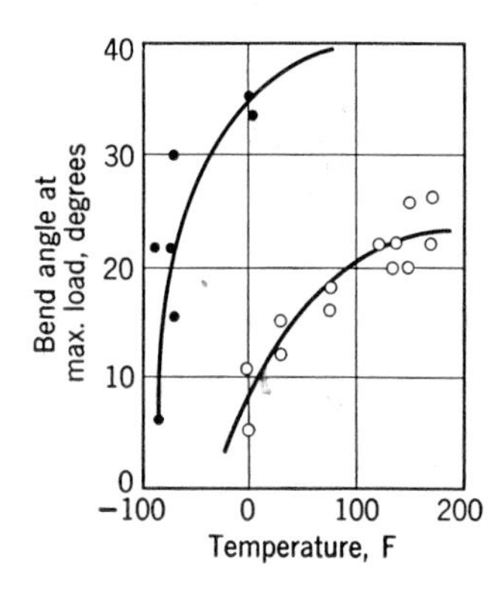

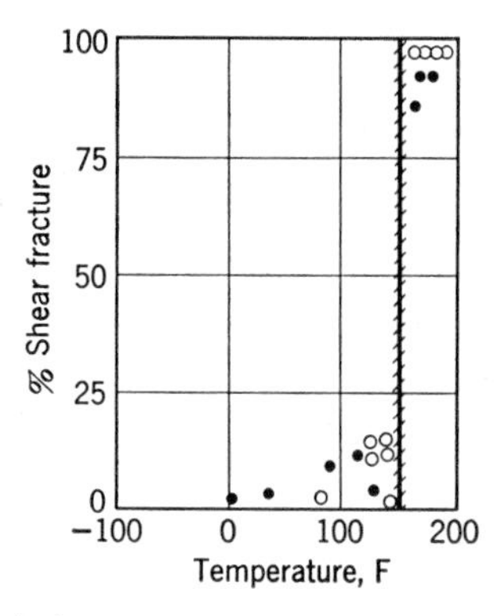

(*a*) Rimmed steel

Notch dimensions: • = 0.04″ radius, 0.08″ deep
○ = 0.01″ radius, 0.125″ deep

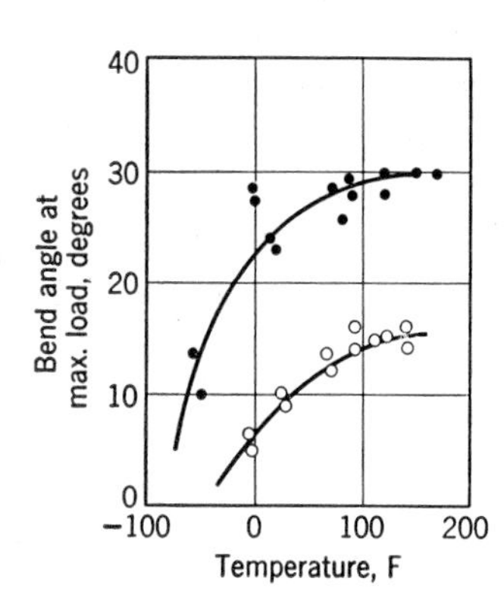

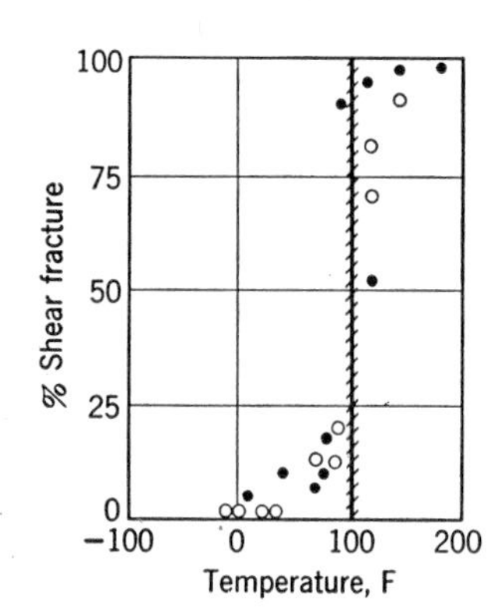

(*b*) Semikilled steel

Notch dimensions: • = 0.04″ radius, 0.08″ deep
○ = 0.01″ radius, 0.125″ deep

Fig. 5.5 Effect of severity of notch on the ductility and fracture appearance transition temperature as evaluated by bend tests.[6]

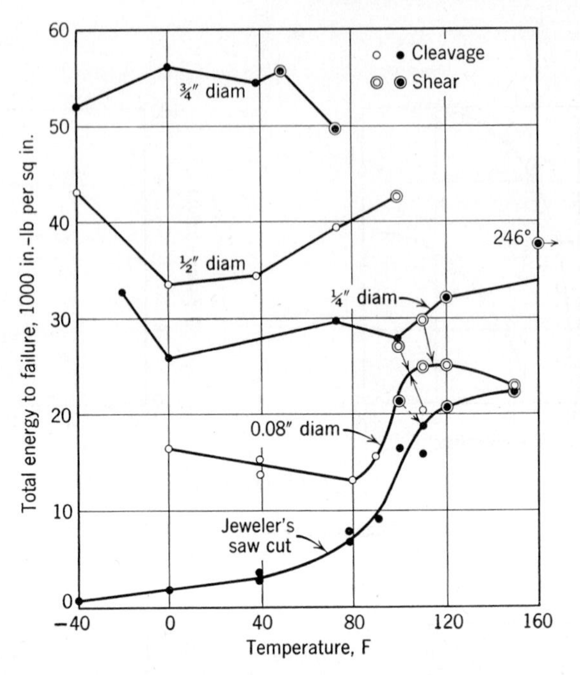

Fig. 5.6 Effect of notch severity on energy absorbed and fracture appearance for specimens of type E steel.[8] (¾-in. by 12-in. wide plate with 3-in. wide central slot.)

geometry, especially for notch diameters of ½ in. and less. The energy-temperature curves, however, differ markedly, and consequently the ductility transition temperatures for the various specimens differed widely. Actually, the final drop to completely brittle behavior was determined only for the specimen with the sharp jeweler's saw cut. For this specimen the ductility transition temperature was 80 F at the arbitrary energy level of 7500 in-lb per sq in. For the specimens with other notches, the ductility transitions must have been below −40 F. Thomas and Windenburg also showed that in these specimens the maximum nominal stress decreased as the notch sharpness increased.

Carpenter and Linsenmeyer [9] determined fracture appearance transition temperatures on tensile specimens 15 in. wide by 40 in. long by ¾ in. thick with various kinds of edge notches, including a jeweler's hack-saw cut and flame-cut notches of several different radii. All of the different notch geometries produced fracture appearance transition temperatures in the range from 25 to 53 F, showing how insensitive the fracture appearance transition temperature is to variations in notch geometry. Other tests [10, 11, 12] on centrally notched flat plate tensile specimens 4 in. to 72 in. wide showed that the fracture appearance transition temperature tends to increase slightly as the plate width increases, the notch radius and plate thickness remaining constant.

Tests on full-scale "hatch corner" specimens were conducted by DeGarmo [13] on a single steel to determine the effectiveness of various modifications of design on strength and ductility. Previous tests on a basic design (using the same steel) had shown that the fracture appearance transition temperature was about 110 F. DeGarmo's tests on the various designs of hatch corner specimens were all conducted at 70 F. It is interesting to note that *all* fractures were granular (i.e., the fracture appearance transition was above 70 F) despite the fact that some specimens absorbed as much as 6,800,000 in-lb of energy, while others absorbed as little as 230,000 in-lb. The fracture transition temperature apparently changed very little, and yet on the basis of energy absorption some designs were much better than others. These results clearly demonstrate that the behavior of steel in a large structure may be quite ductile, even though the fracture is by cleavage and the fracture appearance granular.

The effect of varying the notch severity on the transition temperature was investigated by Zeno and Low [14] with Charpy type specimens. They used two semikilled steels in this investigation. The compositions of these steels are given in Table 5.1. A summary of the transi-

TABLE 5.1

COMPOSITIONS OF STEELS USED FOR NOTCH SEVERITY INVESTIGATION

Steel	C, %	Mn, %	P, %	S, %	Si, %
1	0.17	0.75	0.017	0.035	0.044
2	0.23	0.44	0.015	0.035	0.06

tion temperature data is presented in Table 5.2, where fracture appearance, average energy, and ductility (10 ft-lb) transitions are recorded. These results show that as the notch severity increases the transition temperature rises. They also show that the standard V-notch in the Charpy specimen approaches very closely the most severe condition of stressing that can be imposed on a notched impact specimen.

Zeno and Dolby [15] studied standard and subsize Charpy specimens of SAE 1020 steel and found that the fracture appearance transition temperature was higher for the larger specimens. This evidence is somewhat contradictory to that obtained in the other studies with larger specimens. The evidence seems to indicate that with small specimens a variation in fracture appearance transition temperature may be found when the specimen geometry is altered.

TABLE 5.2

Comparison of Fracture Appearance Transition with Average Energy and 10 Ft-Lb Ductility Transitions

Steel	Standard or Modified Charpy Specimen	Fracture Appearance Transition, F	Average Energy Transition, F	Ductility Transition (10 ft-lb), F
1	V-notch (standard)	50	40	−2
1	Keyhole notch (standard)	15	−10	−50
1	Fatigue crack notch	50	65	15
1	Unnotched, single width	(*)	−255	Below −300
1	Unnotched, double width	(*)	−210	Below −300
2	V-notch (standard)	70	70	32
2	Keyhole notch (standard)	25	−2	−10
2	Fatigue crack notch	85	98	50
2	Unnotched, single width	(*)	−190	−260
2	Unnotched, double width	(*)	−155	−300

* Fracture appearance transition not known. Specimens either broke with 100% granular fracture (low temperatures) or did not crack at all (higher temperatures).

It has been generally observed that the ductility transition temperature increases as the notch depth and sharpness increase and as the specimen size increases. In addition to the examples given previously, the work of Rosenthal and Mitchell[16] also shows that variations in notch depth and notch radius affect the ductility transition temperature appreciably.

In summary, the temperature at which the ductility transition occurs is strongly dependent upon specimen geometry and particularly upon notch geometry, as might be expected. As the notch is made sharper and deeper, the strains are more localized, the strain rates are higher for a given deflection rate, and the degree of triaxiality of the stresses becomes greater; these factors favor higher ductility transition temperatures. The fracture appearance transition temperature is dependent upon the conditions existing at the base of a crack that forms during the early stages of testing. A crack of sufficient depth has effectively the same sharpness regardless of the original notch dimensions. Once the first crack forms, the fracture characteristics are governed by the crack and not by the original notch. It is logical, therefore, to expect the fracture transition temperature to be relatively insensitive to notch geometry; this is indeed the case. Specimens with different sizes and shapes of notches often show widely different ductility transitions and yet show about the same fracture transition temperature.

EFFECT OF STRAIN RATE

The rate at which a specimen is strained has been shown to have an appreciable effect upon the transition curve in some instances, but again the magnitude of this effect seems to depend to a considerable extent upon the criterion used to evaluate behavior. Fig. 5.7 shows

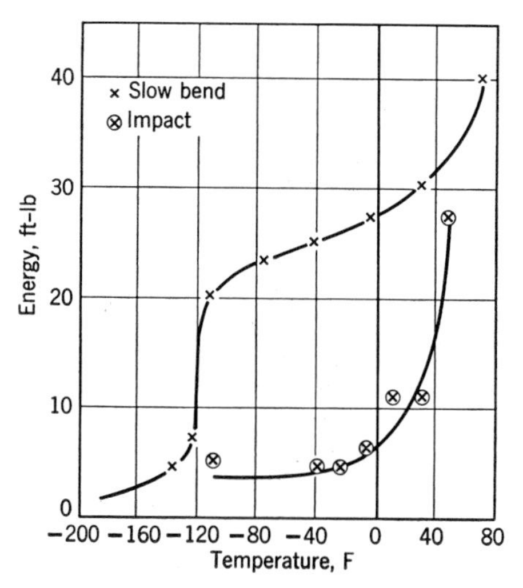

Fig. 5.7 Comparison of impact versus slow loading on energy absorbed in V-notch Charpy specimens (0.16% C plain carbon steel).[17]

data obtained by Offenhauer and Koopman [17] on V-notch Charpy specimens that were bent slowly and by impact. At lower energy levels of 10 to 15 ft-lb (which would be associated with the ductility transition), slow bending produced a transition temperature lower than was obtained by impact loading. At the higher energy levels, however, there is less difference in behavior; in general such curves tend to converge or may even cross.

MacGregor and Grossman [18] conducted bend tests at various deflection rates on disks and on notched bars. Transition temperatures were selected at the highest temperatures at which fractures were obtained with no detectable plastic flow (i.e., less than about 1%). In all cases, it was found that the transition temperature increased with the deflection rate, and a linear relation was found between the logarithm of the deflection velocity and the reciprocal of the absolute temperature of transition. This relationship was also pointed out by Morokovin.[19]

Osborn et al.[20] have conducted both Lehigh slow bend tests and V-notch Charpy impact tests on specimens made from 1¼-in. thick plates of ASTM A-70 and A-201 carbon steels. It is interesting to note the effect that the different testing conditions had on the notch toughness behavior. In Table 5.3 ductility transition temperatures are selected for both tests at 2% lateral contraction just below the notch, and fracture appearance transitions are selected at 50% fibrous fracture appearance. The Lehigh test specimen was ⅝ in. thick by 3 in. wide; the Charpy specimen had the standard dimension of 0.394 in. square. Both specimens contained standard V-notches. The ductility transition obtained with the slow bend test was 45 to 75 F *lower* than transition temperatures found with the Charpy test, while the fracture appearance transitions were found to be 60 to 68 F *higher* in the slow bend test. The two criteria do not even rate the steels in the same order.

TABLE 5.3

COMPARISON OF TRANSITION TEMPERATURES FOR TWO STEELS AND TWO TYPES OF TEST

Grade of Steel	Lehigh Slow Bend: Ductility Transition, F	Lehigh Slow Bend: Fracture Appearance Transition, F	Charpy V: Ductility Transition, F	Charpy V: Fracture Appearance Transition, F
A-201	−75	90	−30	30
A-70	−40	163	35	95

Strain rate seems to have little effect on the fracture appearance transition (except when strain aging occurs). For example, explosion tests, involving very high rates of loading, produce fracture appearance transition temperatures of about 70 to 100 F [21] for semikilled steel plates of ship quality; about the same range was found for similar steels by the Navy tear test.[22]

It is therefore concluded that the ductility transition temperature (or an evaluation at low performance levels on the transition curve) is generally sensitive to changes in the rate of loading; the fracture appearance transition temperature is less sensitive to such changes.

TEST RESULTS ON WELDMENTS

The test results discussed so far have referred principally to unwelded material. Most of the failures experienced in recent years, however, have been in welded structures, a fact that makes it important to evaluate the effects of welding on the over-all notch-toughness behavior. For this reason, various tests on weldments, incorporating both the weld and the base metal, have evolved. There is no definite proof that the extensive use of welding has per se increased the incidence of brittle failure,[23] but it is nevertheless known that welding plays an important role. The influence of welding on the fracture behavior of the base metal is discussed in some detail in Chapter VIII. This section is devoted simply to a description of some of the test results that have been obtained.

Two frequently used tests for evaluating weldment performance are the Kinzel and the Lehigh slow notch-bend tests. In both of these tests specimens are prepared by depositing longitudinal weld beads and then notching the specimens transversely across their entire width,

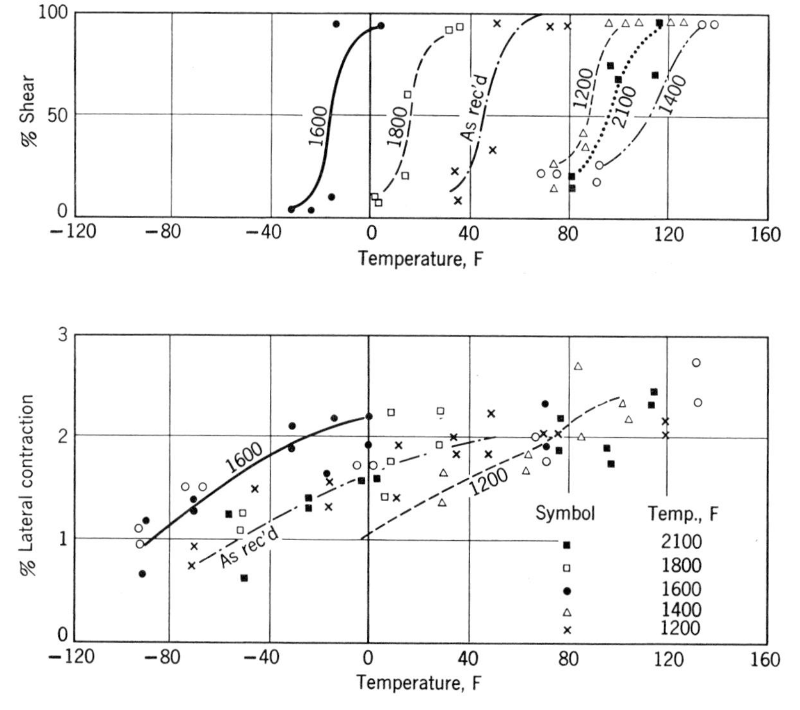

Fig. 5.8 Lehigh bend test transition curves for ½-in. thick unwelded 0.25% carbon steel air-cooled from various temperatures.[24]

the notches crossing both weld metal and base plate, as described in the previous chapter. For comparison with behavior of unwelded material, tests are conducted on similar specimens without the weld bead. Contraction in width just below the notch is usually measured, as well as the percentage of fibrous fracture and the bend angle. The per cent contraction vs. temperature curves are used to obtain a ductility transition temperature. Since the curves do not always show an abrupt change in behavior, it is common practice to select the ductility transition temperature at a low level of performance, such as at 1 or 2% lateral contraction. Fracture appearance transitions are usually selected as the temperature corresponding to 50% fibrous fracture.

Typical results for the Lehigh bend test specimen of unwelded materials are shown in Fig. 5.8; Fig. 5.9 shows similar results for material having a deposited weld bead.[24] These results were obtained on carbon steel plate ½ in. thick that was air-cooled from various tem-

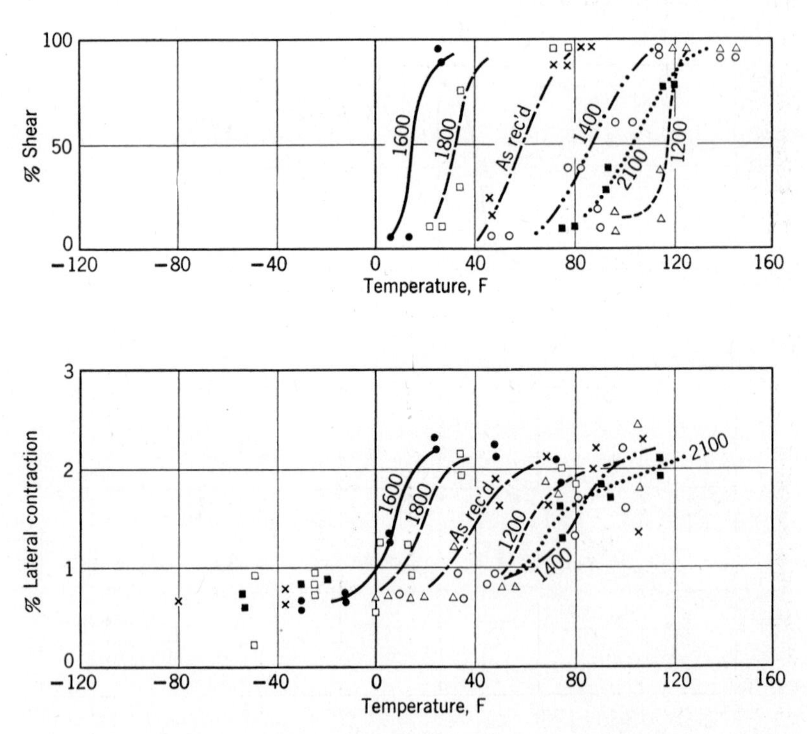

Fig. 5.9 Lehigh bend test transition curves for ½-in. thick welded 0.25% carbon steel, air-cooled from various temperatures before welding. Single weld beads were deposited at 10 in. per min., using 175 amp, E6010 electrode.[24]

peratures. The fracture appearance transition curves in Fig. 5.9 appear at virtually the same positions as they did for the unwelded plate of Fig. 5.8. This behavior indicates that welding does not appear to alter the fracture appearance transition temperature markedly.[24] The ductility transition curves in Fig. 5.9, however, have been displaced to higher temperatures as a result of welding, and they tend to coincide with the fracture appearance transition curves. This shows that the principal effect of welding is to raise the ductility transition temperature (this subject is discussed more fully in Chapter VIII). Stout and McGeady [6] further demonstrate that variations in welding conditions affect the ductility and fracture transitions quite differently. Fig. 5.10 shows both ductility and fracture appearance transition curves for Lehigh bend tests on prime plate and on specimens that were welded under different conditions. The ductility transition was evaluated by measuring the bend angle at maximum load and by selecting a bend angle of 10°. A criterion of 1% lateral contraction below the notch would have given similar results. It may be seen that the fracture appearance transition is about the same for all test conditions, whereas the ductility transition ranges from −70 to +75 F.

Puzak, Eschbacher, and Pellini [21] used explosion tests to evaluate notch-toughness behavior. In their tests a short weld bead of a brittle hard surfacing material was deposited in the center of a 14-in. by 14-in. plate. This bead was sharply notched so that a crack would form at a low value of strain. (It was determined by static load tests that the brittle weld metal cracked when the yield point of the base plate was reached, thus developing an extremely sharp notch.) The test plate was subjected to explosive loading at various temperatures, as in Fig. 5.11, to determine whether the brittle crack that had formed would run through the base plate. The fracture appearance transition was selected as the temperature where cracking was confined to a limited portion of the bulge. A typical series of test plates for a ship plate steel is shown in Fig. 5.12. The fracture transition was selected at 80 F, where the cracks failed to propagate into the hold-down region of the test plate. This test involves welding, a sharp crack, and a high loading rate; but even under these adverse conditions, the fracture appearance transition temperature is about the same as that found for this type of steel with a variety of unwelded, mildly notched, slowly loaded test specimens. Thus the insensitivity of the fracture appearance criterion for transition temperature is again demonstrated.

Ductility transition temperatures were determined by the same test as the temperature at which fracture occurred with no apparent bulg-

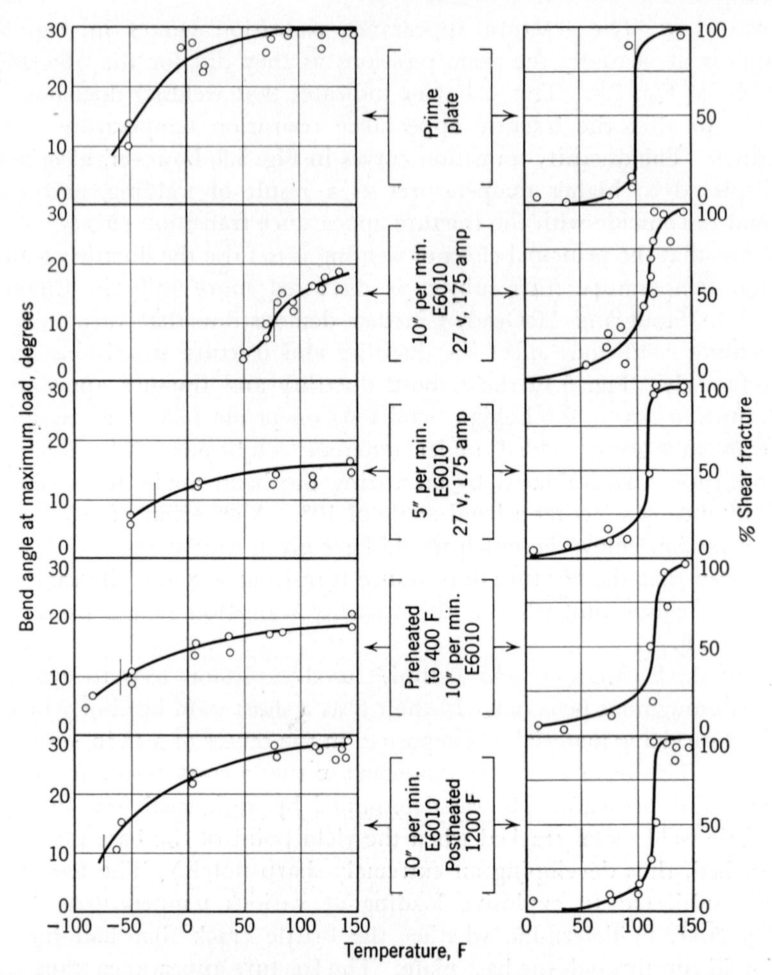

Fig. 5.10 Effect of welding variables on ductility and fracture appearance transition temperatures in the Lehigh bend test, using ¾-in. thick silicon-killed steel containing 0.25% C.

ing (flat break), e.g., as at 20 F in Fig. 5.12. It was found, however, that the same ductility transition temperatures could be obtained by performing drop-weight tests on specimens about 14 in. long and 4 in. wide (dimensions not critical), containing a similarly notched hard-surfacing weld bead. The deflection of the specimen was limited to 5° by a stop. This bend angle was required to develop the ⅓% lateral contraction needed to produce the weld crack. Typical results are shown in Fig. 5.13. The ductility transition was selected as the highest temperature at which complete fracture of the test piece was obtained

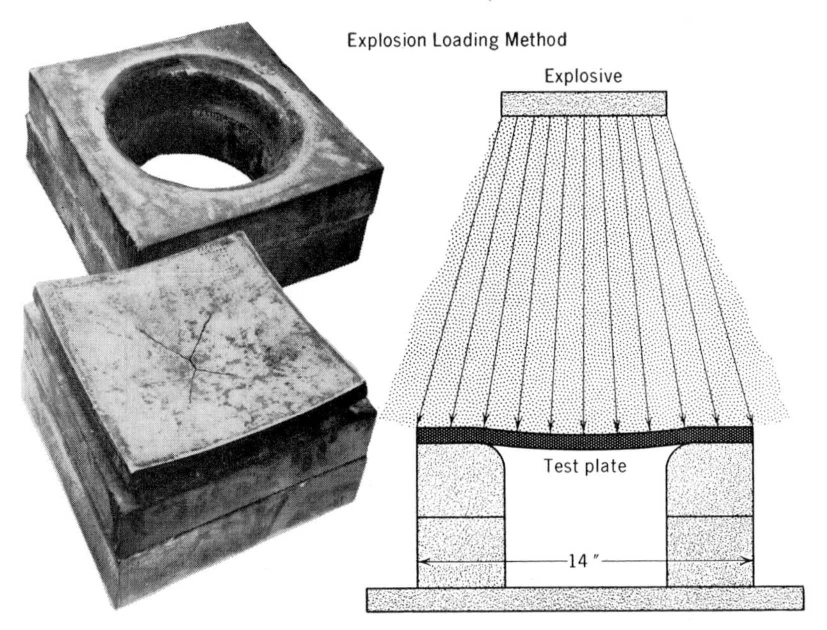

Fig. 5.11 NRL crack starter bulge test by explosion loading method.[21]

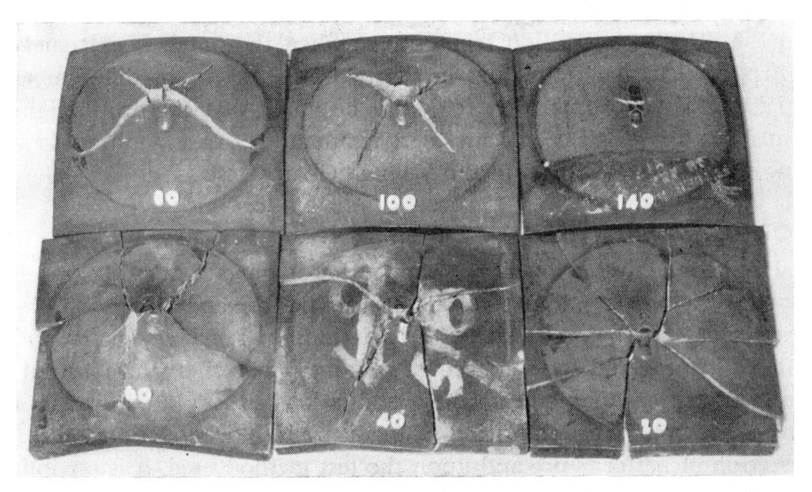

Fig. 5.12 Crack starter bulge test specimens for average quality ship plate steel.[21]

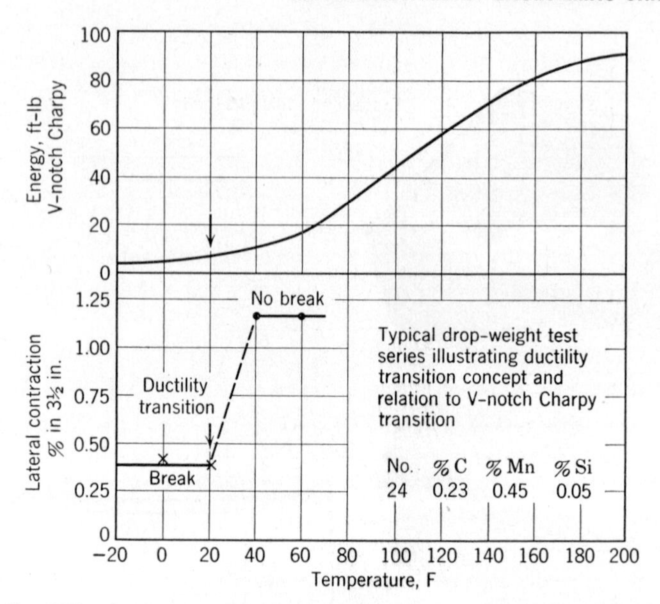

Fig. 5.13 Comparison of drop-weight and V-notch Charpy test results.[21]

under the restricted condition of the test. The same ductility transition temperature was obtained in this test as in the explosion test. This is not in accord with other observations on the effect of loading rate; it may be that the rate of loading does not have much effect on the ductility transition temperature when the notch is extremely sharp, or that the strain rates in the two tests are not as different as might at first be supposed. It should be noted that the drop-weight transition for this steel occurs at a temperature corresponding to a low energy value (7 ft-lb) in the V-notch Charpy test.

CORRELATION BETWEEN TEST RESULTS

In the previous sections it was shown that in general ductility transition temperatures (or evaluations at low performance levels on the transition curves) are sensitive to variations in notch geometry and rate of loading and to the effects of welding, whereas fracture appearance transition temperatures (or evaluations at high performance levels) are not. Since transition temperature is so dependent upon the criterion of performance and upon the test method used, it is obvious that no absolute agreement of results obtained by different techniques can be expected. It might be hoped, however, that steels could be rated in the same relative order with respect to their notch-toughness behavior, regardless of the test specimen or method of evaluation used.

This, of course, would mean that all evaluations of notch toughness could be correlated with each other. Indeed, this claim has more than once been made. Unfortunately, however, this only seems to be true in a very broad sense. For example, with most types of test specimens, steels that have relatively high fracture appearance transition temperatures usually also have relatively high ductility transition temperatures. However, detailed analysis of certain data definitely shows that no precise correlation between results of different tests is possible when the criteria of behavior are indiscriminately mixed. Some examples are given below.

It is rather common practice to select transition temperatures from curves of energy vs. temperature. One criterion commonly used is the temperature corresponding to 50 per cent of the maximum energy. This criterion is sometimes employed for both keyhole and V-notch Charpy impact tests. The correlation obtained between the transition temperatures based on 50 per cent of the maximum energy for the two tests is very poor. The half energy value is usually close to the ductility transition in the keyhole test, whereas it is near the fracture appearance transition in the V-notch test. When the selected criteria of performance are in keeping with the concepts of behavior already discussed, the correlation is quite good. Such a correlation was found by Vanderbeck and Gensamer [1] for the steels used in a number of the ship steel research projects; their data are reproduced in Fig. 5.14. The ductility transition temperature (chosen as the temperature at the center of the range in which the scatter between

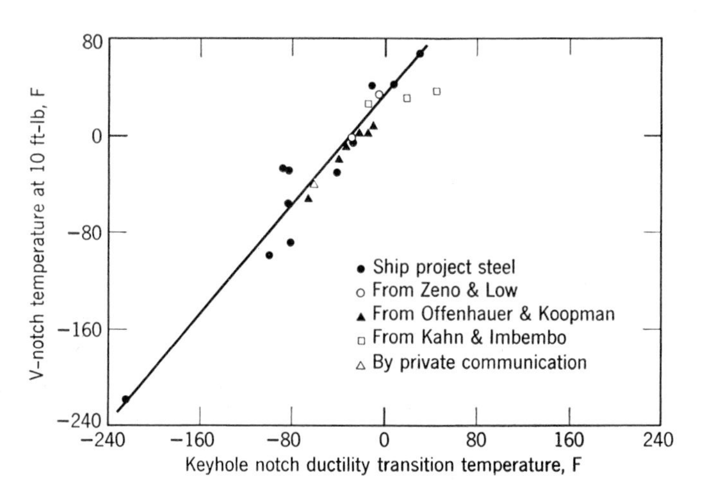

Fig. 5.14 Relationship between temperature at low energy level for V-notch Charpy specimens and ductility transition temperature for keyhole Charpy specimens.[1]

relatively high and low energy values occurs, e.g., 5 F in Fig. 5.1) in the keyhole Charpy test was compared with the temperature at the 10 ft-lb level of energy in the V-notch Charpy test. This low energy level was used in the V-notch test because it is near the bottom of the energy-temperature curve and therefore is in accord with the concept of a ductility transition temperature. Puzak, Eschbacher, and Pellini [21] verified this relation, using a number of rimmed, semi-killed, and killed carbon plate steels, and also some high-tensile-strength steels containing vanadium and titanium. Vanderbeck and Gensamer [1] also pointed out that the previously reported poor correlations between Charpy data and results obtained on internally notched wide plate tests were caused by the indiscriminate mixing of the criteria of performance. They showed that a better correlation could be obtained if the performance criteria in both tests were based upon the low energy portions of the transition curves. Their correlation is reproduced in Fig. 5.15.

Stout and McGeady [6] in 1948 recognized the importance of using comparable criteria of behavior if correlation between test results were to be obtained. Fig. 5.16 shows some of their results. Five tests were made on each of four steels. The steels were rated in the same order by all tests; the variation in transition temperatures for a given steel by the different test methods was found to be about 80 F. In this comparison fracture appearance transition temperatures were used and these were evaluated at 50 per cent fibrous fracture. Stout and McGeady stated that it appeared that any of the testing methods investigated would yield significant information about the steels if the proper criterion for transition were used for evaluation.

Vanderbeck [25] has shown that a poor correlation exists between ductility transition temperatures obtained by keyhole Charpy tests and fracture appearance transition temperatures obtained by slow bend tests for several ship plate steels. He states that there is a general trend for the notch-bend fracture appearance transition temperature to increase as the Charpy ductility transition increases, but the spread is much too large for a satisfactory correlation.

Puzak et al.[21] have obtained a good correlation between results on explosion tests, as previously described, and results on sharply notched Schnadt-type impact specimens. Fracture appearance transitions were selected in the explosion test at the temperature at which the fracture showed only 0.01 to 0.02 in. of fibrous fracture (shear lip) at the plate surface. This temperature corresponds closely to the temperature at which the crack resists extensive propagation. The

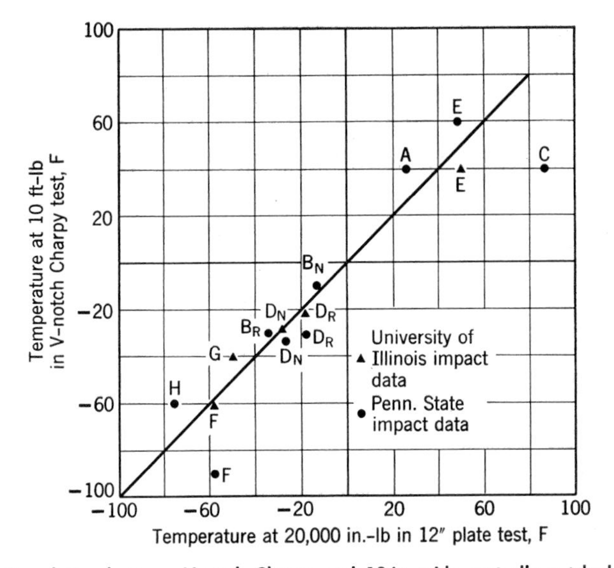

Fig. 5.15 Correlation between V-notch Charpy and 12-in. wide centrally notched plate tests at low energy levels.[1]

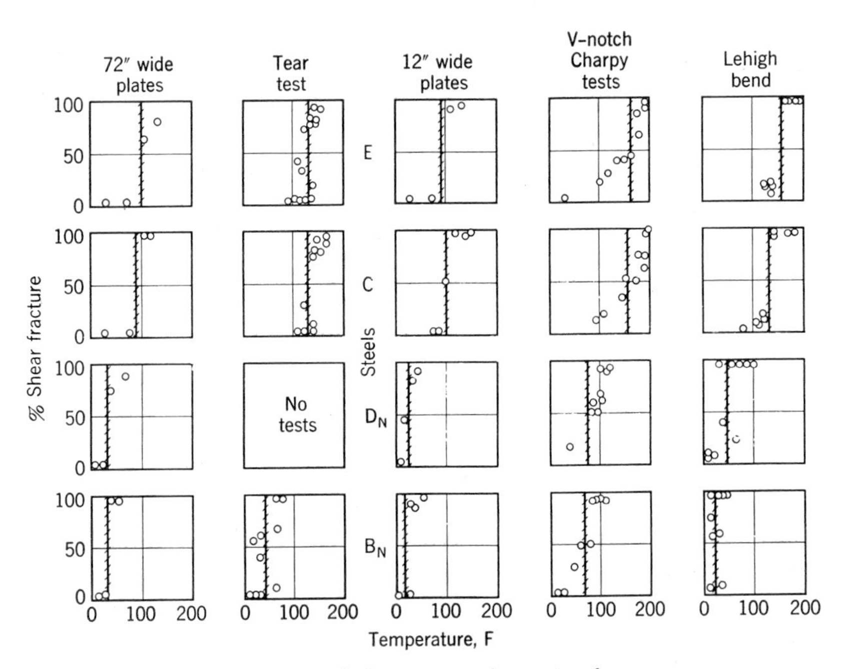

Fig. 5.16 A comparison of test methods on prime plates using fracture appearance as a criterion of behavior.[6]

Schnadt-type specimen used is shown in Fig. 5.17 and is essentially a very sharply notched Charpy specimen with a hardened steel pin inserted at the back of the specimen to form a nonplastic compression zone. Transitions were picked at the 4 ft-lb level, as suggested by Schnadt. The extremely sharp notch in this specimen, in conjunction with a fast rate of loading, gives transitions at relatively high temperatures, even though the transitions are selected at only 4 ft-lb.

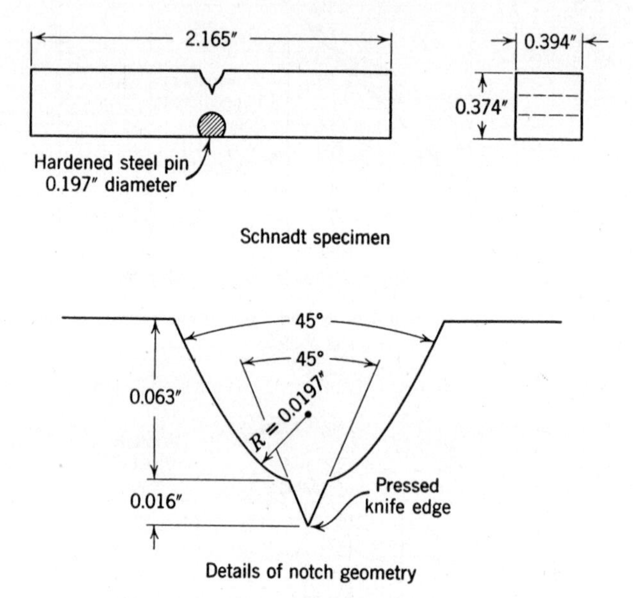

Fig. 5.17 Details of sharply notched Schnadt-type impact specimen.[21]

The transition temperatures evaluated by these two methods are shown in Fig. 5.18, superimposed on V-notch Charpy energy-temperature curves for the same materials. The triangles indicate the Schnadt specimen 4 ft-lb transition temperature, and the black bands, the temperature range of the fracture appearance transition in the explosion test. It may be seen that, while these two transition temperatures agree rather closely, they fall at different energy levels on the Charpy curves for the various kinds of steel. Thus it appears that even though criteria may be selected so that good correlation is obtained between some tests, when an attempt is made to generalize the correlation by including data from certain other types of tests, the correlation becomes poorer.

The correlation between the temperature at which the plates break

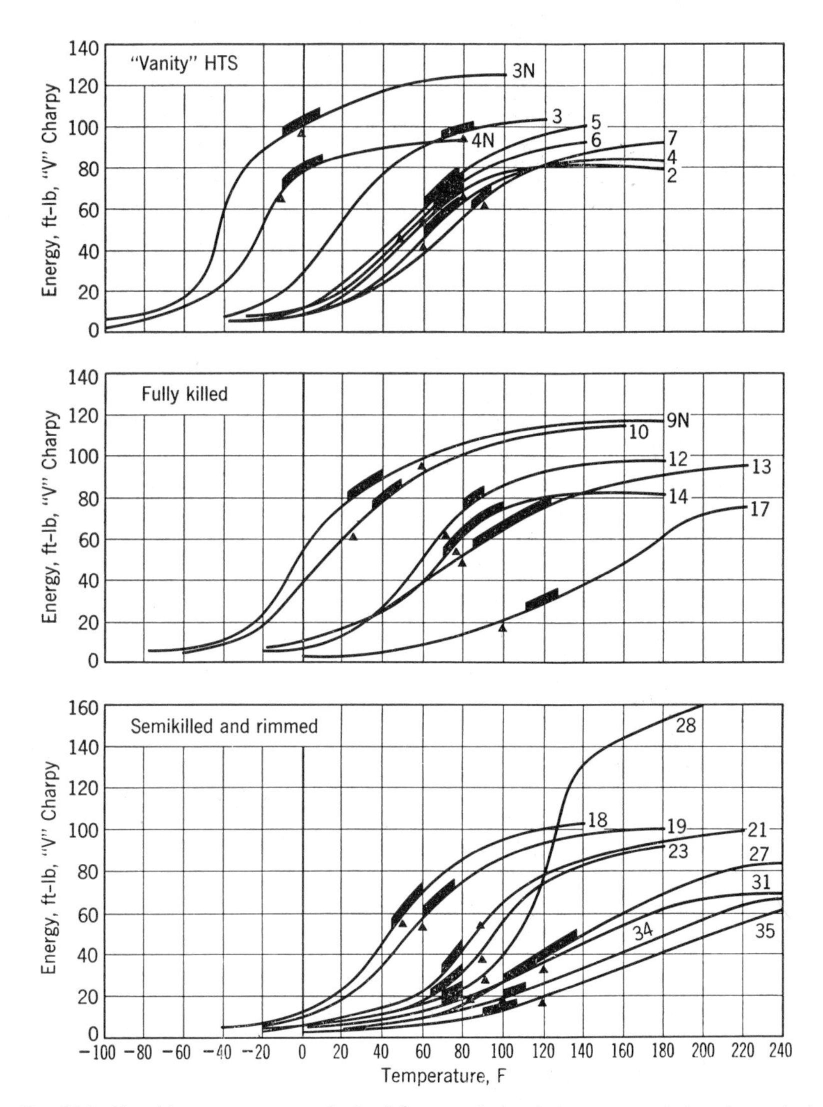

Fig. 5.18 Transition temperatures obtained from explosion bulge tests and sharply notched Schnadt-type impact tests superimposed on V-notch Charpy energy-temperature curves.[21]

flat in the explosion test and the ductility transition temperature in the drop-weight test was mentioned in the preceding section. Puzak et al.[21] also found that the drop-weight ductility transition temperature correlated fairly well with the temperature on the V-notch Charpy curve at which a low value of energy is involved. This energy level falls in the general range of 5 to 10 ft-lb for rimmed and semi-killed carbon plate steels and of 8 to 15 ft-lb for fully killed steels. Recent data have indicated that the corresponding energy level for good correlation may be even higher for certain high strength heat treated steels. Thus, although fairly good correlations have been obtained for individual classes of steel, no general correlation applicable for all classes of steel has been found. At the present time there seems to be little hope for such a correlation.

SUMMARY

The failure in the past to obtain correlations among test results has in many cases been caused by the indiscriminate mixing of the criteria used to judge performance. The criteria used to judge transition temperature may be divided roughly into two groups. Those in the first group are concerned with *initial formation* of the crack and they may be used to measure the transition from relatively tough to completely brittle behavior. This transition is referred to as the ductility transition temperature and it is dependent upon the amount of plastic flow that the material at the base of the notch can undergo before a crack forms. Criteria for the second group are concerned with *propagation* of the crack through the remainder of the specimen and may be used to measure the transition from predominantly fibrous (shear mode) to predominantly granular (cleavage mode) fracture. This transition is referred to as the fracture appearance transition temperature because the appearance of the *entire* fracture surface is involved in the appraisal of behavior. When analyzing notch-toughness data, these two different aspects of behavior must be treated separately or undue confusion will result.

In general, ductility transition temperatures, or evaluations at low performance levels on the transition curves, are sensitive to variations in notch geometry, specimen shape, and rate of loading. Faster rates of loading, changes in notch geometry that increase the notch acuity and increase in specimen size, all raise the ductility transition temperature. In certain specimens welding also raises the ductility transition temperature. Fracture appearance transition temperatures, however, are relatively insensitive to these factors.

The use of different criteria in different tests, i.e., comparing the fracture appearance transitions with ductility transitions, will generally preclude the possibility of rating steels in the same order by different tests. Since fracture appearance and ductility transitions represent distinctly different aspects of fracture behavior and are affected differently by the various testing methods and techniques, it is important to make comparisons based upon like criteria of behavior. When this has been done, some good correlations have been obtained. Even these correlations, however, do not always hold for different classes of steel. This is not too surprising, since the test methods differ widely and some of them even involve welding. A precise correlation of all test results for all steels of a given class, when similar criteria are used, is perhaps possible; but it is too much to expect such a correlation to hold for a variety of classes of steel.

The ultimate test of the specimen suitability and of the criterion of performance is, of course, whether or not there is a correlation between the test results and behavior in service. The only known correlation of this type was obtained with V-notch Charpy specimens by Williams and Ellinger.[26] They found that plates in which failures started had 10 ft-lb transition temperatures at or above the temperature at which the steel had failed in service. This important point is discussed further in Chapters XI and XII.

REFERENCES

1. R. W. Vanderbeck and M. Gensamer, "Evaluating Notch Toughness," *Welding J.*, Res. Suppl., pp. 37-s–48-s (January 1950).
2. N. A. Kahn and E. A. Imbembo, "A Method of Evaluating Transition from Shear to Cleavage Failure in Ship Plate and Its Correlation with Large-Scale Plate Tests," *Welding J.*, Res. Suppl., pp. 169-s–182-s (April 1948).
3. E. P. Klier, F. C. Wagner, and M. Gensamer, "The Correlation of Laboratory Tests with Full-Scale Ship Plate Fracture Tests," *Welding J.*, Res. Suppl., pp. 71-s–96-s (February 1948).
4. A. Boodberg, H. E. Davis, E. R. Parker, and G. E. Troxell, "Causes of Cleavage Fracture in Ship Plate—Tests of Wide Notched Plates," *Welding J.*, Res. Suppl., pp. 186-s–199-s (April 1948).
5. R. W. Vanderbeck, R. W. Lindsay, H. D. Wilde, W. T. Lankford, and S. C. Snyder, "Effect of Specimen Preparation on Notch Toughness Behavior of Keyhole Charpy Specimens in the Transition Temperature Zone," presented at ASTM meeting in Atlantic City, June 1953.
6. R. D. Stout and L. J. McGeady, "The Meaning and Measurement of Transition Temperature," *Welding J.*, Res. Suppl., pp. 299-s–302-s (June 1948).
7. C. J. Osborn, A. F. Scotchbrook, R. D. Stout, and B. G. Johnston, "Comparison of Notch Tests and Brittleness Criteria," *Welding J.*, Res. Suppl., pp. 24-s–34-s (January 1949).

8. H. R. Thomas and D. F. Windenburg, "A Study of Slotted Tensile Specimens for Evaluating the Toughness of Structural Steels," *Welding J.*, Res. Suppl., pp. 209-s–215-s (April 1948).
9. S. T. Carpenter and R. F. Linsenmeyer, "Cracking of Simple Structural Geometries: The Effects of Edge Notch Geometry on Flat Steel Plates," Ship Structure Committee Report, Serial No. SSC-51, May 12, 1952.
10. S. T. Carpenter, "The Strength, Energy Absorption, and Transition Temperature of Internally Notched Flat Steel Plates," Ship Structure Committee Report, Serial No. SSC-47, January 19, 1953.
11. A. Boodberg, H. E. Davis, E. R. Parker, and G. E. Troxell, "Cause of Cleavage Fractures in Ship Plate—Tests of Wide Notched Plates," *Welding J.*, Res. Suppl., pp. 186-s–199-s (April 1948).
12. W. M. Wilson, R. A. Hechtman, and W. H. Bruckner, "Cleavage Fracture of Ship Plates as Influenced by Size Effect," *Welding J.*, Res. Suppl., pp. 200-s–208-s (April 1948).
13. E. P. DeGarmo, "Tests of Various Designs of Welded Hatch Corners for Ships," *Welding J.*, Res. Suppl., pp. 50-s–68-s (February 1948).
14. R. S. Zeno and J. R. Low, Jr., "The Effect of Variation in Notch Severity on the Transition Temperature of Ship Plate Steel in the Notched Bar Impact Test," *Welding J.*, Res. Suppl., pp. 145-s–147-s (March 1948).
15. R. S. Zeno and J. L. Dolby, "The Effect of Specimen Geometry on Impact Transition Temperature," *Welding J.*, Res. Suppl., pp. 190-s–197-s (April 1953).
16. D. Rosenthal and W. D. Mitchell, "The Influence of Biaxiality on Notch Brittleness," *Welding J.*, Res. Suppl., pp. 409-s–421-s (September 1950).
17. C. M. Offenhauer and K. H. Koopman, "Factors Affecting the Weldability of Carbon and Alloy Steels," *Welding J.*, Res. Suppl., pp. 234-s–252-s (May 1948).
18. C. W. MacGregor and N. Grossman, "The Effect of Combined Stresses on the Transition Temperature for Brittle Fracture," *Welding J.*, Res. Suppl., pp. 7-s–16-s (January 1948).
19. D. Morokovin, Discussion of paper by L. R. Jackson entitled "Some Speculations Regarding the Plastic Flow and Rupture of Metals under Complex Stresses," *Trans. Inst. Mining Met. Engrs., 162,* 595–601 (1945).
20. C. J. Osborn, A. F. Scotchbrook, R. D. Stout, and B. G. Johnston, "Effect of Plastic Strain and Heat Treatment," *Welding J.*, Res. Suppl., pp. 337-s–353-s (August 1949).
21. P. P. Puzak, E. W. Eschbacher, and W. S. Pellini, "Initiation and Propagation of Brittle Fracture in Structural Steels," *Welding J.*, Res. Suppl., pp. 561-s–581-s (December 1952).
22. N. A. Kahn and E. A. Imbembo, "Notch Sensitivity of Steel Evaluated by Tear Test," *Welding J.*, Res. Suppl., pp. 153-s–165-s (April 1949).
23. M. E. Shank, "A Critical Survey of Brittle Failure in Carbon Plate Steel Structures Other Than Ships," Ship Structure Committee Report, Serial No. SSC-65, December 1, 1953. (Also reprinted as Welding Research Council Bull. No. 17.)
24. R. D. Stout and L. J. McGeady, "Notch Sensitivity of Welded Steel Plate," *Welding J.*, Res. Suppl., pp. 1-s–9-s (January 1949).
25. R. W. Vanderbeck, Discussion of paper entitled "Some Metallurgical Aspects of Ship Steel Quality," *Welding J.*, Res. Suppl., pp. 192-s–194-s (April 1951).
26. M. L. Williams and G. A. Ellinger, "Investigation of Fractured Steel Plates Removed from Welded Ships," Ship Structure Committee Report, Serial No. NBS-1, February 25, 1949.

CHAPTER

VI

Summary of Test Results on Special Steels

INTRODUCTION

A number of "project steels" were manufactured during the period 1944–1946 to facilitate investigations concerned with the brittle behavior of steel. These materials were commercial open-hearth heats made under carefully observed conditions. Accurate records were kept of the manufacturing practice, the chemical composition, and, of course, the test results. A number of different kinds of specimens were made from these steels, and many laboratories throughout the country participated in the testing and evaluation program. In all there were 10 different steels (3 of these were tested in two heat-treated states) and 20 different investigations. A summary of the transition temperatures found for the various steels is presented in bar graph form in Fig. 6.1. It should be noted, however, that various criteria of brittle behavior were employed, and consequently, indiscriminate comparisons are likely to yield confusing and misleading correlations. Although the scatter is quite large, it is evident that the various tests rate the steels in more or less the same order. The results from the tests, however, differ from each other in some ways, with certain tests being more discriminating than others. For example, the V-notch Charpy test shows a fairly uniform spread of transition temperatures over a range of 200 F; the keyhole Charpy shows a range of only 100 F for 11 of the 12 steels, with results for the 3½ per cent nickel steel being completely out of line with results from any other type of test;

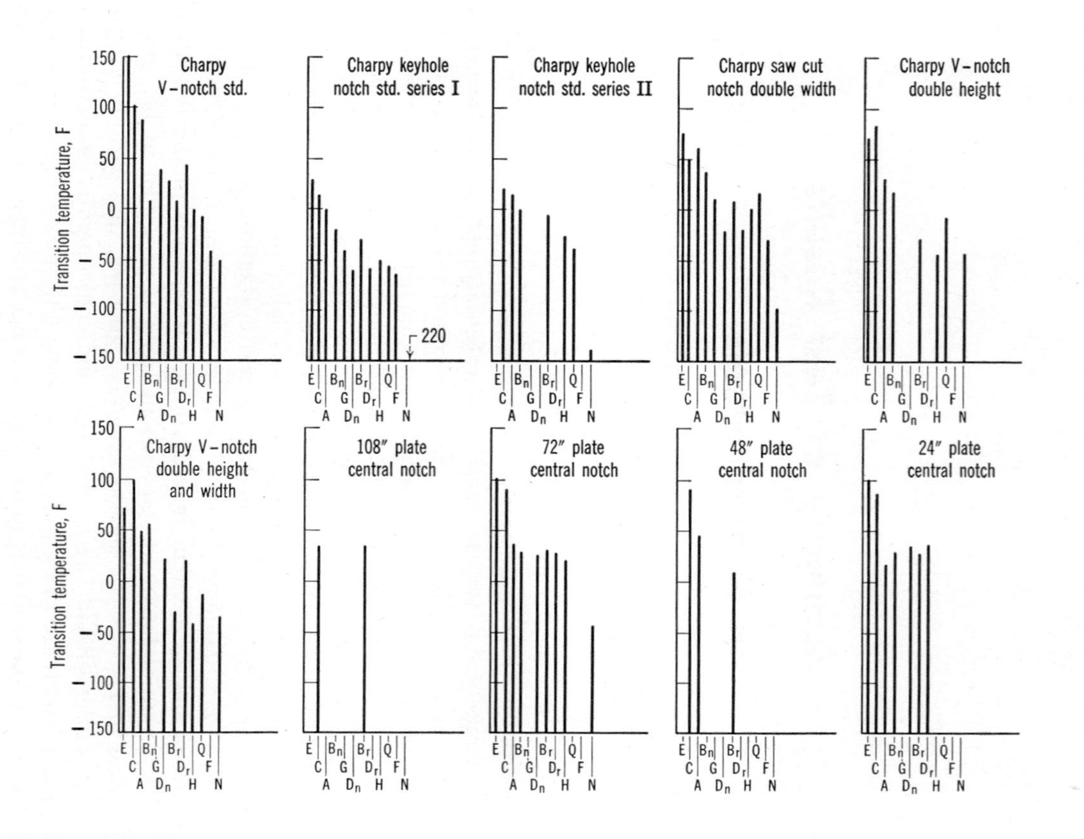
Transition temperature, F
150
100
50
0
−50
−100
−150
Charpy V-notch std.
Charpy keyhole notch std. series I
220
Charpy keyhole notch std. series II
Charpy saw cut notch double width
Charpy V-notch double height
Charpy V-notch double height and width
108″ plate central notch
72″ plate central notch
48″ plate central notch
24″ plate central notch
E C Bn A G Br Dn Dr Q H F N

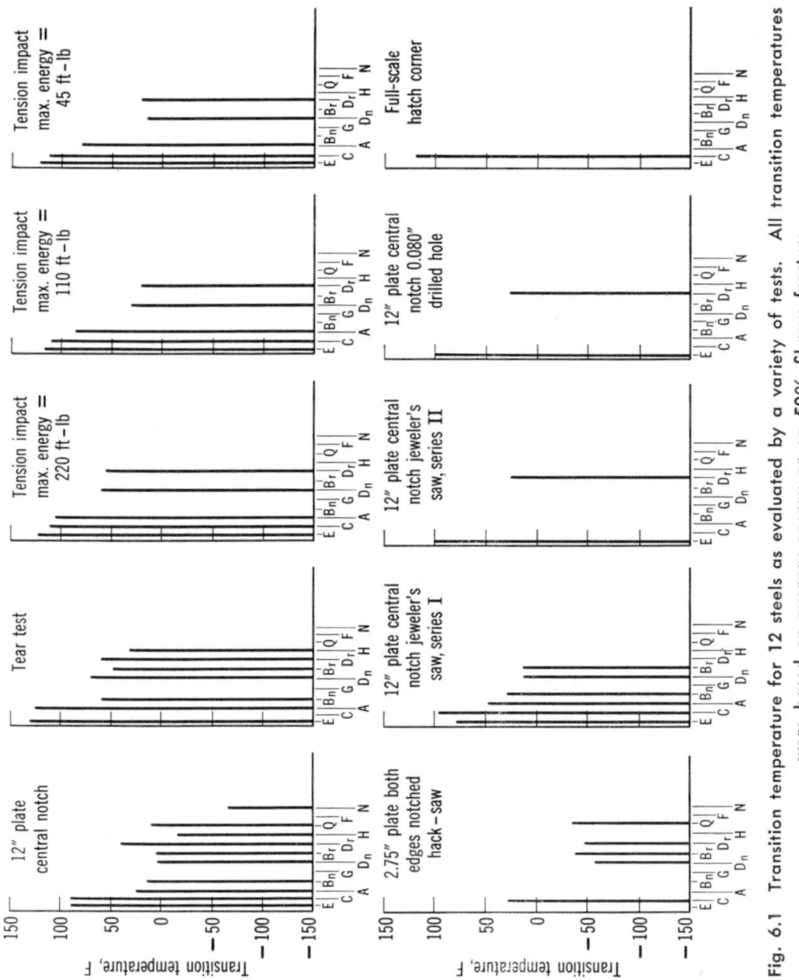

Fig. 6.1 Transition temperature for 12 steels as evaluated by a variety of tests. All transition temperatures were based on average-energy or on 50% fibrous fracture.

the 72-in. wide internally notched plates have a range of transition temperatures of about 150 F, but the transition temperatures are grouped at three values (−50, 32, and 100 F) instead of being spread uniformly over the entire range.

The compositions of the steels are given in Table 6.1, and the ordinary mechanical properties are listed in Table 6.2. Results from

TABLE 6.1

Chemical Analyses of Project Steels [1,2]

	Element, %											
Steel	C	Mn	Si	P	S	Ni	Al	Cu	Cr	Mo	Sn	N
A	0.26	0.50	0.03	0.012	0.039	0.2	0.012	0.03	0.03	0.006	0.003	0.004
B	0.18	0.73	0.07	0.008	0.030	0.05	0.015	0.07	0.03	0.006	0.012	0.005
C	0.24	0.48	0.05	0.012	0.026	0.02	0.016	0.03	0.03	0.005	0.003	0.009
D	0.22	0.55	0.21	0.013	0.024	0.16	0.020	0.22	0.12	0.022	0.023	0.005
E	0.20	0.33	0.01	0.013	0.020	0.15	0.009	0.18	0.09	0.018	0.024	0.005
F	0.18	0.82	0.15	0.012	0.031	0.04	0.054	0.05	0.03	0.008	0.021	0.006
G	0.20	0.86	0.19	0.020	0.020	0.08	0.045	0.15	0.04	0.018	0.012	0.006
H	0.18	0.76	0.16	0.012	0.019	0.05	0.053	0.09	0.04	0.006	0.004	0.004
N	0.17	0.53	0.25	0.011	0.020	3.39	0.077	0.19	0.06	0.025	0.017	0.005
Q	0.22	1.13	0.05	0.011	0.030	0.05	0.008	0.13	0.03	0.006	0.018	0.006

TABLE 6.2

Ordinary Mechanical Properties of Project Steels [1,2]

Steel *	Yield Point, psi	Ultimate Strength, psi	Elongation in 2 in., %	Elongation in 8 in., %	Reduction Area, %	Hardness Rockwell B
A	36,000	59,000	41	34	58	60
B_{ar}†	33,000	57,500	44	34	64	61
B_n‡	36,000	57,000	44	34	63	60
C	36,000	65,000	39	30	56	67
D_{ar}†	37,500	65,000	..	30	54	..
D_n‡	35,000	60,000	..	32	59	..
E_{ar}†	30,000	57,000	..	32	56	..
E_n‡	35,000	57,500	..	31	56	..
F	34,000	61,000	..	31	62	..
G	41,500	70,000	..	28	56	..
H	36,000	63,500	42	30	63	70
N	58,000	80,000	35	26	65	84
Q§	46,000	72,000	45	23	62	81

* All steels in the as-rolled condition unless otherwise noted. Steels A, B, C were semikilled; D, F, G, H were fully deoxidized; E was a rimmed steel; N was an alloy steel; Q was a quenched and drawn 1% Mn steel.

† Subscript ar refers to as-rolled condition.

‡ Subscript n refers to normalized condition.

§ Quenched and drawn.

the individual notched specimen tests will now be presented and discussed; subsequently, appropriate correlations between the results from various tests will be shown.

TEST RESULTS

Gensamer and co-workers [3] made Charpy impact tests on all of the project steels. A summary of their results with V-notch specimens is presented in Fig. 6.2. Similar results with keyhole Charpy specimens

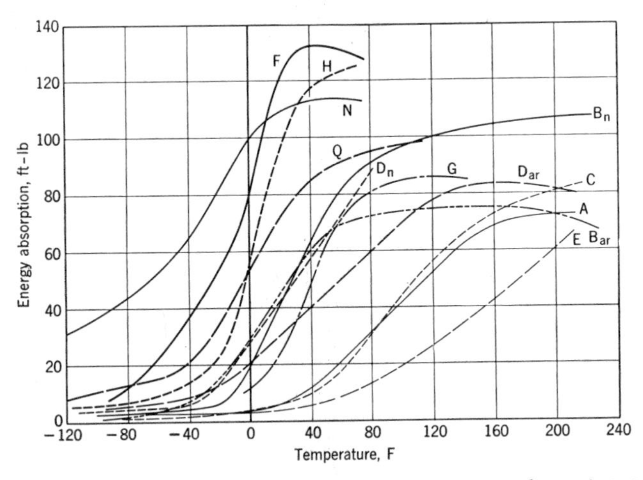

Fig. 6.2 Summary of V-notch Charpy energy-temperature curves for project steels.[1]

obtained by the same investigators are shown in Fig. 6.3. The 3½ per cent nickel steel (N) was markedly superior in both cases, and the rimmed steel (E) was notably inferior. The fully deoxidized steels (D, F, G, H) were generally better than the semikilled steels (A, B, C), but the transition ranges overlapped.

The need for an understanding of the meanings of the various transition temperature criteria can be nicely illustrated by this work. For example, in Fig. 6.2 the "fracture appearance" transition temperature * for steel (N) was only 20 to 40 F below those for steels (F) and (H). However, the 10 ft-lb transition (ductility transition) was well over 100 F lower for the (N) steel. Similarly, the "fracture appearance" transition for steel (E) was about 60 F higher than those for steels (A) and (C), but the ductility transitions (10 ft-lb level) were

* Fracture appearance transitions were not actually determined for Charpy specimens, so the temperature at 80 per cent of maximum energy has been arbitrarily selected as the "fracture appearance" transition temperature for comparison and correlation purposes.

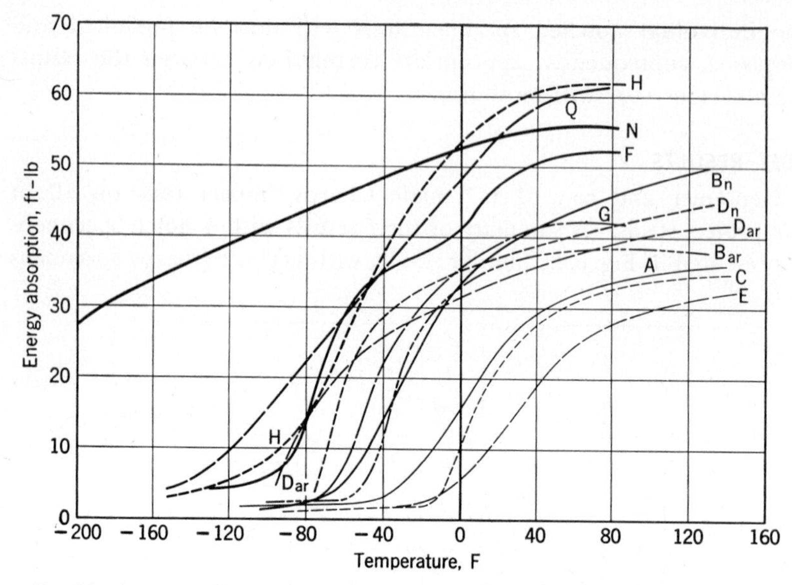

Fig. 6.3 Summary of keyhole Charpy energy-temperature curves for project steels.[1]

only about 30 F apart. In certain cases, such as that of steels (B_n) and (D_{ar}), the order was actually reversed, with the "fracture appearance" transition being higher for steel (D_{ar}) and the ductility transition being higher for steel (B_n). Similar behaviors were exhibited by keyhole Charpy specimens, as a study of Fig. 6.3 will show.

Tests were made on full thickness plates of the various steels in widths ranging from 12 in. up to 72 in. Steels A, B, C, N, H, and Q were tested at the University of California,[2] and steels D, E, F, and G were tested at the University of Illinois.[3] The results for some of the ¾-in. thick by 72-in. wide centrally notched plates are shown in Fig. 6.4. The reason for the difference in the energy scales is that the energy to maximum load was reported for steels A, B, C, H, and N, and the total energy to failure for steels D and E. Both groups of investigators [2,3] used a gage length equal to three fourths of the plate width and obtained the energy by integrating the load elongation curves. The reported transition temperatures were, however, not significantly affected by the numerical differences, and so the discrepancy is of little consequence. Details of the notch geometry are given in Fig. 6.5.

The curves and data in Fig. 6.4 give the impression that the fracture appearance and apparent ductility transitions (as indicated by energy absorption) are generally only about 10 F apart. This is a mislead-

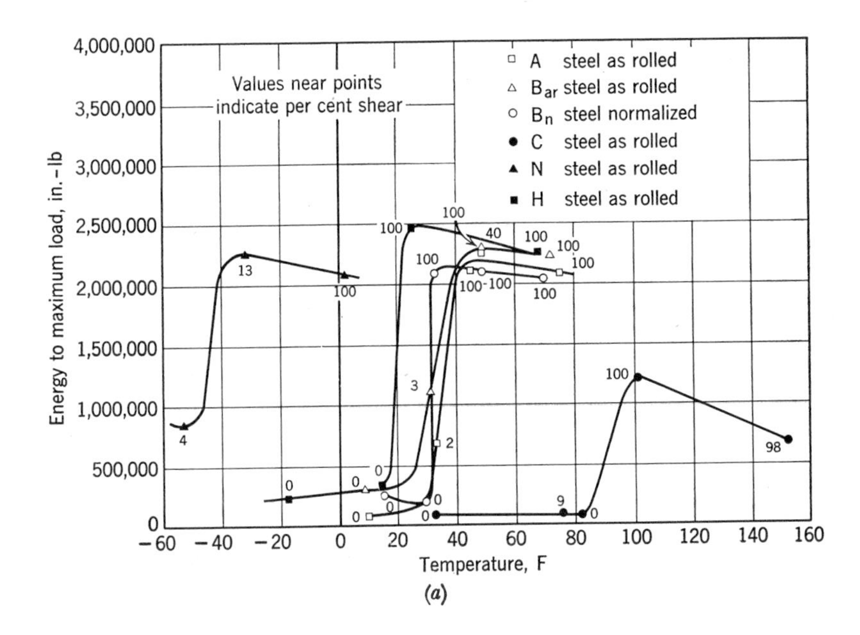

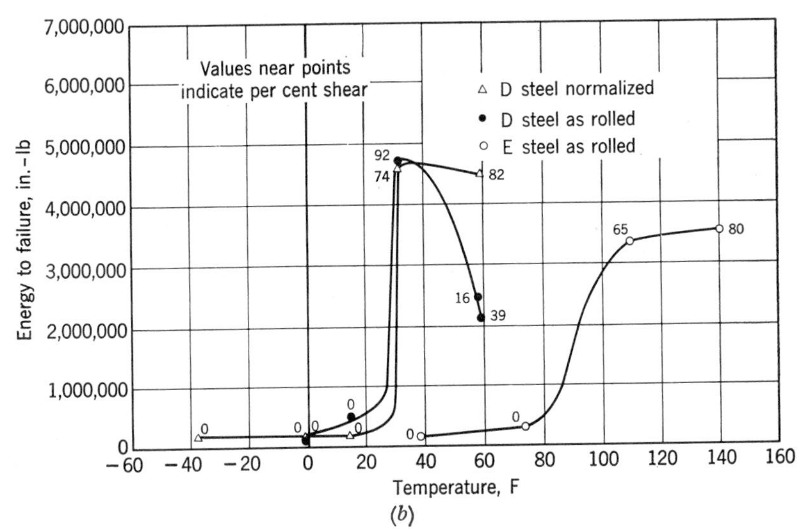

Fig. 6.4 Energy-temperature curves for 72-in. wide centrally notched plates. (a) Steels A, B, C, N, and H [2]; (b) steels D and E.[3]

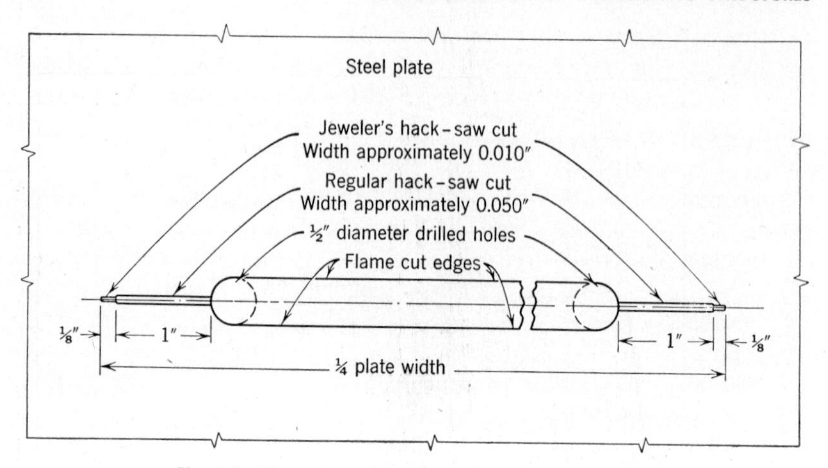

Fig. 6.5 Dimensions of notch used in flat plate tests.[4]

ing and an erroneous interpretation, however, because the ductility transition (as measured by 1 per cent lateral contraction at the base of the notch) is far below the temperature at the bottom of the sharp drop in the energy-temperature curve. Fig. 6.6, taken from the original data,[4] shows the elongation across the fracture, as measured on a 1-in. gage length, for the most brittle specimen tested and reported in Fig. 6.4(*a*)—that of C steel at 32 F. Elongation in a 1-in. gage length across the fracture and at the base of the notch was about 6 per cent; the elongation decreased to a minimum of about 3 per cent as the distance from the notch increased. Unfortunately, local

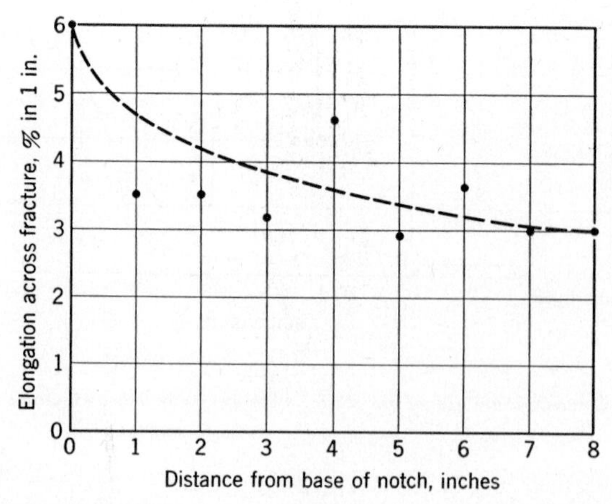

Fig. 6.6 Elongation in 1-in. gage length of 72-in. wide notched plate of steel C tested at 32 F.[4]

ductility measurements were not reported for all of the plates tested, nor were any of the wide plates tested at a low enough temperature to establish the 1 per cent lateral contraction ductility transition. Thus the internally notched wide plate tests established fracture appearance transitions but not ductility transition temperatures. Comparisons of results from wide plate tests with other tests should therefore be made only on the basis of fracture appearance and should not be made with ductility transitions obtained in other types of tests.

Results for 12-in. wide centrally notched plates are shown in Fig. 6.7. These specimens provide substantially the same kind of results as those obtained with the wider plates. With the narrower plates, however, the fracture appearance transition temperatures were somewhat lower. Table 6.3 shows the transition temperature for plates of

TABLE 6.3

FRACTURE APPEARANCE TRANSITION TEMPERATURES [2,3] FOR NOTCHED PLATES

Steel	Transition Temperature, F							
	Charpy V-notch *	3-in. Tension		Centrally Notched Flat Plate Specimens				
		Edge Notched	Sheared Edge	12-in.	24-in.	48-in.	72-in.	108-in.
A	130	45	35	25	Between −7 and 37	Below 48	35	—
B_{ar}	40	5	..	5	Below 32	Between 9 and 45	33	Below 32
B_n	60	−5	..	15	Below 32	..	31	..
C	160	90	120	90	88	90	90	Above 32
D_{ar}	110	..	..	40	33	35	30	..
D_n	80	..	..	15	36	40	32	..
E_{ar}	200	..	..	95	Above 120	110	95	..
E_n	..	..	..	65	..	..	..	..
F	20	..	..	30	20	..	..	..
G	60	..	..	20	..	..	..	..
H	30	20	10	−15	..	..	20	..
N	0	..	..	−64	..	..	−45	..
Q	30	35	..	10	..	..	..	..

* Temperature at 80 per cent of maximum energy arbitrarily selected for comparison as representative of fracture appearance transition in Charpy tests.

various widths. Some of the steels were not tested in all widths, and consequently there are several blanks in the table. However, enough data are available to establish the general behavior of notched plates.

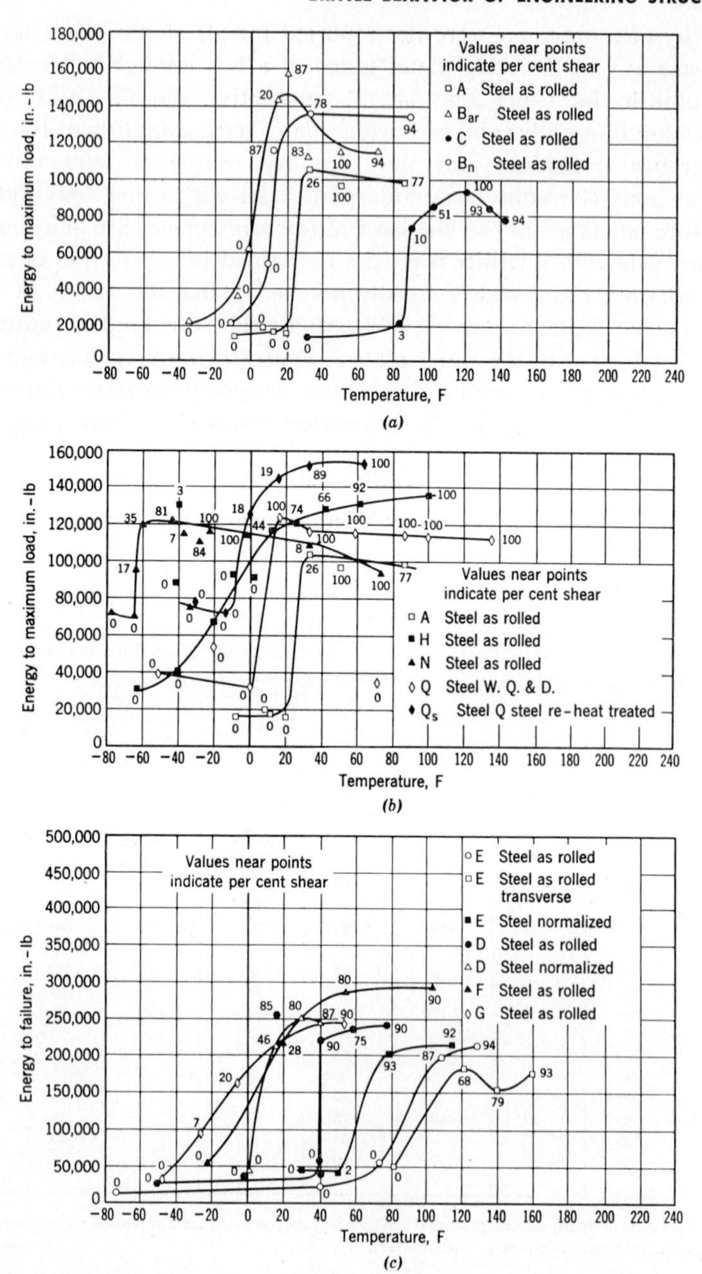

Fig. 6.7 Energy-temperature curves for 12-in. wide centrally notched plates. (*a*) Steels A, B, and C; [2] (*b*) steels A, H, N, and Q; [2] (*c*) steels D, E, F, and G.[3]

There is no valid quantitative correlation for all of the tests and steels, but it is immediately apparent that the C and E steels always had the highest transition temperatures and the H and N steels always had the lowest. The values for other steels scattered irregularly, with the order varying with the test.

The effects of various edge preparations and notch geometries on the fracture appearance transition temperature of 3-in. wide plate specimens is shown in Fig. 6.8. Sheared edges are as bad as hacksaw notches in promoting cleavage fractures and in lowering the ductility transition. This result has been substantiated by results of tests on other steels. Edge notches are somewhat more severe than central notches, and thicker plates in the as-rolled state have higher fracture appearance transitions. The influence of plate thickness is further illustrated in Figs. 6.9, 6.10, and 6.11. Fracture appearance transitions are shown for proportional edge-notched specimens of steel C rolled to various thicknesses. The transition temperature rises in a regular manner with increasing plate thickness until a maximum value is reached above which the transition temperature no longer

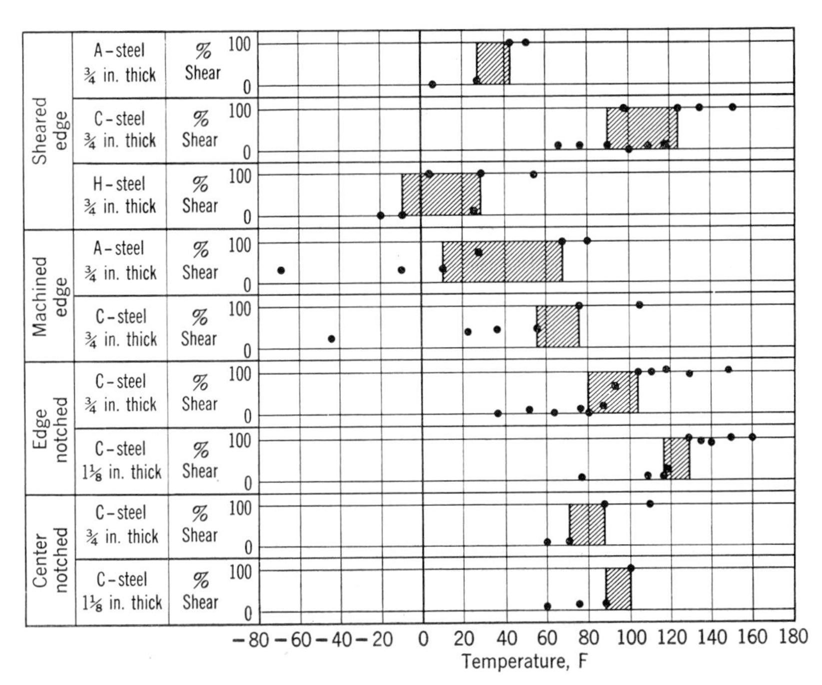

Fig. 6.8 Fracture appearance transition temperatures for various types of 3-in. wide specimens.[2]

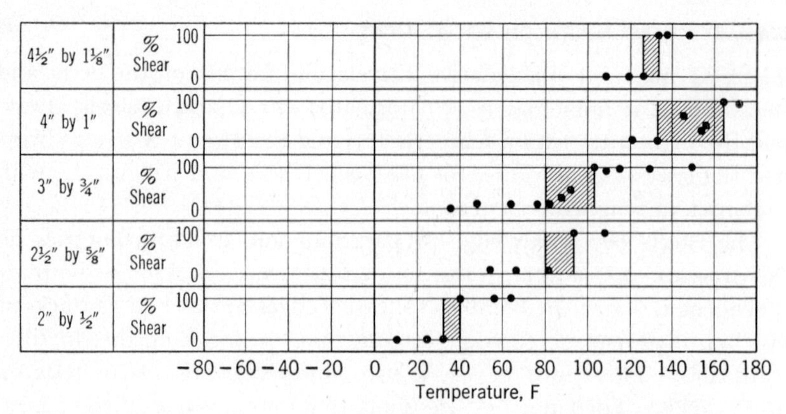

Fig. 6.9 Fracture appearance transition temperatures for proportional edge-notched specimens of steel C, plates of various thickness, net section 5/6 of plate width.[2]

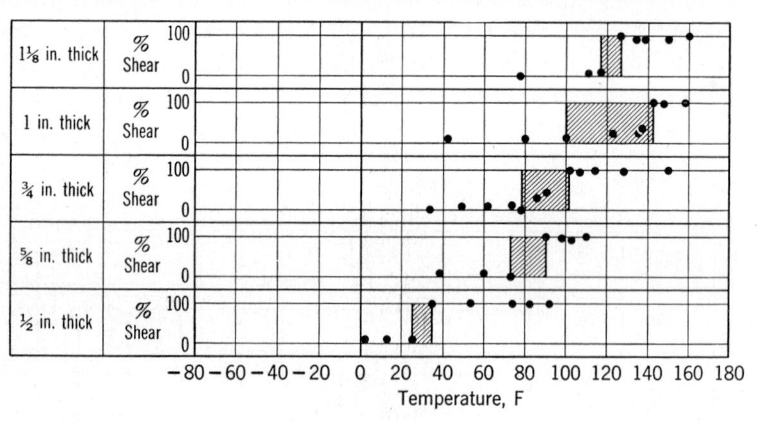

Fig. 6.10 Fracture appearance transition temperatures for 3-in. wide edge-notched specimens of steel C cut from plates rolled to different thicknesses.[2]

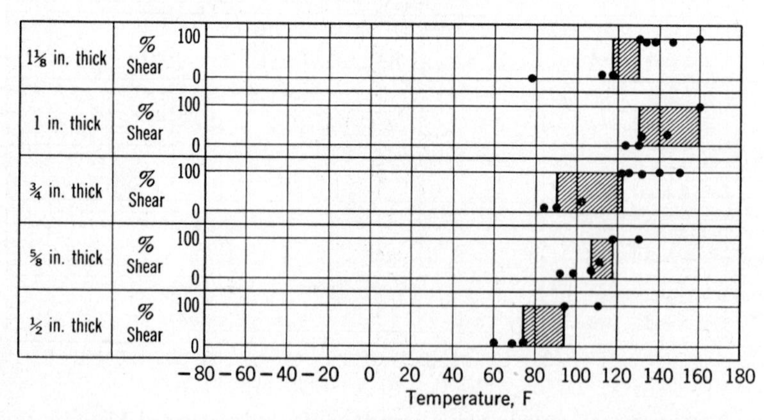

Fig. 6.11 Fracture appearance transition temperatures for 3-in. wide edge-notched specimens of steel C machined to various thicknesses from a single 1⅛-in. thick plate.[2]

increases with increasing plate thickness. This trend was further verified by the tests reported in Fig. 6.10, which shows similar results for 3-in. wide edge-notched specimens having the same type and depth of hacksaw notch. These specimens were also made from plates of steel C that had been rolled to various thicknesses ranging from ½ to 1⅛ in. The transition temperatures ranged from 30 F for the ½-in. plates to 120 F for the thicker plates. This large range in transition temperatures was shown to be partly due to metallurgical differences in the various thicknesses of plate. Fig. 6.11 shows the results obtained with a series of specimens having identical dimensions, but in this case the test bars were all machined from a single 1⅛-in. thick plate, with the midthickness being the plate center. Thus the metallurgical variable was largely eliminated and the thickness effect revealed. The spread in transitions was thereby reduced from 90 to 60 F.

The plate thickness is an important factor because of the influence it has on the stress in the thickness direction. As discussed in Chapter I, this stress must fall to zero at each face of the plate. The maximum value that this stress will reach (with a given sharpness of notch) will depend upon the absolute thickness of the plate. In very thin plates this component of stress will be low. As the plate thickness increases, the maximum value reached by the stress in the thickness direction will also increase. However, as the plate thickness increases, the rate at which this stress rises gradually decreases until at some plate thickness the rate becomes zero. Further increases in thickness would produce no change in the state of stress, and thus the transition temperature would become independent of plate thickness. The results shown in Figs. 6.9, 6.10, and 6.11 indicate that a thickness of 1 in. is sufficient to establish the maximum value of thickness direction stress. It should be borne in mind, however, that thicker plates may have higher transition temperatures because of metallurgical factors. Thicker plates are worked less, are finished at higher temperatures, and cool more slowly from the hot rolling temperature. Consequently, the ferrite grain size will be larger, and this will have an adverse effect upon the transition temperature. The metallurgical factors are discussed in detail in Chapter VII.

The specimen size effect was investigated further with a series of geometrically similar specimens.[5] According to the theory of elasticity, geometrically similar specimens should behave identically. To determine whether or not model laws could be applied to plastically strained metal, a series of special experiments was performed. The steel used in this series was not one of the "project steels" but was a hot-rolled plate of the medium carbon structural steel class that contained 0.25% carbon and 0.40% manganese. It was 1 in. thick and was large enough so that all specimens could be cut from a single plate. The material was annealed to relieve all internal stresses. The thinner specimens were made by machining equal amounts of material from each face. Three sizes of internally notched plate specimens were prepared. They were ¾, ⅜, and 3/16 in. thick; 12, 6, and 3 in. wide, and long enough to avoid end effects. All specimens had square central holes oriented with the sides at 45° to the loading axis. The diagonal of the hole, running transversely across the plate, was one third of the width of the plate. The radii at the corners of the holes were 1/32, 1/64, and 1/128 in. Four specimens of each size were made. The ones tested at room temperature were marked with a fine photographic grid so that the strain distribution could be determined as a function of load. The test results are summarized in Table 6.4. The fracture appearance transition temperature was

TABLE 6.4

SUMMARY OF RESULTS OF TESTS ON GEOMETRICALLY [5] SIMILAR SPECIMENS

Size of Specimen	Temp. of Test, F	Type of Fracture	Nominal Stress of Max. Load, psi	Reduction in Thickness, %	
				Maximum	Minimum
3″ wide	0	Shear	47,900	30.0	18.9
9″ long	32	Shear	45,200	26.7	15.6
3/16″ thick	74	Shear	47,700	30.0	18.5
	74	Shear	45,800	33.3	....
6″ wide	32	Cleavage	45,500	22.3	9.0
18″ long	50	Mixed	44,200	23.1	7.8
⅜″ thick	70	Shear	44,500	25.7	15.1
	90	Shear	44,400	25.6	17.7
12″ wide	32	Cleavage	40,900	16.2 *	1.4
36″ long	70	Cleavage	39,900	17.9 *	1.4
¾″ thick	102	Cleavage	39,100	19.7 *	1.7

* At base of notch.

found to be a function of the specimen size, with the transition for the thickest specimens being above 100 F and that for the thinnest being below 0°F.

The three sizes of specimens tested at room temperature apparently behaved alike until cracks formed at the base of the notch; thereafter they differed in behavior. It is evident that as soon as a crack forms at the base of a notch similitude is destroyed and a size effect is introduced.

Additional work on 12-in. wide centrally notched plates was done at Swarthmore by Carpenter and Roop.[6] They tested ¾-in. thick plates of A, B_n, B_{ar}, C, D_n, and E steels with notches of the same geometry as that shown in Fig. 6.5. Their data are given in Table 6.5, along with values of transition temperatures from the earlier work. The results show reasonable agreement, with the differences probably being due to the normal variations between plates.

TABLE 6.5

SUMMARY OF TRANSITION TEMPERATURES FOR 12-INCH WIDE CENTRALLY NOTCHED PLATES

	Swarthmore Data			
Steel	Energy to Max. Load, F	Fracture Appearance, F	Univ. of Illinois, F	Univ. of California, F
A	42	41	. .	25
B_{ar}	9	11	. .	5
B_n	26	27	. .	15
C	95	94	. .	90
D_n	18	19	0 to 30	. .
E	85	77	80 to 120	. .

A number of full-scale tests[7] were also made on welded specimens of the "hatch corner type" (see Fig. 4.12 in Chapter IV). The results of tests on 26 specimens are tabulated in Table 6.6. The energy absorption values shown in the table correspond to the energy at the time the longitudinal girder broke away from the hatch end beam. For the specimens that failed by cleavage, this corresponded to complete failure of the deck; when the failure was of the shear type, however, the fracture did not extend very far into the deck plate. The beneficial effects of preheating are shown by the results of tests numbered as 5, 12, 13, 21, and 23. Preheating increased the fracture stress by a substantial amount and raised the energy absorption so much that specimens of steel C broken at 70 F absorbed more energy than specimens not preheated did at temperatures 30 to 70 F higher. However, the fracture appearance transition was apparently unaffected, since all specimens failed by cleavage. This is to be expected because the properties of the plates through which the fracture passed were unaltered by the preheat. Thus welding conditions affect initiation of failure but not the propagation of a crack. It appears that pre-

TABLE 6.6

RESULTS OF FULL-SCALE HATCH CORNER TESTS [7]

Steel	Ref. No.	Test Temp., F	Nominal Stress at Failure, psi	Total Energy in 1000 in-lb Units		Thickness Reduction at Fracture, % Distance from Corner, in.						Type of Failure
				Max. Load	At Failure	0	1/16	1/4	1/2	3/4	1	
A	1	32	24,200	...	...	26.0	2.8	1.8	0.7	...	...	Cleavage
B	2	32	25,700	340	522	26.0	2.3	1.8	1.1	0.6	0.2	Cleavage
B	3	66	27,000	...	...	*	*	*	*	*		Shear
B_n	4	32	26,900	...	...	25.0	2.4	1.3	0.9	...	...	Cleavage
B 400 F preheat	5	75	32,400	2012	2758	*	*	*	*	*		Shear
C	6	32	23,200	...	...	24.0	1.1	0.4	0	...	...	Cleavage
C	7	68	24,000	...	...	27.0	2.1	1.0	0.2	0	0	Cleavage, shear lip
C	8	72	24,800	...	...	27.0	2.1	1.9	1.5	1.1	0.5	Cleavage at corner
C	9	100	27,400	342	788	19.0	1.5	1.3	1.1	0.9	0.8	Cleavage
C	10	120	25,600	284	484	*	*	*	*	*		Shear at corner
C	11	142	29,200	544	860	*	*	*	*	*		Shear
C 400 F preheat	12	70	32,600	1046	...	27.0	1.3	0.2	0	0	0	Cleavage, shear in welds
C 400 F preheat	13	70	32,800	1358	...	....	...	...	...	...	...	Cleavage
C riveted	14	70	20,900	790	...	....	...	...	...	...	...	Cleavage at corner
C riveted	15	70	20,600	412	588	....	...	...	...	...	...	Cleavage at corner
C low hydrogen alloy weld	16	32	23,600	180	180	27.0	1.8	1.1	0.4	0.1	0	Cleavage
C 25Cr-20Ni electrode	17	32	27,700	232	232	27.0	1.8	0.5	0.1	0	0	Cleavage
C 1100 F after welding	18	72	30,000	...	...	27.0	1.9	1.1	0.5	0.3	0.2	Cleavage
D_n	19	32	25,900	...	...	25.0	2.4	1.3	0.9	...	...	Cleavage
D_n	20	72	27,800	514	1196	*	*	*	*	*		Shear
D_{ar} 400 F preheat	21	32	32,600	390	920	†	†	†	†	†		Cleavage in doubler plate
E	22	32	23,100	...	...	27.0	1.9	0.4	0.1	0	0	Cleavage
H 400 F preheat	23	31	35,400	1570	1622	27.0	0.8	0.5	0.3	0.1	0	Cleavage
H	24	72	31,200	910	1210	*	*	*	*	*		Shear
N 100 F preheat 25Cr-20Ni electrode	25	35	40,400	972	...	*	*	*	*	*		Shear

* High (no measurements possible).
† No failure in deck plate.

heating lowers the ductility transition, but there is no direct evidence for this conclusion in this series of tests. The energy-temperature curve for steel C is reproduced in Fig. 6.12. Shear failures occurred above 120 F and cleavage fractures below. The curve does not show an abrupt discontinuity, however, and the ductility at the base of the notch was always above 19 per cent. After the crack had progressed only $\frac{1}{16}$ in., the ductility had dropped to 1 or 2 per cent regardless of the test temperature, provided the fracture was of the cleavage

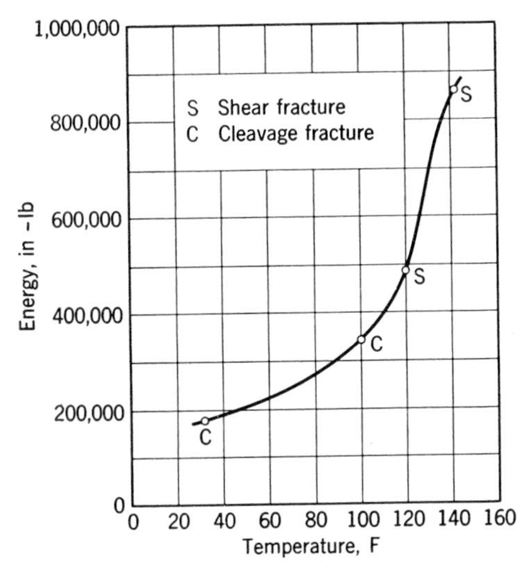

Fig. 6.12 Energy-temperature curve for hatch corner specimens of steel C.[8]

type. When the crack had progressed 1 in., the reduction in thickness was substantially zero for all specimens failing by the cleavage mode. Steel B behaved slightly better than steel C in this respect, and steels H and N behaved better than B, as might be anticipated from the V-notch Charpy and wide plate test results.

Some model tests were also made on welded hatch corner specimens made of steel C.[8] The results, as reproduced in Fig. 6.13, show a decrease in strength from 48,500 psi for the $\frac{1}{4}$-scale model to 24,500 psi for the full-scale specimen. These results and the more recent tests of Robertson [9] and of Feely and co-workers [10] indicate that heavy massive structures may fail at nominal stresses of 15,000 psi or lower when severe stress raisers are present. The data on service failures reported in Chapters XI and XII bear out the validity of this conclusion. Many of the service failures occurred at nominal stresses of 10,000 to 15,000 psi.

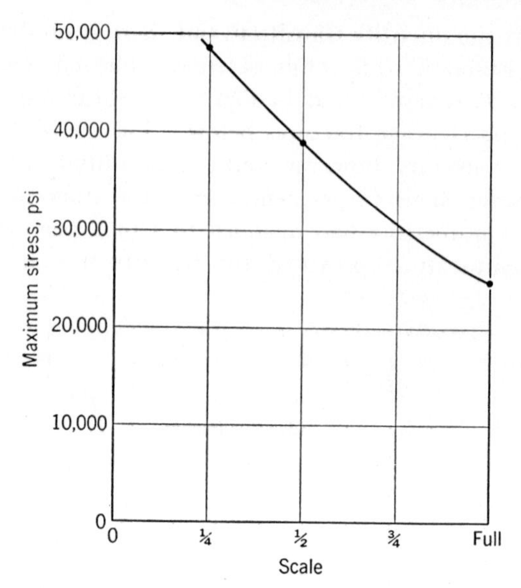

Fig. 6.13 Effect of size on strength of scale model hatch corner specimens.[8]

Kahn and Imbembo[11] determined the "tear test" transition temperatures for the A, B, C, E, and H steels. Their specimen was an eccentrically loaded edge notch specimen of the type shown in Fig. 4.11(*c*) in Chapter IV. The specimen was 5 in. long and 3 in. wide, with the distance between loading pins being 2½ in. These pins were directly in line with the base of the notch, a slot 1 in. deep that terminated in a drilled hole 0.039 in. in diameter. The tear test fracture appearance transition temperatures are given in Table 6.7

TABLE 6.7

Comparison of Fracture Appearance Transition Temperatures for Tear Test, Charpy V-Notch, and 72-Inch Wide Plate Specimens

	Tear Test			
Steel	Energy, F	Fracture Appearance, F	Charpy V-Notch,* F	72″ Wide Plates, F
A	60	63	130	35
B	45	45	40	33
C	127	127	160	90
E	130	130	200	95
H	28	30	30	20

* Temperature at 80 per cent of maximum energy is arbitrarily selected for comparison as representative of fracture appearance transition.

along with values for V-notch Charpy specimens and for 72-in. wide plates for comparison. The results from the tear test are consistently higher than those for the 72-in. plates. The V-notch Charpy transition temperatures do not correlate very well with either the tear test or the wide plate transition temperatures. If the V-notch Charpy fracture appearance transition temperatures had been based on actual fracture appearance rather than on 80 per cent of maximum energy, the correlation might have been somewhat better.

Direct explosion tests of the type illustrated by Fig. 4.10 in Chapter IV were also made on some of the project steels.[12] Explosive charges generate stress waves with a sharp wave front, which travels at high velocity through the steel. For explaining the action of an impulsive load, the wave may be considered as a triaxial compression pulse that travels through the plate and is reflected from the opposite face as a triaxial tension wave. It is this reflected wave that causes the plate to break. Thus even in unnotched plates the stress is triaxial tension in nature, and it is the "hydrostatic tension" component of the shock wave that causes the plate to break in a brittle manner. In addition to the triaxial nature of the stress, the high rate of loading also raises the yield point of the steel, as described in Chapter II. This results in an increase in the ratio of yield stress to cleavage fracture stress, thereby favoring brittle behavior.

Notch sensitive steels (as evaluated by other tests, e.g., 72-in. wide plates) fractured with comparatively little deformation in the explosion tests, whereas the notch tough steels deformed extensively. In a single steel the performance varied with temperature, the lower temperature tests resulting in brittle fracture. Explosion test data were too incomplete to provide an adequate comparison with wide plate test results, but a rough correlation was found. For example, in the 72-in. wide plate tests the fracture appearance transition temperature for steel C was found to be about 70 F higher than that for steel D; correspondingly, steel C required less energy than steel D to cause fracture in the explosion test. Furthermore, steel D deformed considerably prior to fracture, while steel C deformed very little at the same test temperature.

Tests were also made on other steels in both the unwelded and the welded states, with the welding conditions being varied over a wide range. The performance of welded specimens ranged from 25 to 90 per cent of the prime plate, depending upon the quality of the plate and the welding procedure employed. The performance of unnotched butt welded plates was never as good as that of unwelded plates.

The performance, as measured by the charge required to cause fracture, was generally about one half that of the unwelded plate. Both low temperature stress relieving and furnace stress relieving improved the performance 15 to 25 per cent. The effect of preheating was not determined. The use of low-hydrogen high-tensile electrodes doubled the energy required to fracture. An example of the type of transition curve obtained with the explosion test is shown in Fig. 6.14. These data, taken from the work of Mikhalapov,[13] show the minimum energy required to cause fracture as a function of temperature for

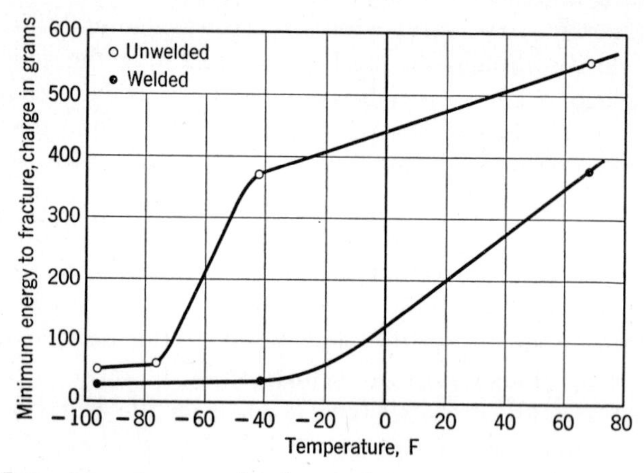

Fig. 6.14 Energy-temperature curve for direct explosion test on 1-in. thick mild steel plates showing effect of welding. All plates were unnotched.[13]

both welded and unwelded mild steel plate. The welds were made with E6010 electrodes and without preheat.

CORRELATION OF TEST RESULTS

Precise correlations of transition temperatures are difficult to obtain. Furthermore, any correlation based on fracture appearance transitions will not in general hold for the ductility transitions in the same series of tests. There may, indeed, even be reversals in the order of rating. There are two reasons for this: (1) the fracture appearance transitions are near the top of the energy-temperature curves, while the ductility transitions are near the bottom; and (2) the slope of the steeply rising portion of the curve varies with the type of test and the type of steel. A study of Fig. 6.15 will be helpful in clarifying this. Energy-temperature curves for six specimen types and for three steels

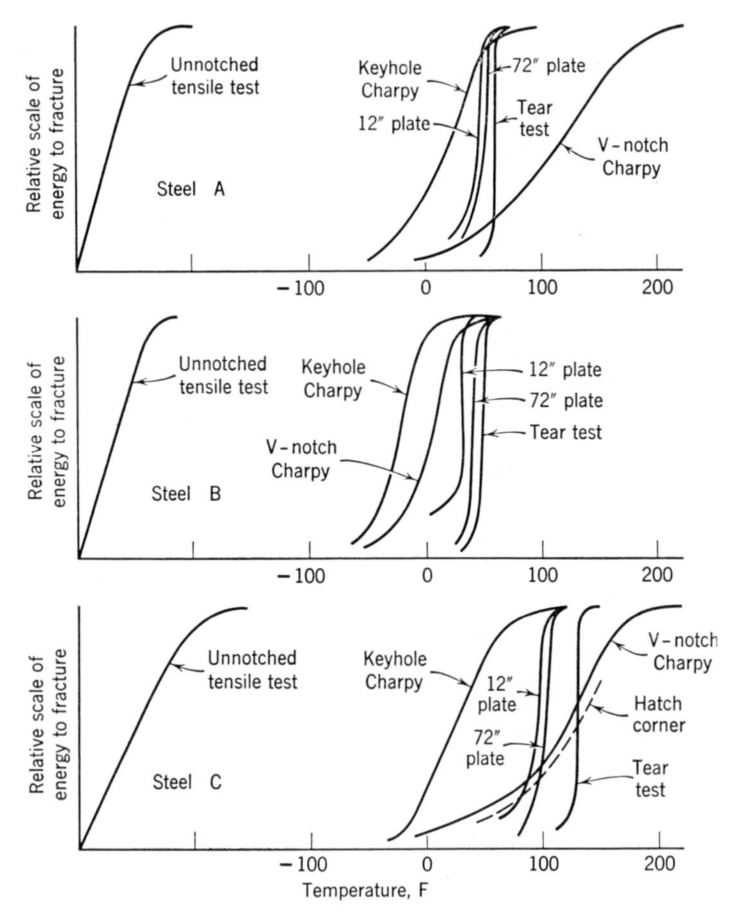

Fig. 6.15 Composite plot showing energy-temperature curves for various specimens made from A, B, and C steels.

are shown on composite plots. Some of the curves diverge at the top, some at the bottom, and others cross in an irregular manner.

Some reasonably good ductility transition temperature correlations have been worked out by Vanderbeck and Gensamer.[14] Fig. 6.16 shows the correlation they obtained between the 10 ft-lb V-notch Charpy transition temperature and the keyhole Charpy "ductility" transition temperature. The transition for the keyhole specimens was selected as the temperature corresponding to the middle of the scatter zone. The relation found to hold for all project steels and for several similar steels can be expressed as follows:

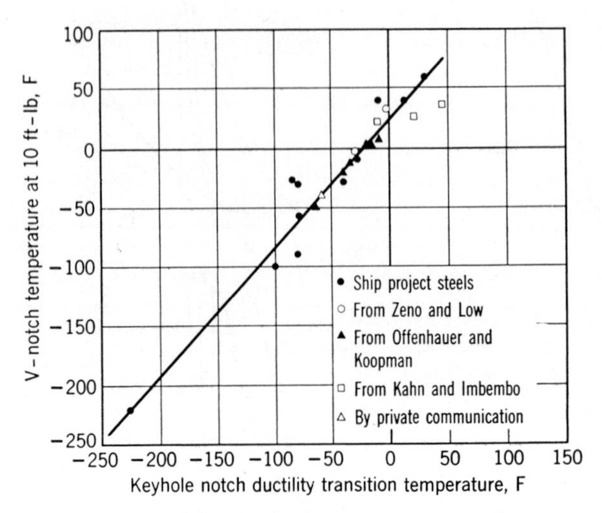

Fig. 6.16 Relation between 10 ft-lb V-notch Charpy temperature and temperature at middle of scatter band for keyhole Charpy specimens.[14]

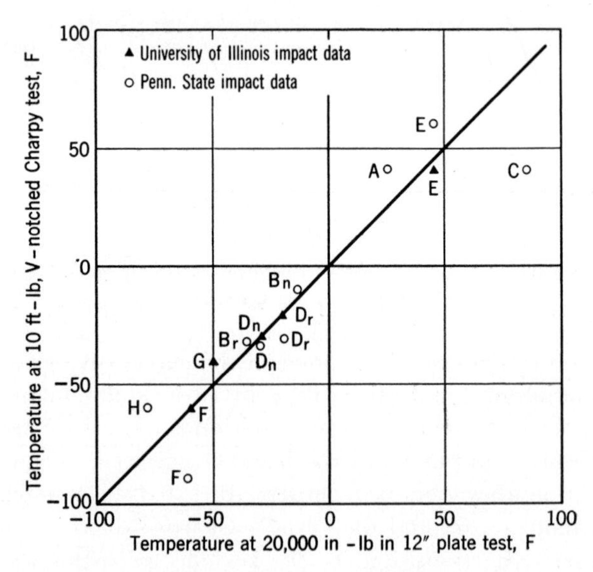

Fig. 6.17 Relation between 10 ft-lb V-notch Charpy temperature and temperature at 20,000 in-lb level for 12-in. wide centrally notched plates.[14]

$$V = 30 + 1.12K$$

where V = the 10 ft-lb transition temperature for V-notch Charpy specimens, F.

K = temperature at middle of scatter band for keyhole Charpy specimens, F.

Deviations from this relation of 40 F occurred, but most of the data fell within a ±10 F scatter band. For other classes of steel the constants vary somewhat from those given above.

The same investigators also found a reasonably good correlation between the 10 ft-lb V-notch Charpy transition temperature and the temperature at which the energy required to break a 12-in. wide internally notched plate was 20,000 in-lb. Their results are reproduced in Fig. 6.17. Again the extreme limit of scatter is about 40 F, but the normal scatter is within ±20 F. This seems very good when it is realized that two plates rolled from the same heat of steel may vary by this amount. Thus, within the limits of sampling errors, these correlations may be considered valid.

An interesting summary of transition temperatures has been prepared by Gensamer[15] and is reproduced in Fig. 6.18. There is a regular downward trend for all six steels, but there is no rigorous correlation because of the mixed criteria used in the various tests.

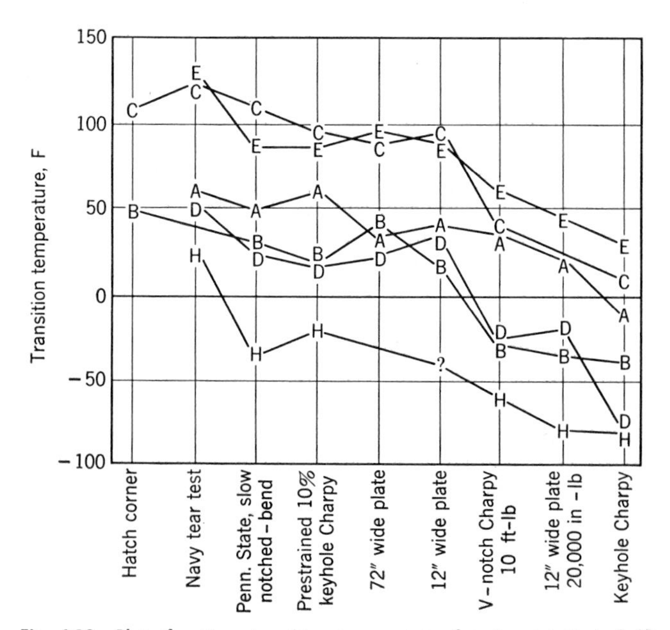

Fig. 6.18 Plot of various transition temperatures for six project steels.[15]

CONCLUSIONS

General correlations exist between transition temperatures (either fracture appearance *or* ductility) determined by various tests for a number of steels, but the best correlations have been obtained for those transitions based on notch ductility. In particular it has been shown that the 10 ft-lb V-notch Charpy temperature correlates well with the ductility transition of the keyhole Charpy specimen. A similar relation was found to exist between the V-notch Charpy transition and the temperature at the 20,000 in-lb energy level for 12-in. wide centrally notched plates. These correlations, however, hold only for the particular class of steel under consideration.

The only known correlation between service failures and notched bar tests is with the V-notch Charpy specimen. Williams and Ellinger [16] found that the 10 ft-lb transition temperature for V-notch Charpy specimens corresponded approximately to the temperature at which the plate failed in ship service. Details of service failures are presented in Chapters XI and XII.

Ductility and fracture transitions do not correlate with each other. The ductility transition seems to be a criterion of whether or not a brittle fracture might start in service, whereas the fracture appearance transition temperature seems to be a criterion of whether or not a crack, once started, will continue to propagate through the structure.

REFERENCES

1. A. Boodberg, H. E. Davis, E. R. Parker, and G. E. Troxell, "Causes of Cleavage Fracture in Ship Plate—Tests of Wide Notched Plates," *Welding J.*, Res. Suppl., pp. 186-s–199-s (April 1948).
2. W. M. Wilson, R. A. Hechtman, and W. H. Bruckner, "Cleavage Fracture of Ship Plates as Influenced by Size Effect," *Welding J.*, Res. Suppl., pp. 200-s–208-s (April 1948).
3. M. Gensamer, E. P. Klier, T. A. Prater, F. C. Wagner, J. O. Mack, and J. L. Fisher, "Correlation of Laboratory Tests with Full-Scale Ship Plate Fracture Tests," Ship Structure Committee Report, Serial No. SSC-9, March 19, 1947.
4. H. E. Davis, G. E. Troxell, A. Boodberg, E. R. Parker, and M. P. O'Brien, "Causes of Cleavage Fracture in Ship Plate: Flat Plate Tests," Ship Structure Committee Report, Serial No. SSC-2, August 23, 1946.
5. H. E. Davis, G. E. Troxell, E. R. Parker, and M. P. O'Brien, "Final Report on Cleavage Fracture of Ship Plate as Influenced by Design and Metallurgical Factors: Part II—Flat Plate Tests," OSRD Report No. 6452, Serial No. M-608, January 10, 1946.
6. S. T. Carpenter and W. P. Roop, "The Strength, Energy Absorption, and Transition Temperature of Internally Notched Flat Steel Plates," Ship Structure Committee Report, Serial No. SSC-47, January 19, 1953.

7. E. P. DeGarmo, J. L. Meriam, and M. P. O'Brien, "Causes of Cleavage Fracture in Ship Plate: Hatch Corner Tests," Ship Structure Committee Report, Serial No. SSC-5, October 23, 1946.
8. E. P. DeGarmo, J. L. Meriam, and R. C. Grassi, "Some Tests of Large Welded Structures," *Welding J.,* Res. Suppl., pp. 257-s–267-s (May 1947).
9. T. S. Robertson, "Brittle Fracture of Mild Steel," *Engineering* (*London*), *172,* 445–448 (1951).
10. F. J. Feely, Jr., D. Hrtko, S. R. Kleppe, and M. S. Northup, "Report on Brittle Fracture Studies," *Welding J.,* Res. Suppl., pp. 99-s–111-s (February 1954).
11. N. A. Kahn and E. A. Imbembo, "A Method of Evaluating Transition from Shear to Cleavage Failure in Ship Plate and Its Correlation with Large-Scale Plate Tests," *Welding J.,* Res. Suppl., pp. 169-s–182-s (April 1948).
12. G. S. Mikhalapov, "Structural Strength of the Welded Joint" (Adams Lecture for 1947), *Welding J.,* Res. Suppl., pp. 193-s–206-s (March 1948).
13. G. S. Mikhalapov, "Direct Explosion of Welded Joints," *Welding J.,* Res. Suppl., pp. 109-s–122-s (March 1950).
14. R. W. Vanderbeck and M. Gensamer, "Evaluating Notch Toughness," *Welding J.,* Res. Suppl., pp. 37-s–48-s (January 1950).
15. M. Gensamer, "General Survey of the Problem of Fatigue and Fracture of Metals," *Fatigue and Fracture of Metals.* New York: John Wiley & Sons, 1952.
16. M. L. Williams and G. A. Ellinger, "Investigation of Fractured Steel Plates Removed from Welded Ships," Ship Structure Committee Report, Serial No. NBS-1, February 25, 1949.

CHAPTER

Influence of Chemical Composition and Manufacturing Practice

INTRODUCTION

The transition temperature, regardless of the criterion selected, depends upon many factors, including specimen geometry, chemical composition, heat treatment, grain size, rolling procedure, and deoxidation practice. In this chapter the discussion is limited to the effects of variations in composition and manufacturing practice on selected "transition temperatures" for hot-rolled medium carbon structural steel.

CHEMICAL COMPOSITION

Unfortunately, there have been very few comprehensive investigations of the effect of variations in chemical composition on transition temperatures of hot-rolled structural carbon steel. Data from two fairly complete investigations are available,[1,2] however; and even though there is a lack of agreement about certain details, the general effects of composition seem fairly clear. Part of the observed differences are perhaps due to the fact that the microstructure varies with composition when the various alloys are treated alike. The results reported in the following pages represent an incomplete story, and so the conclusions may have to be modified somewhat when additional data have been accumulated.

Frazier, Boulger, and Lorig[2,3] obtained the following relation between composition and mechanical properties from a number of laboratory heats of semikilled medium carbon steel. The ingots were rolled into ¾-in. thick plates; the rolling was at a controlled temperature of 1850 F. These relations were obtained with a variety of compositions, including variations in carbon from 0.15% to 0.35% and in manganese from 0.20% to 1.50%. All steels contained approximately 0.015% phosphorus, 0.004% nitrogen, 0.05% silicon, and 0.01% aluminum.

Upper yield point in pounds per square inch

$$= 23{,}000 + 39{,}200 \times \%C + 7200 \times \%Mn$$

(Standard error = 1500 psi)

Lower yield point in pounds per square inch

$$= 20{,}700 + 39{,}800 \times \%C + 8400 \times \%Mn$$

(Standard error = 1300 psi)

Tensile strength in pounds per square inch

$$= 30{,}800 + 104{,}000 \times \%C + 13{,}000 \times \%Mn$$

(Standard error = 2200 psi)

$$\text{Elongation in per cent} = 38.2 - 32.6 \times \%C - 3.2 \times \%Mn$$

(Standard error = 2.4%)

50% fibrous fracture tear test transition temperature * (in F)

$$= 17 + 330 \times \%C - 23 \times \%Mn$$

(Standard error = 10 F)

20 ft-lb keyhole Charpy transition temperature † (in F)

$$= K - 19 + 349 \times \%C - 74 \times \%Mn$$

(Standard error = 12 F)

The value of K in the Charpy transition relation was found to vary in an irregular way with the manganese content, as indicated below:

* This transition temperature was selected as the highest temperature at which one or more of a group of four test specimens exhibited a fracture area having less than 50% of fibrous appearance.

† The Charpy transition temperature was selected as the temperature on the average temperature-energy curve corresponding to the 20 ft-lb level.

%Mn	K	%Mn	K
0.2	+6	1.0	−5
0.4	+1	1.2	+2
0.6	−3	1.4	+8
0.8	−8	1.5	+12

Other factors, such as plate thickness, finishing temperature, and cold work, are known to affect the mechanical properties. Commercial heats may vary considerably from the properties predicted by the above equations because of the presence of other elements or because of variations in thermal and mechanical history. Furthermore, these equations are valid only over the indicated limits of composition.

Frazier et al.[2,3] stated that the formulas presented above for tensile properties agreed well with those reported for commercial steels.[4] Furthermore, they calculated the 50% fibrous fracture tear test transition temperature and the 20 ft-lb keyhole Charpy transition temperature and compared these calculated values with actual test results obtained by Kahn [5] on 25 commercial steels. These data are plotted in Fig. 7.1, where the calculated and experimental values of transition temperature are compared for both Charpy and tear test specimens. The correlation is far from ideal. The scatter is about ±25 F for the keyhole Charpy 20 ft-lb transition temperature and about ±35 F for the fracture appearance transition temperature of the tear test. The average Charpy transition temperatures (20 ft-lb) of the steels containing about 0.22% of carbon and 0.45% of manganese were almost identical for laboratory and commercial heats, being +21 F and

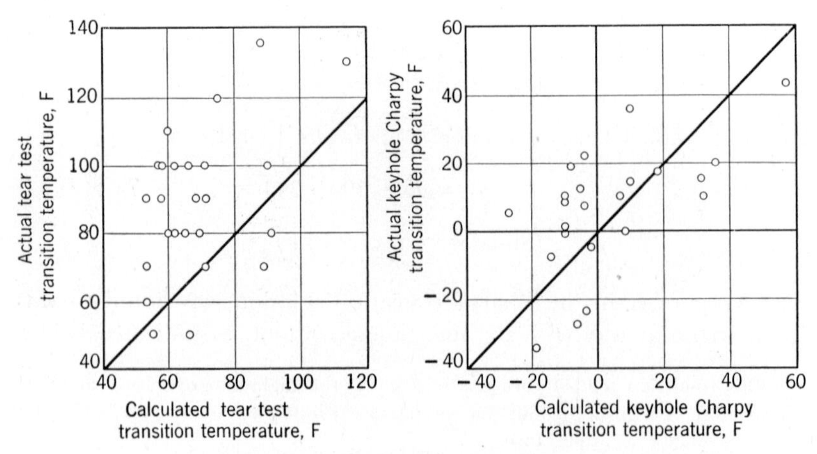

Fig. 7.1 Comparison of actual and calculated transition temperatures of commercial semi-killed ¾-in. ship plate.[2]

+20 F, respectively. The agreement between laboratory and commercial heats of steels containing about 0.20% carbon and 0.76% manganese was not quite so good but still reasonably satisfactory. The laboratory heats had an average 20 ft-lb transition of +2 F; the commercial heats averaged −15 F. Discussion of other factors that influence the transition temperature is presented later in this chapter.

Carbon. An increase in carbon content causes an increase in the strength, a reduction in ductility, a lowering of the maximum energy in the Charpy test, and an increase in both the fracture appearance and the ductility transition temperatures.

Lorig [6] determined the effect of carbon on the 50% fibrous fracture transition temperature for the Kahn (Navy) tear test. His results for hot-rolled semikilled pearlitic steels are reproduced in Fig. 7.2. The effect of carbon was to increase this transition temperature about 30 F for each 0.1% increase in the carbon content. Curve 1 is for a 0.45% manganese steel, and Curve 2 is for steel containing 0.75% manganese. The 20 ft-lb energy level for the keyhole Charpy transition temperature corresponded to a position on the energy-temperature curve that was often far above the scatter band indicating the ductility transition range. The 20 ft-lb temperature represented neither the fracture appearance transition nor the ductility transition. A replot of the original data indicated that a 0.1% increase in carbon caused an upward shift of only about 20 F in the 10 ft-lb (ductility transition) temperature instead of 35 F as indicated by the misleading 20 ft-lb criterion. The 10 ft-lb temperature was always within the scatter band associated

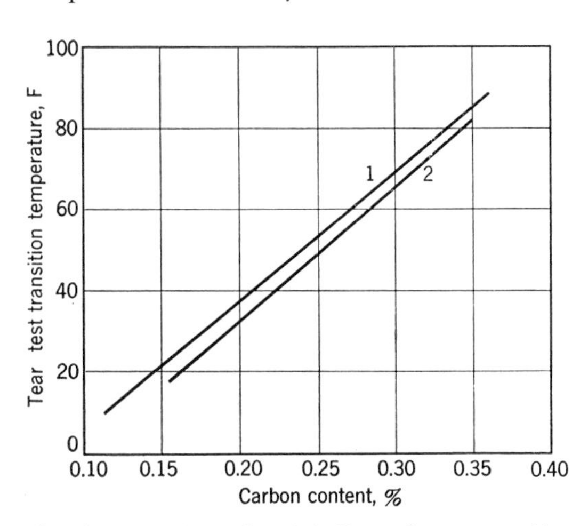

Fig. 7.2 Effect of carbon content on the 50% fibrous fracture transition temperature as determined by Kahn (Navy) tear test.[6]

with the ductility transition for this type of specimen. The same comments apply to the use of the 20 ft-lb energy level for appraising the effect of manganese, but the difference obtained between the 20 and the 10 ft-lb criteria seems to be within the limits of experimntal error.

In a similar investigation on fully deoxidized steels, Rinebolt and Harris [1] found that the average-energy transition temperature for V-notch Charpy specimens was raised about 50 F for each increase of 0.1% in the carbon content, whereas the ductility transition temperature (15 ft-lb) was increased only 25 F for the same increase in carbon. These results were valid, however, only for carbon contents in the range 0 to 0.3%. At higher carbon concentrations the effect was

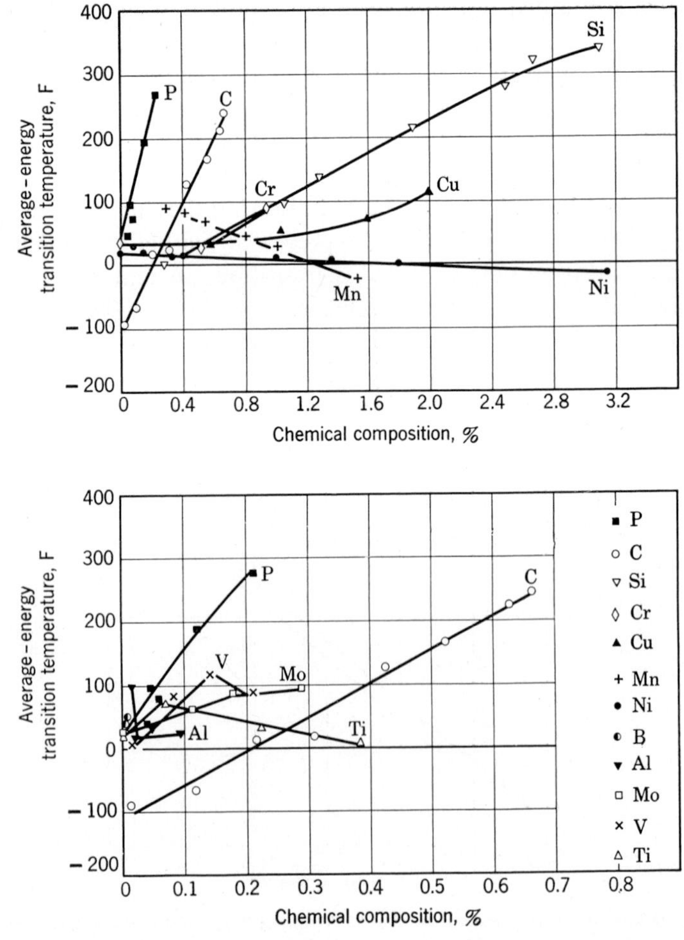

Fig. 7.3 Effect of chemical composition on average-energy transition temperature.[1]

larger. The average-energy transition temperatures obtained by Rinebolt and Harris with steels of various carbon contents are shown in Fig. 7.3, along with the results found for steels in which other elements varied. In this series of experiments the base analysis for all melts was 0.30% carbon, 1.00% manganese, and 0.30% silicon, except as indicated for the variable element whose effect was being measured. All heats were deoxidized with silicon and with 1.5 lb of aluminum per ton of steel, added just before pouring.

The average-energy transition temperature did not correspond to either the fracture appearance transition or the ductility transition. Figs. 7.4 and 7.5, also taken from Rinebolt and Harris,[1] are helpful in understanding why this is so. The three transitions are shown in Fig. 7.4, where the ductility transition (as represented by the 15 ft-lb energy level) is about −65 F, the average-energy transition is at 0°F, and the fracture appearance transition (50% cleavage) is 40 F. The absolute difference in degrees between these three temperatures will vary with the shape of the temperature-energy curve and with the maximum energy. Fig. 7.5 illustrates this nicely. For steels containing less than 0.1% carbon, the three transition temperatures are practically identical; but as the carbon content is increased, the transition range becomes broader, the maximum energy becomes less, and the spread between the three criteria increases. Furthermore, if the ductility transition is based upon the 10 ft-lb energy level instead of the 15 ft-lb value, the effect of the carbon will appear to be less, par-

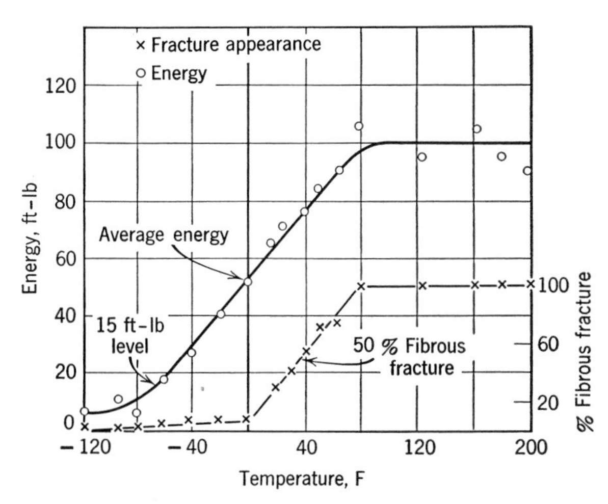

Fig. 7.4 Typical curves showing lack of correspondence between three transition temperature criteria.[1]

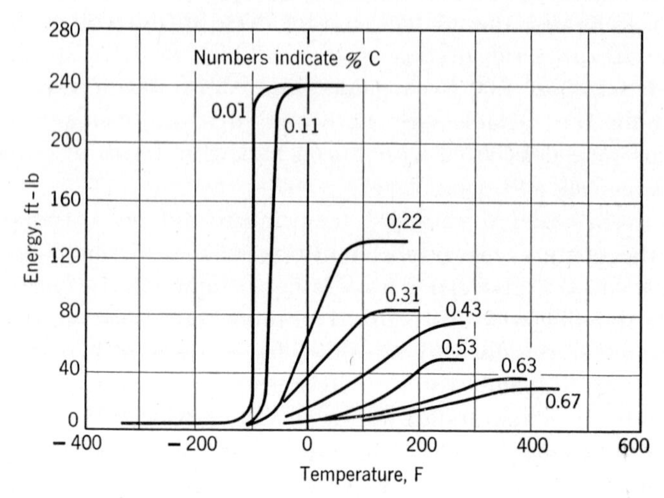

Fig. 7.5 Effect of carbon content on the shape of the energy transition temperature curves.[1]

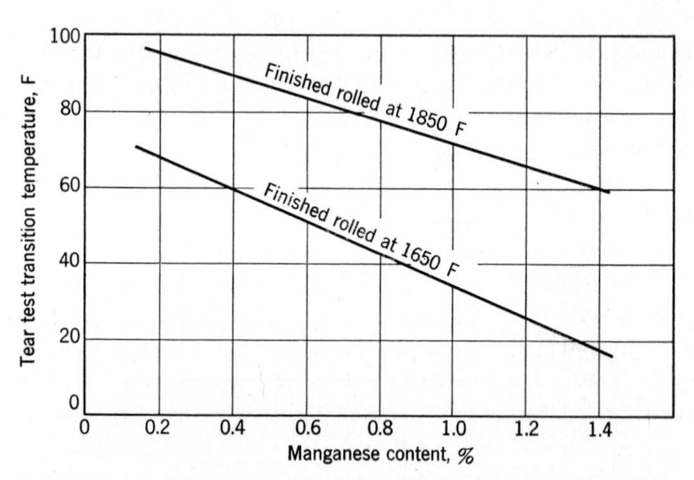

Fig. 7.6 Effect of manganese content on the 50% fibrous fracture transition temperature as determined by the Kahn (Navy) tear test.[6]

ticularly at the higher carbon concentrations. In the range below 0.3% carbon, however, the difference is small, the 10 ft-lb ductility transition changing about 20 F for each 0.1% increase in carbon content instead of the 25 F change obtained with the 15 ft-lb criterion.

Smith, Fostini, and Brick [7] determined the tensile and V-notch Charpy properties of vacuum melted high purity iron-carbon alloys with carbon ranging from 0.02% to 0.22%. They found that the ductility transition temperature (15 ft-lb) ranged from −53 F for the 0.02% carbon alloy to 90 F for the 0.22% carbon steel; the average-energy transition temperatures for these materials were −33 F and 161 F, respectively. Their data, however, did not vary in a regular way with variation in carbon content, apparently because their melting and heat treating methods were not the same for all melts and the grain size was apparently not held constant.

Manganese. Manganese is added to steel because it is a fairly good deoxidizer and also because it prevents hot shortness (high temperature brittleness) of the steel by sulphur. Much more important from the standpoint of brittle fracture, however, is its beneficial lowering of the transition temperature.[7,8,9,10,11] Lorig [6] reported the effect of manganese content on the 50% fibrous fracture transition temperature for the tear test as shown in Fig. 7.6. This transition temperature is also affected by the ferrite grain size (which in as-rolled products is largely determined by the final rolling temperature) as indicated in the figure. The grain size factor will be more fully discussed in a later section of this chapter. Manganese lowers the 50% fibrous fracture tear test transition temperature 4 F or less for each 0.1% increase in manganese content. Manganese was found to have a greater effect on both the 10 ft-lb and the 20 ft-lb keyhole Charpy transition temperatures, lowering each about 7 F for each 0.1% increase in manganese content.

Rinebolt and Harris [1] found that for fully killed steels the average-energy transition temperature for V-notch Charpy specimens was lowered about 10 F for each 0.1% increase of manganese. In addition they also found that the ductility transition temperature (15 ft-lb) for V-notch Charpy specimens was lowered about 10 F for each 0.1% increase in manganese content; the results would have been substantially the same for a 10 ft-lb ductility transition.

Silicon. Evaluation of the effect of silicon is complicated by the fact that silicon acts as a deoxidizer and also as an alloying element. Consequently, the influence of silicon on the ductility transition or fracture transition temperature will depend upon the concentration of other deoxidizing elements such as manganese and aluminum.

Figs. 7.7 and 7.8 taken from the Battelle work [3] show the effect of silicon on both tear test transition temperature and the 20 ft-lb keyhole Charpy transition temperature. Both transitions decrease with increasing silicon until the silicon content reaches some critical value; higher concentrations of silicon seem to raise the transition

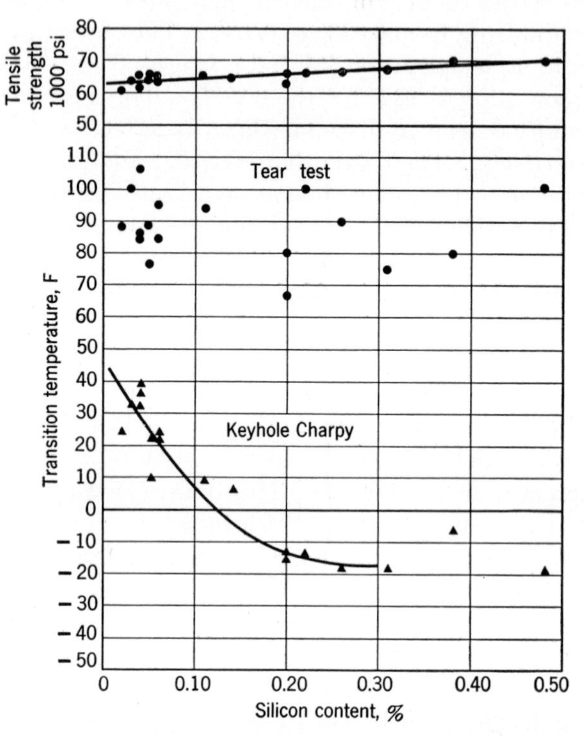

Fig. 7.7 Effect of silicon content on tensile strength, on tear test transition, and on 20 ft-lb keyhole Charpy transition temperatures for steel containing 0.25% C and 0.45% Mn.[3]

temperature slowly. These two figures show that the effect of silicon varies with the manganese content. The minimum transition temperature is reached at a lower concentration of silicon in the higher manganese steel, a result in accord with the concept that the beneficial effect of silicon is due to its deoxidizing action.

Rinebolt and Harris [1] investigated the properties of laboratory heats of fully deoxidized steels having a base composition of 0.30% carbon, 1.0% manganese, and 0.30% silicon. Fig. 7.9 shows the effect of silicon on three of the V-notch transition temperatures. Within the range of 0.2 to 3.0% silicon, all three transitions rose at a rate of 13 F for each additional 0.1% of silicon.

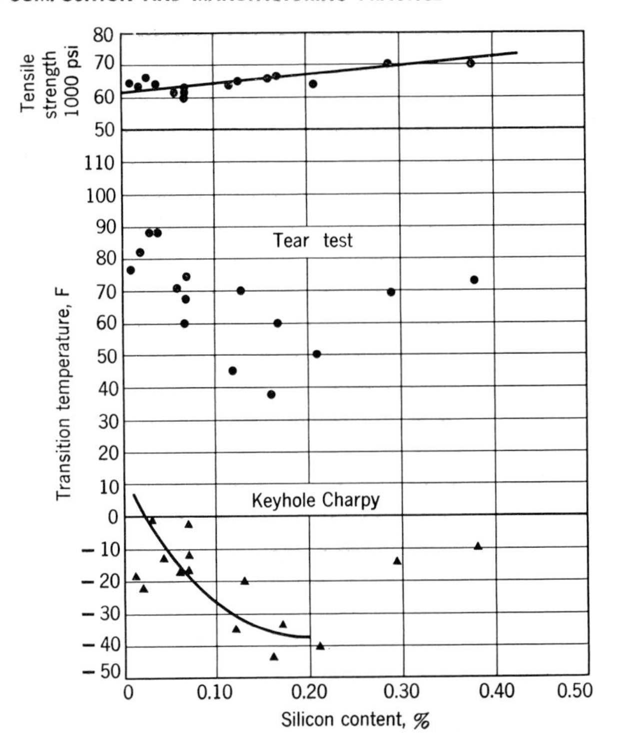

Fig. 7.8 Effect of silicon content on tensile strength, on tear test transition, and 20 ft-lb keyhole Charpy transition temperature for steel containing 0.21% C and 0.75% Mn.[3]

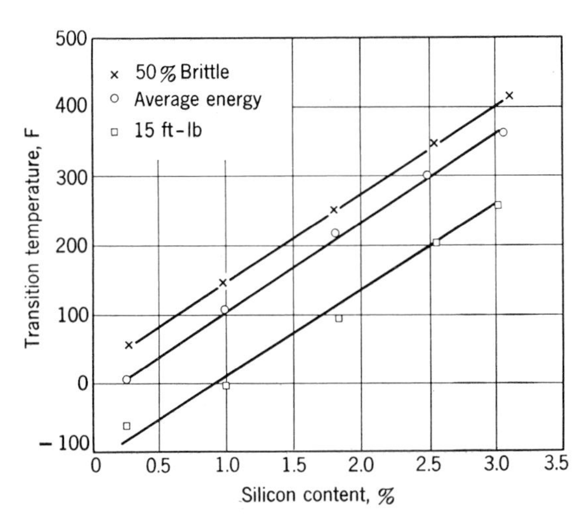

Fig. 7.9 Effect of silicon content on three V-notch Charpy transition temperatures for fully deoxidized steels containing 0.30% C and 1.00% Mn.[1]

Phosphorus. This element increases the various transition temperatures at a rate that equals or exceeds that of carbon. The effect varies slightly with the manganese content of the steel,[3] as shown in Fig. 7.10. The tear test transition temperature was increased about 5 F for each 0.01% increase in the phosphorus content, while the 20 ft-lb keyhole Charpy transition was increased about 4 F for the same increase.

Rinebolt and Harris [1] found that in fully deoxidized steels phosphorus raised the V-notch Charpy transition temperature about 13 F for each 0.01% increase in phosphorus content, as shown in Fig. 7.11.

McGeady and Stout [12] tested 18 commercial steels having a wide variation in composition and deoxidation practice. Using the Lehigh bend test (transverse notch 0.080 in. deep, root radius = 1 mm, specimen width 3 in., length 8 in., thickness ½ to ¾ in.) and taking the transition temperature as that temperature at which the lateral contraction at the root of the notch was 2%, they found that the phosphorus seemed to be about 20 times as effective as carbon in raising the transition temperature. This adverse effect of phosphorus was found for both prime plate and plates having longitudinal weld beads. The magnitude of the phosphorus effect is, however, open to question and the factor of 20 is probably much too high.

Sulphur. Sulphur in the form of sulphide inclusions may produce laminations in rolled steel plate.[1] Laminations, whether of the sulphide or oxide type, are plate-like inclusions that have little strength. Stresses acting normal to the laminations cause fissures to form, thus preventing the build-up of thickness direction stresses. Laminated plate tends to act like several thinner plates stacked together to form a thicker one. When laminated steel is tested, the results tend to scatter over a wide range, making accurate analysis difficult. Sulphur increases the energy absorption when it is present in plate-like inclusions, but it seems to lower the maximum energy for specimens without laminations. The meager results available indicate that sulphur has little if any effect upon the ductility transition temperature.

Nitrogen. The effect of nitrogen is difficult to evaluate accurately because of its interaction with other elements. However, there is little room for doubt that nitrogen is effective in raising certain of the transition temperatures. Rinebolt and Harris [1] found that nitrogen had little effect on the V-notch Charpy average-energy transition temperature for fully deoxidized steels. Frazier, Boulger, and Lorig [2,3] found, however, that nitrogen raised the fracture appearance and the keyhole Charpy transition temperatures of semikilled steels. Their results for the 50% fibrous fracture transition temperature (as deter-

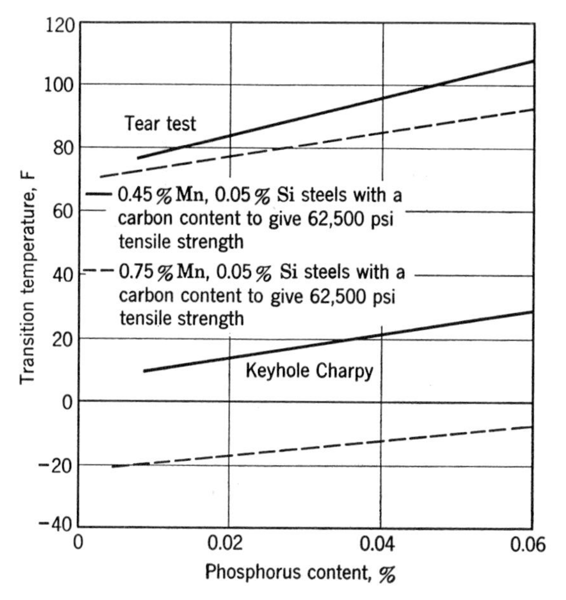

Fig. 7.10 Effect of phosphorus content on tear test and 20 ft-lb keyhole Charpy transition temperatures[3] (carbon content to give 62,500 psi tensile strength).

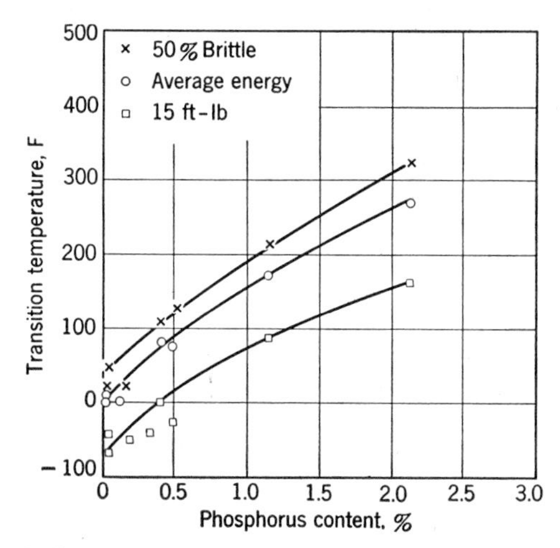

Fig. 7.11 Effect of phosphorus content on three V-notch transition temperatures for fully deoxidized steels containing 0.30% C and 1.00% Mn.[1]

mined by the tear test) are plotted in Fig. 7.12 against the nitrogen content. A similar plot is shown in Fig. 7.13 for the 20 ft-lb keyhole Charpy transition temperature. An increase of 0.01% in the nitrogen content raised the fracture appearance transition temperature about 50 F but raised the 20 ft-lb keyhole Charpy transition temperature only about 25 F. The same investigators added 0.017% aluminum to one heat of steel to see if aluminum would react with the nitrogen and

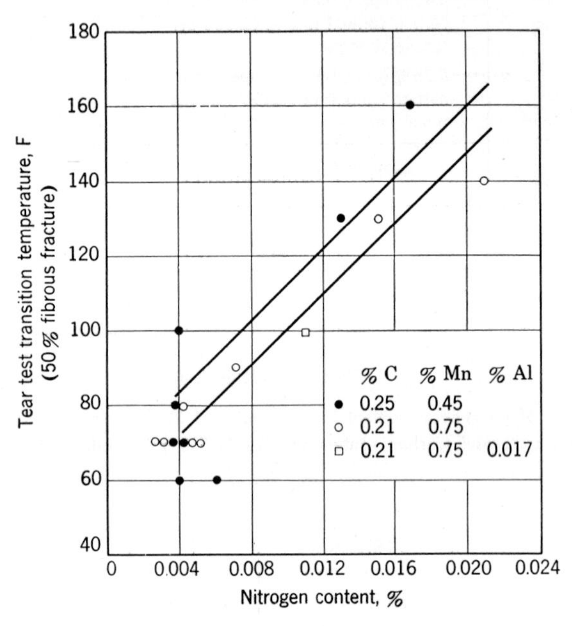

Fig. 7.12 Effect of nitrogen content on tear test transition temperature (50% fibrous fracture).[2]

reduce its embrittling action. The results as shown in the figures indicate that the aluminum was ineffective in this respect. The embrittling effect of nitrogen, however, was found by Geil, Carwile, and Digges [13] to be largely overcome by aluminum, which reacted to form aluminum nitride. It appears, however, that aluminum cannot always be depended upon to overcome the deleterious effect of nitrogen. It is apparently ineffective when added in small amounts to semikilled steels, possibly because these steels contain enough oxygen to combine with the aluminum added. In fully deoxidized heats, however, the aluminum in excess of that required for deoxidation can combine with the nitrogen and thus reduce its embrittling action. Normalizing seems to increase the effectiveness of aluminum in counteracting the deleterious effect of nitrogen.

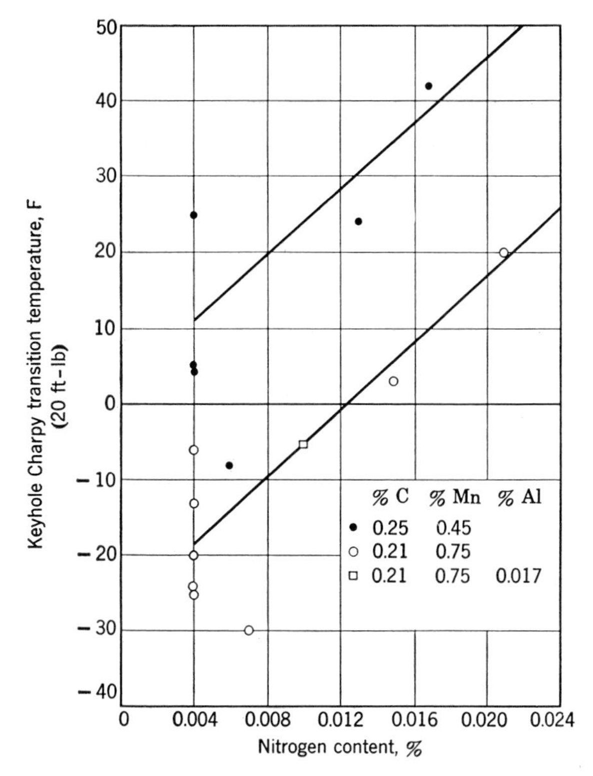

Fig. 7.13 Effect of nitrogen content on 20 ft-lb keyhole Charpy transition temperature.[2]

Enzian and Salvaggio [14] investigated the effect of nitrogen on the brittle behavior of a number of commercial plate steel heats. The steels were made with deliberate variations in open hearth practice, which included methods in common use by the steel industry. Most heats contained about 0.22% carbon and 0.50% manganese, but a few were made with about 0.18% carbon and 0.90% manganese. Nitrogen contents ranged from 0.005% to 0.01%. The effect of nitrogen was found to vary for the two types of steel, and the magnitude of the effect varied with the criterion of brittle behavior selected. The results obtained by the investigators on specimens cut from hot-rolled plates are reproduced in Figs. 7.14, 7.15, and 7.16. Points for project steels A and C previously described are plotted on some of the graphs for comparison. It is evident that the effect of nitrogen varies with the manganese and carbon contents, being small for the low manganese series and fairly large for the higher manganese steels. (These results are at variance with those obtained by Lorig [2,3] and co-workers,

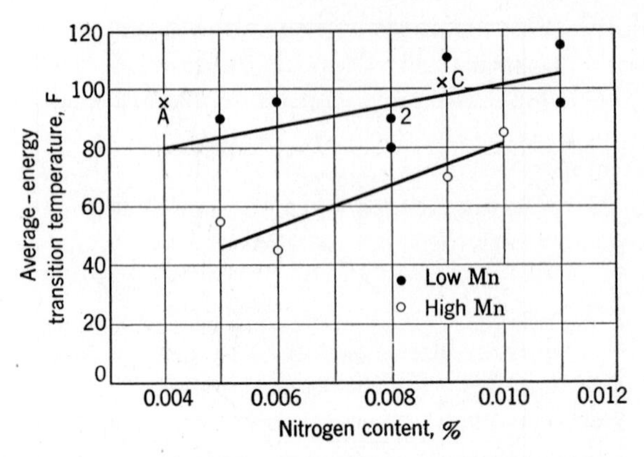

Fig. 7.14 Effect of nitrogen content on the average-energy transition temperature as determined with V-notch Charpy tests.[14]

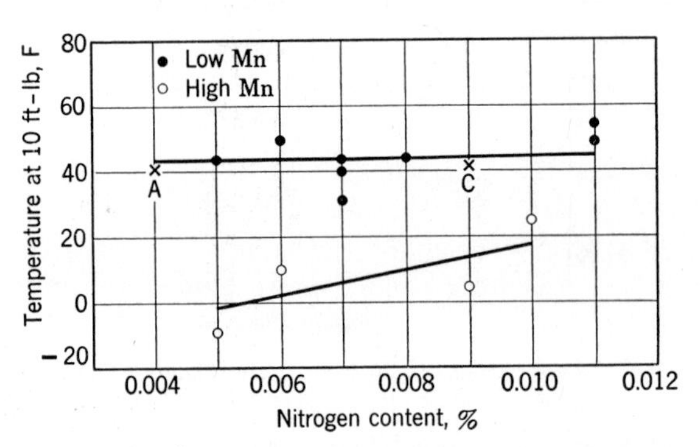

Fig. 7.15 Effect of nitrogen content on the 10 ft-lb transition temperature (ductility transition) as determined with V-notch Charpy impact tests.[14]

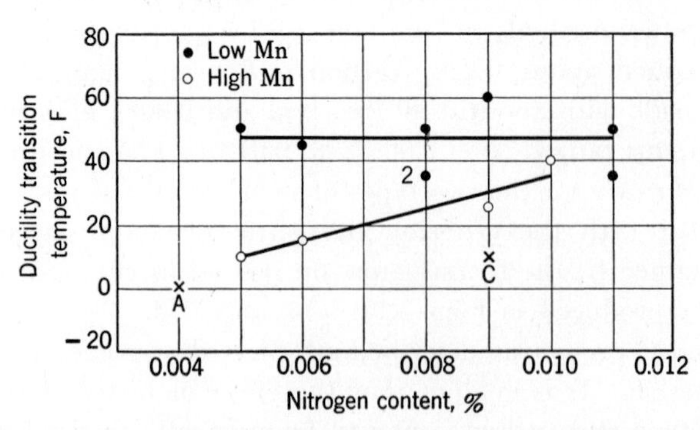

Fig. 7.16 Effect of nitrogen content on the ductility transition temperature (taken at midpoint of transition range) with keyhole Charpy impact tests.[14]

who found the effect of nitrogen greater in low manganese semikilled steels.) In the V-notch Charpy test, the addition of 0.005% nitrogen increased the average-energy transition temperature about 20 F for the low manganese steels and 35 F for the high manganese group. The same change in nitrogen, however, had no influence upon the 10 ft-lb transition temperature (ductility transition) for the low manganese steels and increased the ductility transition temperature for the higher manganese steels by only 20 F. The ductility transition for the keyhole Charpy tests is taken as the temperature at the midpoint of the transition range. Again, with this test, the effect of nitrogen was observed only for the higher manganese steels.

Oxygen. Oxygen plays a complex role in steel because of its reactions with iron and with the other elements present. Oxygen is known to have a detrimental effect upon the toughness and ductility of low carbon steel. The data shown in Fig. 7.17 on high purity ingot iron containing various amounts of oxygen were reported by Schmidt.[15] He found that increasing the oxygen content lowered the maximum energy considerably but raised the transition temperature very little unless unusually large quantities of oxygen were present. Similar observations were made by Rees and Hopkins,[16] who found that the

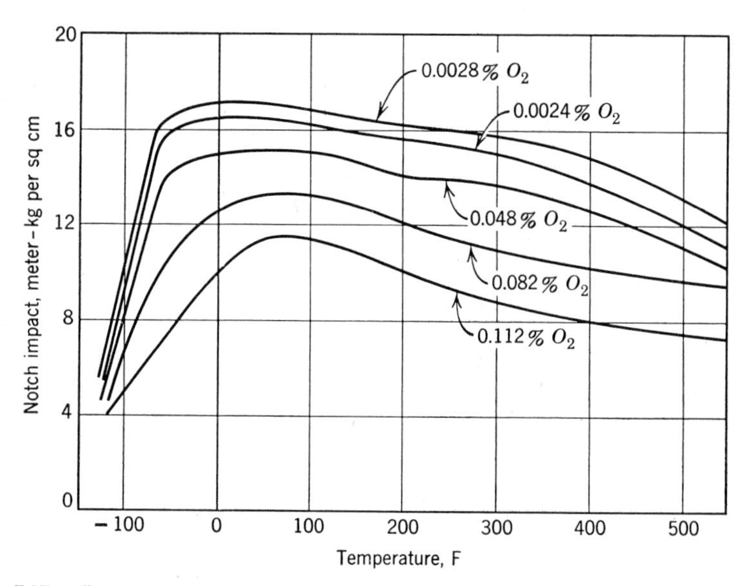

Fig. 7.17 Effect of oxygen content on the notch impact strength of iron.[15] (To convert impact strength in meter-kg per sq cm to ft-lb per sq in. multiply notch impact values by 46.7. The values on this figure have not been converted to the usual units, i.e., ft-lb, because the specimen cross section is not known.)

transition temperature in pure iron was unaffected unless the oxygen content was nearly 0.003%; for larger oxygen concentrations, however, the transition temperature rose steeply, appreciably more than reported by Schmidt. Fracture under conditions of oxygen concentrations in excess of 0.003% appeared predominantly to follow the ferrite grain boundaries with a consequent reduction in energy absorption in the V-notch Charpy impact test. Increasing the oxygen content from 0.001% to 0.057% lowered the maximum impact energy by approximately 40% and raised the transition temperature from 5 F to 650 F.

Brick [17] has discussed the effect of oxygen on the low temperature ductility of high purity iron. He has shown that with vacuum melted iron containing a trace of carbon, but no oxygen, the ductility is quite high. When the carbon was low and oxygen was present, however, the iron lost its ductility even at room temperature. The fracture followed the grain boundaries rather than a path through the grains. A photograph of this type of fracture is shown in Fig. 7.18. Ductility at room temperature can be restored by addition of 0.02% carbon or an equiva-

(*a*) (*b*)

Fig. 7.18 Photomicrographs showing fracture along ferrite grain boundaries in iron.[17]

lent amount of aluminum or titanium. This embrittlement usually does not occur in the composition range found in commercial use, although Rees and Hopkins found grain boundary cracks in a normalized mild steel (Fig. 7.19) which they attributed to the presence of

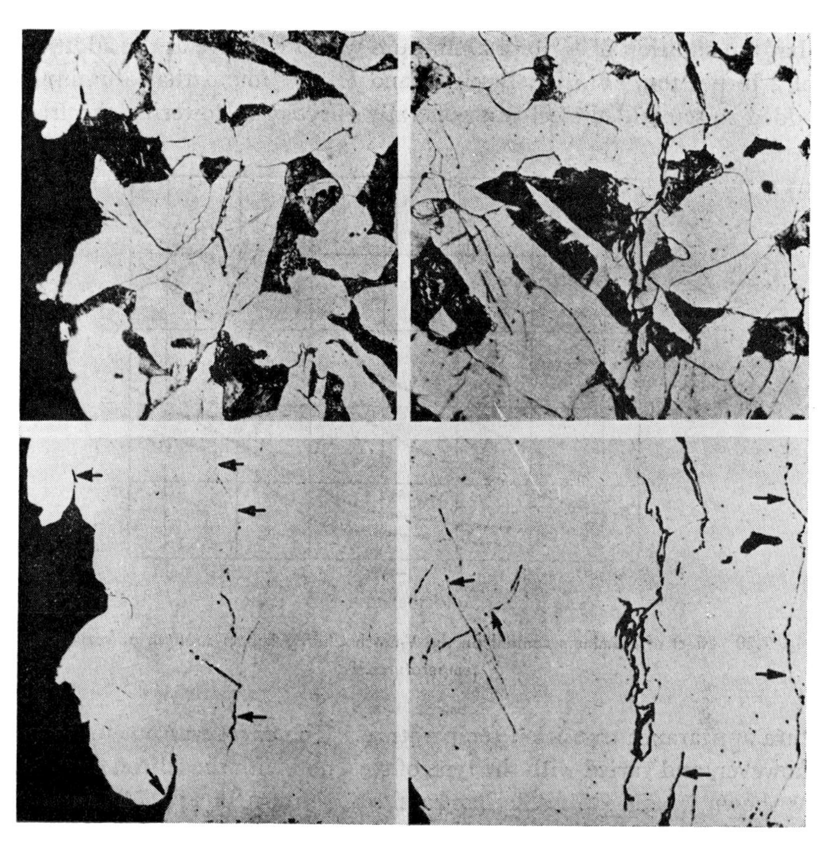

Fig. 7.19 Photomicrographs showing grain boundary cracks presumably due to oxygen in a normalized mild steel.[16] Upper—etched. Lower—unetched. 300×

oxygen. The effects of oxygen in commercial steels are not exactly known, but the presence of oxides is known to lower the notch ductility, even when the fracture is 100% shear; this, of course, reduces the maximum energy for any type of specimen.

Aluminum. Aluminum modifies the embrittling effect of oxygen; it alters the structure of sulphide inclusions, and it tends to combine with nitrogen. The effect of aluminum on the V-notch Charpy impact properties of medium carbon cast steel in the normalized and drawn condition was reported in an SAE special publication.[18] These results are reproduced in Fig. 7.20; they show that the addition of aluminum is beneficial up to 1.5 to 2 lb per ton but that further additions may be detrimental.

The effect of aluminum on the transition temperature of silicon killed steel was investigated by Rinebolt and Harris.[1] They found that the addition of ½ lb of aluminum was as effective as the addition of 2 lb per ton. Frazier, Boulger, and Lorig [2] found that aluminum added to semikilled steel was generally effective in lowering the frac-

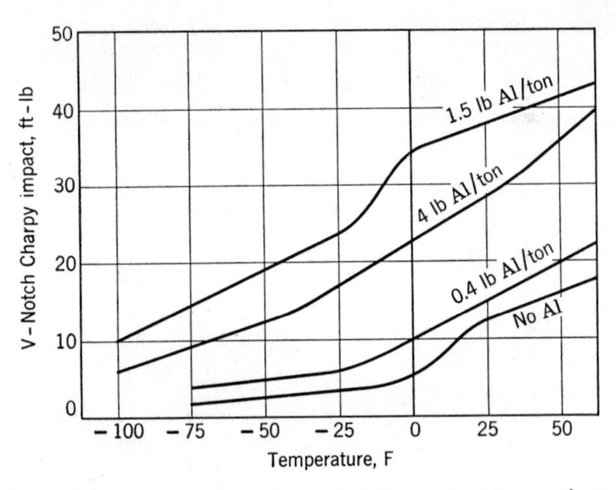

Fig. 7.20 Effect of aluminum content on the V-notch Charpy impact strength at various test temperatures.[18]

ture appearance transition temperature. The effect was not uniform, however, and varied with the type of steel and with the silicon content, as shown in Fig. 7.21. Similar results are shown in Fig. 7.22 for the keyhole Charpy test.

Nickel. Nickel is recognized as being beneficial. In increasing amounts, it slowly lowers the transition temperature of hot-rolled and normalized steel,[1] as shown in Fig. 7.23. Both fracture appearance and ductility transition temperatures decrease progressively with increasing nickel content. As shown in Fig. 7.23, nickel becomes increasingly beneficial until at 13% nickel there appears to be no transition from ductile to brittle behavior even at temperatures as low as −300 F.[19] The effect of nickel varies with the criterion of brittleness selected for comparison. For example, Rinebolt and Harris [1] found that in the V-notch Charpy test 3% of nickel lowered the average-energy transition about 40 F, the 50% fibrous fracture transition about 45 F, and

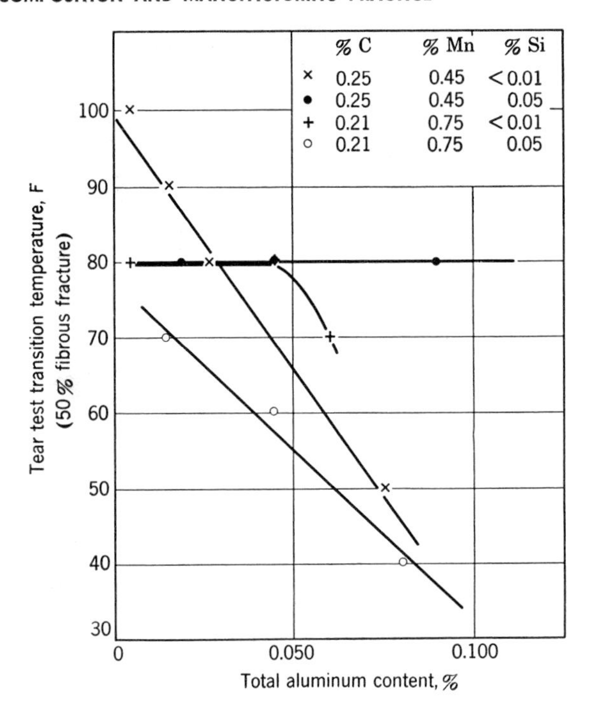

Fig. 7.21 Effect of aluminum content, as determined by spectrographic analysis, on tear test transition temperature (50% fibrous fracture).[2]

the 15 ft-lb transition by 110 F. Thus, nickel seems to be particularly beneficial in lowering the ductility transition.

GRAIN SIZE

It has long been known that the ferrite grain size has a marked influence on the transition temperature of steel. The effect of grain size has been reported by Frazier et al.[2] for two types of semikilled ship steel. Their results are reproduced in Figs. 7.24 and 7.25. Both fracture appearance (tear test) and 20 ft-lb keyhole Charpy transition temperatures decreased linearly as the number of grains per square inch of cross section increased. The influence of grain size was substantially the same for both classes of steels tested.

The ferrite grain size of hot-rolled steel is governed by the chemical composition and by the rolling practice in the steel mill, i.e., by the final rolling temperature and the finished plate thickness. When hot-rolled steel is heat treated, e.g., normalized, the ferrite grain size is altered in a manner that depends upon the maximum temperature to which the steel is heated and upon the rate of cooling from this tem-

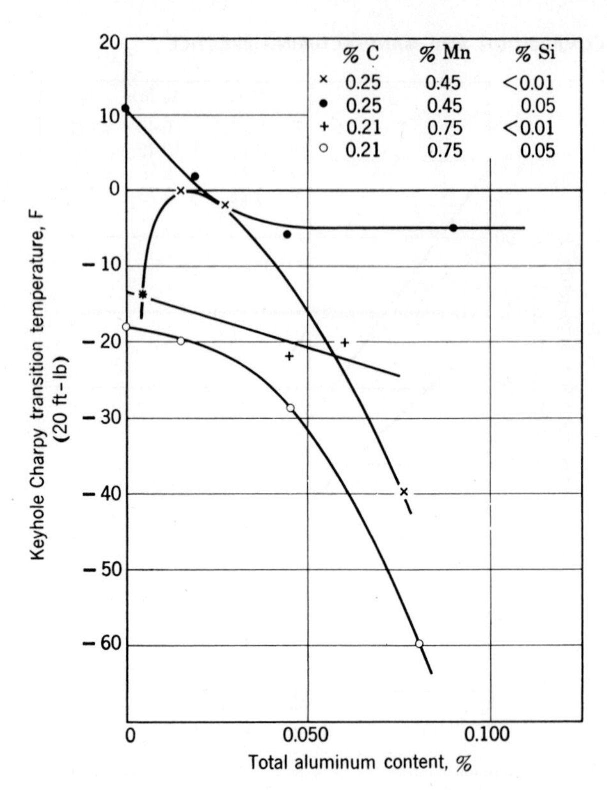

Fig. 7.22 Effect of aluminum content, as determined by spectrographic analysis, on the keyhole Charpy test (20 ft-lb).[2]

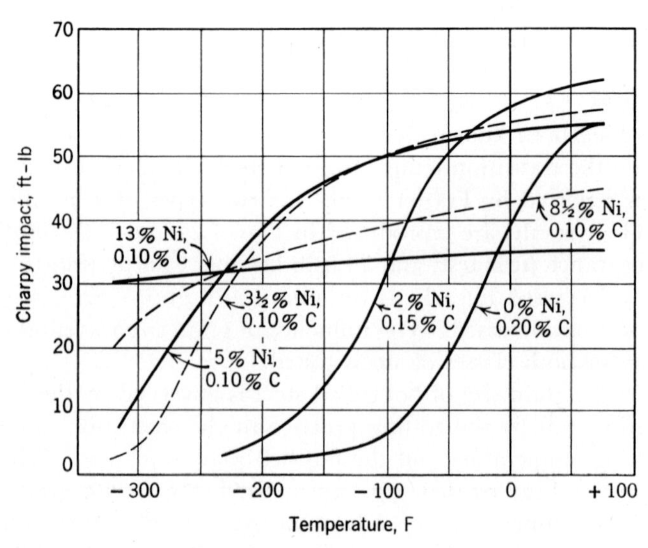

Fig. 7.23 Effect of nickel content on keyhole Charpy impact energy in normalized low carbon steels.[19]

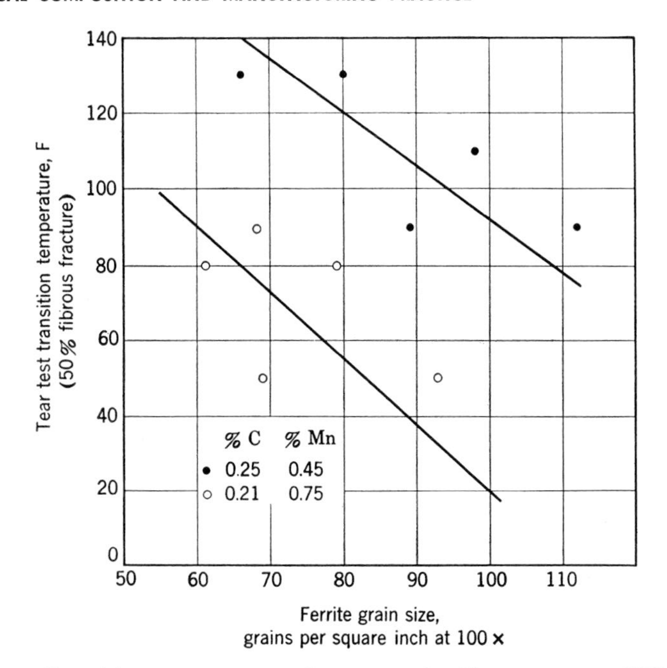

Fig. 7.24 Effect of ferrite grain size on the tear test transition temperature (50% fibrous fracture appearance).[2]

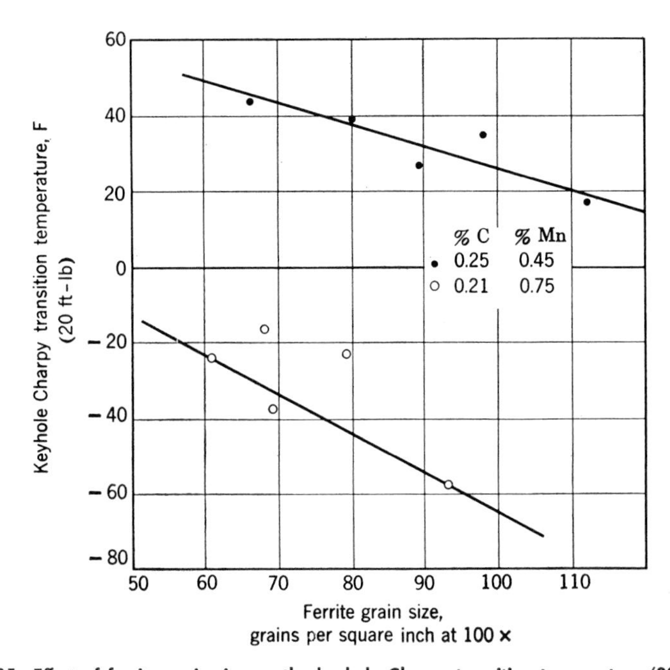

Fig. 7.25 Effect of ferrite grain size on the keyhole Charpy transition temperature (20 ft-lb).[2]

perature. Fig. 7.26, taken from Frazier et al.,[2] illustrates the effect of normalizing temperature on the fracture appearance transition temperature as determined by the tear test.

The influence of finishing temperature on the 20 ft-lb transition temperature for keyhole Charpy specimens was determined by the Battelle group.[3] Their data are shown in Fig. 7.27 for both low and high manganese semikilled steels. The grain size was substantially the

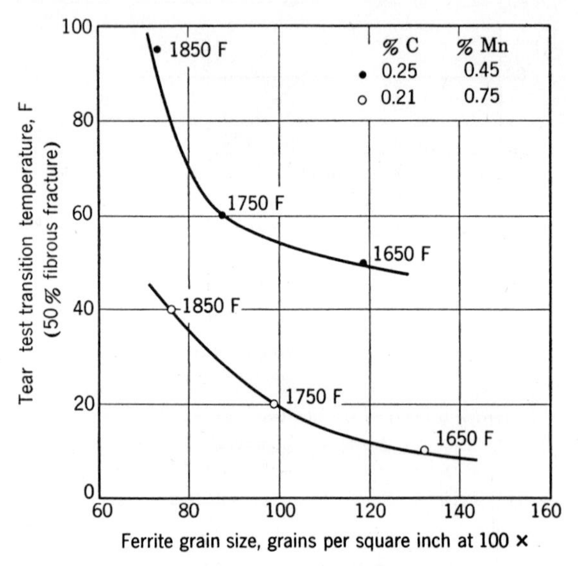

Fig. 7.26 Effect of normalizing temperature on the tear test transition temperature (50% fibrous fracture) and ferrite grain size.[2]

same for each class of steel at any one finishing temperature, and so the lower transitions for the higher manganese steels can be attributed directly to the higher value of this element and the lower concentration of carbon. Since increasing the normalizing temperature results in an increase in the grain size, the transition temperature for any steel rises with an increase in the heat treating temperature. Steels completely deoxidized with silicon plus aluminum will have somewhat smaller grain size than semikilled steels when normalized from ordinary temperatures, hence fully killed and normalized steels are superior to semikilled steels. (The beneficial effect of aluminum deoxidation is, however, not always realized in hot-rolled steels.) The increase in transition temperature with normalizing temperature is not linear for fully killed steels,[20] probably because of the different grain growth behavior of fully deoxidized steels. Such steels show little grain coarsen-

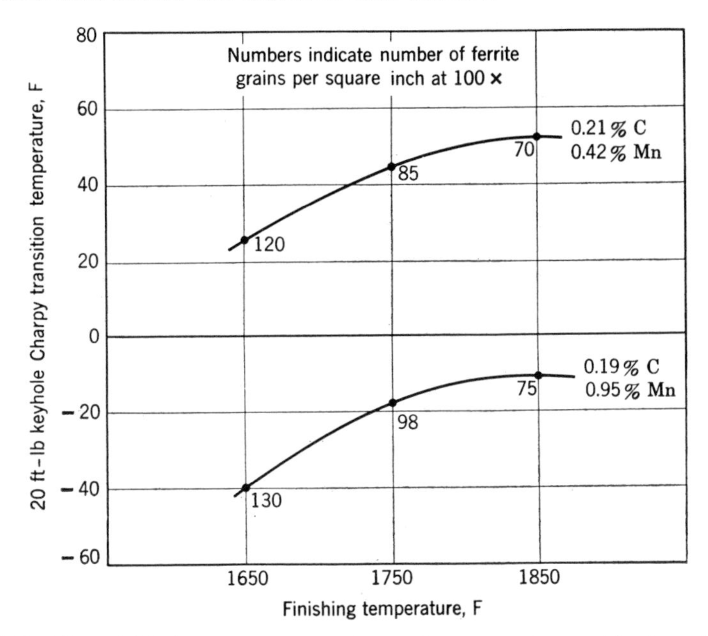

Fig. 7.27 Effect of finishing temperature on the transition temperature and ferrite grain size for two laboratory steels.[3]

ing until heated several hundred degrees above the ferrite-austenite transformation temperature. At still higher temperatures, however, grain size increases rapidly as the temperature is raised; when this occurs, there is a correspondingly accelerated increase in transition temperature.

COLD WORK AND STRAIN AGING

It has been repeatedly shown that cold working, even without aging, may raise both the fracture appearance and ductility transition temperatures.[21, 22, 23, 24] However, cold work plus aging is more effective in raising the transition temperatures of hot-rolled structural carbon steel than is either cold work or aging alone. This effect was investigated by Gensamer and co-workers.[25] They prestrained a number of medium carbon structural steels 2, 5, and 10%. After aging for one month at room temperature, keyhole Charpy transition curves were determined. The results for project steel C are shown in Fig. 7.28. These results are characteristic of those obtained with all types of steels except that this steel was slightly more sensitive to straining and aging than most of the other steels tested. Five per cent prestrain raised both the average-energy transition temperature and the 10 ft-lb transition temperature 40 to 60 F for hot-rolled semikilled steels, about

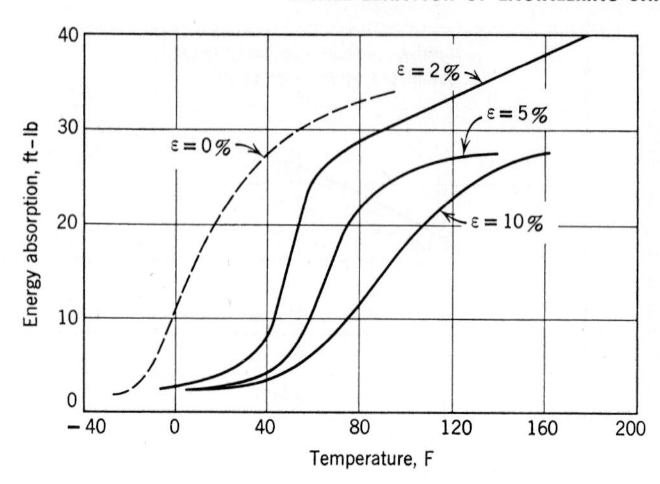

Fig. 7.28 Effect of prestrain and subsequent aging for one month on the keyhole Charpy transition energy.[25]

40 F for a rimmed steel, and about 60 F for a fully killed steel. Normalizing prior to cold working seemed to reduce the embrittling action of the cold working. The average-energy transition temperatures were raised only about 25 F for normalized semikilled and for normalized fully killed steels that had been prestrained 5%.

In addition to room temperature strain aging embrittlement, medium carbon structural steels are sensitive to embrittlement when strained and aged for a short period of time at an elevated temperature. Enzian and Salvaggio [14] investigated this effect for a number of commercial steels having various nitrogen contents. Fig. 7.29 taken from their work shows that the Izod impact strength at room temperature is markedly affected by aging for one hour at 450 F after cold working. The magnitude of the strain aging effect depended upon the amount of cold work and upon the chemical composition. These investigators found that all steels with low manganese contents were sensitive to strain aging embrittlement regardless of the nitrogen content. Steels having higher manganese contents were relatively insensitive to such embrittlement when the nitrogen content was low, e.g., 0.005%, but were badly embrittled by strain aging when the nitrogen content was 0.010%. It will be recalled that in the earlier section under *Nitrogen* it was shown that the transition temperature was raised more by nitrogen when the manganese content was higher. Thus it can be seen that the role of nitrogen is complex and that its effect depends strongly upon the composition of the steel, the amount of prior strain, and the thermal history of the steel.

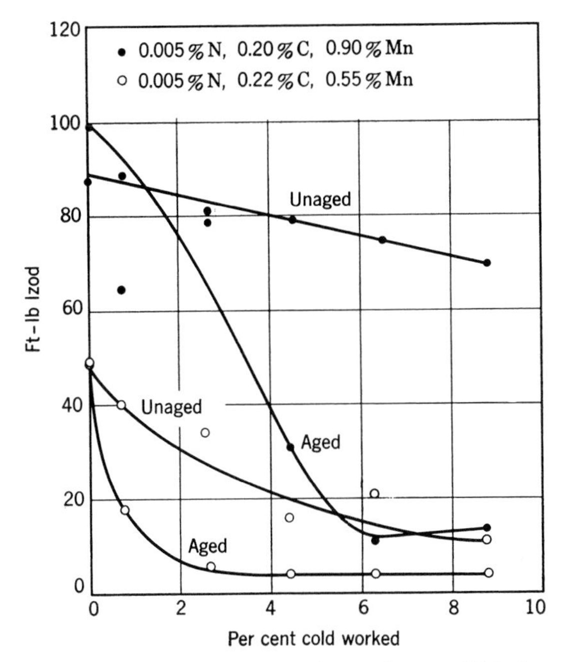

Fig. 7.29 Effect on Izod impact strength of aging for one hour at 450 F after cold working.[14]

SUMMARY

Data illustrating the influence of chemical composition are too incomplete to permit a reliable quantitative estimate of the effect of the individual elements. However, enough tests have been made on laboratory heats of steel to define the approximate effects of the elements present in carbon structural steel. Carbon was found to raise the 50% fibrous fracture transition temperature for the tear test by about 33 F for each 0.1% increase in the carbon content and the 20 ft-lb keyhole Charpy transition by about the same amount. The 15 ft-lb transition temperature for V-notch Charpy specimens was raised about 25 F for each increase of 0.1% carbon; the 10 ft-lb transition was raised about 20 F. Carbon has a marked effect on maximum energy for fracture; the higher the carbon content, the lower the maximum energy.

Manganese lowers the transition temperature of steel at a much slower rate than carbon raises it. The 50% fibrous fracture tear test transition temperature is lowered only about 4 F for each 0.1% increase in manganese content. The 15 ft-lb keyhole Charpy transition, however, was lowered about 10 F for each 0.1% increase.

Silicon apparently acts in a complex manner, and its effect is still somewhat uncertain. Up to about 0.3% it appears to be slightly beneficial, but larger amounts raise the transition temperature.

Phosphorus increases the transition temperature even more rapidly than equal amounts of additional carbon. Consequently, it is important to restrict the phosphorus to the lowest practicable amount.

Sulphur seems to have little, if any, direct effect on low temperature brittleness, but it does create nonmetallic inclusions, which reduce ductility and which influence brittle behavior in a minor manner.

Nitrogen is apparently effective in raising the transition temperature, but the effect varies markedly with the criterion selected and with the composition of the steel. Some investigators report large effects; others, none. The effect of nitrogen seems to depend largely upon the deoxidation practice employed during melting and casting. The embrittling effect of nitrogen was found to be largely overcome by aluminum in steels fully deoxidized with silicon and aluminum, particularly when the steels were normalized; aluminum additions to incompletely deoxidized steels were ineffective in reducing the effectiveness of nitrogen, probably because the aluminum was completely converted to oxide—leaving none to react with the nitrogen.

Oxygen appears to have an embrittling effect on mild steel, as has been reported, and may cause grain boundary cracking. The effect of oxygen on the properties of commercial steel is not understood; the presence of oxides, however, is known to lower the notch ductility, even when the fracture is 100% shear.

Aluminum, as mentioned above, is effective in neutralizing the deleterious effect of nitrogen in fully deoxidized steels. Aluminum is beneficial in normalized steels at least in amounts up to 2 pounds per ton. In hot-rolled steels the effect of aluminum is generally beneficial, but its effectiveness varies with the type of steel and particularly with the silicon content.

Nickel is generally recognized as being effective in lowering the transition temperature. However, it is not as potent in this respect as manganese.

The ferrite grain size generally has a marked effect on transition temperature, but the magnitude of the effect varies with the manufacturing and heat treating practice. The smaller the ferrite grain size, the lower the transition temperature in a given test. The ferrite grain size depends upon the final rolling temperature and the rate of cooling from above the transformation temperature. Hot-rolling practice thus has a predominant influence in establishing the grain size. Low finishing temperatures and fast cooling favor the formation of small ferrite crystals. Thinner plates normally cool faster than thicker ones, hence have a more favorable grain structure.

Cold work, particularly when combined with aging, raises the transition temperature. The average-energy transition temperature for keyhole Charpy specimens is raised about 25 F for steels prestrained 5% and aged.

The effects of various elements on the tear test and Charpy transition temperatures are summarized in Table 7.1.

TABLE 7.1

APPROXIMATE CHANGE IN TRANSITION TEMPERATURES PRODUCED BY VARIOUS ELEMENTS

Change in Transition Temperature, F

Element Varied	Tear Test	20 ft-lb Charpy Keyhole	10 ft-lb Charpy Keyhole	Average-Energy Charpy V-Notch	15 ft-lb Charpy V-Notch	10 ft-lb Charpy V-Notch
0.1% C	+33	+35	+20	+50	+25	+20
0.1% Mn	−4	−7	−7	−10	−10	−10
0.1% Si (0.2% max.)	−30	−30	....	....	....	....
0.1% Si (0.3% min.)	+15	+15	....	+13	+13	+13
0.01% P	+5	+3	....	+15	+13	+11
0.01% N (low Mn)	+50	+25	....	+40	....	0
0.01% N (high Mn)	+20	+3	....	+70	....	+40
1.0% Ni	....	....	....	−10	−35	....
0.1% Al	−30	−30	....	....	....	....
S (0.06% max.)	0	0	....	0	0	....
Change from 50 to 100 ferrite grains/sq in. at 100 ×	−80	−50	....	....	....	....

REFERENCES

1. J. A. Rinebolt and W. J. Harris, Jr., "Effect of Alloying Elements on Notch Toughness of Pearlitic Steels," *Trans. Am. Soc. Metals, 43,* 1175–1214 (1951).
2. R. H. Frazier, F. W. Boulger, and C. H. Lorig, "An Investigation of the Influence of Deoxidation and Chemical Composition on Notched-Bar Properties of Semikilled Ship Steel," Ship Structure Committee Report, Serial No. SSC-53, November 28, 1952.
3. Advisory Committee for Project SR-110. "A Review of the Influence of Composition and Deoxidation on the Properties of Ship Plate Steels," Ship Structure Committee Report, Serial No. SSC-73, November 16, 1953.

4. C. F. Quest and T. S. Washburn, "Tensile Strength and Composition of Hot-Rolled Plain Carbon Steels," *Trans. Am. Inst. Mining Met. Engrs., 140,* 489–496 (1940).
5. N. A. Kahn and E. A. Imbembo, "Further Study of Navy Tear Test," *Welding J.*, Res. Suppl., pp. 84-s–96-s (February 1950).
6. C. H. Lorig, "Influence of Metallurgical Factors," *Behavior of Metals at Low Temperatures,* pp. 71–105. Cleveland: American Society for Metals, 1953.
7. R. L. Smith, R. V. Fostini, and R. M. Brick, "The Low Temperature Properties of Relatively High Purity Iron-Carbon Alloys," Ship Structure Committee Report, Serial No. SSC-52, August 29, 1952.
8. H. M. Banta, R. H. Frazier, and C. H. Lorig, "Some Metallurgical Aspects of Ship Steel Quality," *Welding J.*, Res. Suppl., pp. 79-s–90-s (February 1951).
9. J. Görrissen, "Some Notes on Brittleness in Mild Steel," *J. Iron Steel Inst. (London), 162,* 16–28 (1949).
10. W. Barr and A. J. K. Honeyman, "Effect of the Manganese Carbon Ratio on the Brittle Fracture of Mild Steel," *J. Iron Steel Inst. (London), 157*:2, 239–242 (1947).
11. W. Barr and A. J. K. Honeyman, "Some Factors Affecting the Notched-Bar Impact Properties of Mild Steel," *J. Iron Steel Inst. (London), 157*:2, 243–246 (1947).
12. L. J. McGeady and R. D. Stout, "Notch Sensitivity of Welded Steel Plate," *Welding J.*, Res. Suppl., pp. 243-s–251-s (May 1950).
13. G. W. Geil, N. L. Carwile, and T. G. Digges, "Influence of Nitrogen on the Notch Toughness of Heat-Treated 0.3% Carbon Steels at Low Temperatures," *J. Research Nat. Bur. Standards, 48,* 3, 193–200 (1952).
14. G. H. Enzian and G. J. Salvaggio, "The Effect of Nitrogen on Brittle Behavior of Mild Steels," *Welding J.*, Res. Suppl., pp. 537-s–544-s (November 1950).
15. G. Schmidt, "Influence of Impurities in Commercial Iron on Impact" (Einfluss der im technischen Eisen enthaltenen Verunreinigungen auf die Kerbzähigkeit), *Arch. Eisenhüttenw., 8*:6, 263–267 (1934).
16. W. P. Rees and B. E. Hopkins, "Intergranular Brittleness in Iron-Oxygen Alloys," *J. Iron Steel Inst. (London), 172*:3, 403–409 (1952).
17. R. M. Brick, "Behavior of Single Crystals and of Pure Metals," *Behavior of Metals at Low Temperatures,* pp. 1–38. Cleveland: American Society for Metals, 1953.
18. "Low Temperature Properties of Ferrous Materials," Society of Automotive Engineers, Inc., Special Publications Department (SP-65), reference Fig. 31, 41 pp.
19. "Properties of Nickel Alloy Steels at Low Temperatures," *Nickel Alloy Steels,* 2d ed., sec. 6, data sheet D, p. 12, International Nickel Co., 1946.
20. "Effect of Deoxidation on the Impact Strength of Carbon Steel at Low Temperatures," Cooperative Bull. 67, Mining and Metallurgical Advisory Boards to Carnegie Institute of Technology and Bureau of Mines, Pittsburgh, 1934.
21. R. D. Stout and L. J. McGeady, "Notch Sensitivity of Welded Steel Plate," *Welding J.*, Res. Suppl., pp. 1-s–9-s (January 1949).
22. C. J. Osborn, A. F. Scotchbrook, R. D. Stout, and B. G. Johnston, "Comparison of Notch Tests and Brittleness Criteria," *Welding J.*, Res. Suppl., pp. 24-s–34-s (January 1949).

23. A. F. Scotchbrook, L. Eriv, R. D. Stout, and B. G. Johnston, "Effect of Welding on Pressure Vessel Steels," Welding Research Council Bull. Series, No. 4, pp. 6–12 (February 1950).
24. A. B. Kinzel, "Ductility of Steels for Welded Structures," *Welding J.*, Res. Suppl., pp. 217-s–234-s (May 1948).
25. M. Gensamer, E. P. Klier, T. A. Prater, F. C. Wagner, J. O. Mack, and J. L. Fisher, "Correlation of Laboratory Tests with Full-Scale Ship Plate Fracture Tests," Ship Structure Committee Report, Serial No. SSC-9, March 19, 1947.

CHAPTER

VIII

The Role of Welding

INTRODUCTION

It is true that engineering structures can fail in a brittle manner, even when no welds are present; this fact is amply emphasized in Chapter XI, which deals with service failures. It is equally true, however, that defective welding has been largely responsible for most of the recent structural failures. Almost without exception the origins of cleavage cracks in welded steel ships have been at weld defects. Very rarely have cracks been observed to start in sound welds in any type of engineering structure.

The notch toughness of weld metal varies from one deposit to another. Consequently, the effect of a certain type of weld defect may be expected to vary with the nature of the deposit. Unfortunately, there is no experimental evidence that would enable one to estimate the severity or seriousness of a particular weld defect. Work is progressing along this line, however, and in a few years some degree of standardization may be expected to develop that will aid inspectors in evaluating the seriousness of defects.

Much is already known about many of the factors that influence the notch brittleness of weld deposits, details of which are discussed in this chapter. The origin and effect of residual welding stresses is treated at length in Chapter IX.

Welding is the only satisfactory means for joining many metal parts. It is defined by the American Welding Society [1] as "A metal-joining process wherein coalescence is produced by heating to suitable temperatures, with or without the application of pressure and with or without the use of filler metal." Many joining processes used today fall under the above classification; they are used for light and heavy gage sections, small and large structures, and for ferrous and nonferrous metals. A complete discussion of all welding processes is beyond the scope of this book. It is sufficient to note that the joining by welding of the type of large steel structures with which this book is concerned is done almost exclusively by two types of fusion welding, namely, manual shielded arc and automatic submerged arc welding. Hence, the following discussion on welding will be restricted to these two processes.

There are two common types of arc welded joints: fillet welds, which are used to join two plates at right angles, and butt welds, which are used to join two plates lying in the same plane. Either type of welding may be employed, and the deposits may be made with multiple or with single pass techniques. Manual welding is done by feeding a filler rod or electrode into the arc zone at such rate that the arc length remains substantially constant as the rod melts. The current for welding is supplied from a d-c welding machine or from a transformer; the voltage between the base plate and the welding electrode is generally in the range of 20 to 30 volts. The nonmetallic coating of the electrode burns and melts off as the electrode is consumed during welding. Coating ingredients stabilize the arc and shield the molten metal from the atmosphere during and after transfer to the base plate. Machine welding is usually done by the submerged arc welding process. With this process joints can be made in a single pass even in plate several inches thick. The welding action in the submerged arc process takes place under a burden of granular flux, and the arc action is hidden from the view of the observer. In this process a bare electrode is automatically fed into the welding zone, and the magnitude of current and voltage are automatically maintained by the welding machine and rod feed control. While manual welding is normally restricted to the use of currents of the order of 50 to 500 amperes, submerged arc welds can be made with currents as high as 3000 amperes. The electrode burn-off rate is largely determined by the welding current; hence it is evident that the submerged arc process is capable of depositing weld metal at a much higher rate than can be attained with coated electrodes.

When a welded joint is sectioned, polished, and etched, three distinctly different structural regions are discernible, as illustrated in Fig. 8.1. The central portion is the weld metal and consists of metal

Fig. 8.1 The three structural regions in a fusion weld.

from the electrode that has been mixed with the melted portion of the base plate. This metal has an unusual microstructure characterized by large columnar grains. The heat-affected zone in the base plate adjacent to the weld etches dark; the microstructure of this region is almost always bainite in medium carbon structural steel. This portion of the metal was not molten at any time but had been heated in the range between the transformation temperature and the melting point. The region adjacent to the weld was heated almost to the melting point, hence the coarse grain structure. Near the outer rim of the heat-affected zone, smaller grains are present because the temperature in this area never exceeded about 1400 F. Occasionally the grains in this location are even finer than those in the original plate, particularly when the initial grain size is rather large. There is a third region of interest in the outer rim of the heat-affected zone; it consists of the material that was heated just below the lower transformation temperature. At this temperature the cementite plates of the original pearlite coalesce and form a spheroidized structure. The metal beyond the heat-affected zone is the unaffected base plate, which was not subject to a metallurgical change of any kind. Because of the numerous and complex microstructures present in a welded joint and because of defects and discontinuities introduced during welding, the prediction of service performance is not a simple problem. It involves a detailed knowledge of the action and interaction of the weld metal, heat-affected zone, and unaffected base plate under various types of loading and environmental conditions.

THE WELD METAL

The metal deposit during arc welding is cast metal, but because of the unusual conditions of solidification, it does not have a characteristic cast steel structure. It consists of small dendrites and columnar grains. The composition of this metal is determined by the composition of the core wire, the amount of base metal that is melted, the base metal composition, and the gases absorbed during deposition. When the welding is done with bare metal electrodes, the arc is surrounded by air; hence, during the transfer from the electrodes and after deposition on the plate, oxygen and nitrogen have an opportunity to react with the molten metal. When the welding is done with shielded or coated electrodes, the reaction between the air and the weld metal is inhibited. Contamination by oxygen and nitrogen is reduced because the gaseous constituents that are liberated from the electrode coating act to exclude the air from the arc zone. Further benefit may be derived from deoxidizers, such as ferrosilicon and ferromanganese, which are present in some coatings, and from the fluxes, which form a molten slag covering for the deposited weld metal. In the case of inert gas welding, the arc zone is surrounded by an envelope of inert gas, such as argon or helium; the additional shielding from a molten slag is not present. The metal is not perfectly protected, and trouble from gas holes is frequent. This process has not as yet found wide application in the welding of mild steel and will not be discussed further. In the submerged arc welding process, the arc is effectively shielded from the atmosphere by a molten envelope of flux, which surrounds the arc and is completely buried under a burden of unfused flux. Hence, gaseous constituents derived from the air are not in contact with the weld metal and therefore are not absorbed either during or after transfer from the electrode. Thus, for each welding process, the properties of the deposit vary depending upon the electrode composition, the amount of base metal melted, the condition under which the filler metal passes through the arc, and the rate at which the deposit cools.

Coated electrodes for manual welding are classified according to the operating characteristics, the type of coating, and the characteristics of the deposited metal. This grouping is shown in Table 8.1

TABLE 8.1 [2]

OPERATING CHARACTERISTICS OF MILD STEEL AND LOW ALLOY STEEL ELECTRODES

Classification	Current and Polarity	Welding Positions	Type of Covering	Penetration	Surface Appearance	Nature of Flux Deposit
EXX10	dc, reverse polarity (electrodes positive)	All	High-cellulose sodium silicate binder	Deep	Flat, wavy	Thin
EXX11	ac or dc, reverse polarity (electrode positive)	All	High-cellulose potassium silicate binder	Deep	Flat, wavy	Thin
E6012	dc, straight polarity (electrode negative) or ac	All	High-titania sodium silicate binder	Medium	Convex, rippled	Heavy
EXX13	ac or dc, straight polarity (electrode negative)	All	High-titania potassium silicate binder	Shallow	Flat or concave, slight ripple	Medium
EXX15	dc, reverse polarity (electrode positive)	All	Low-hydrogen sodium silicate binder	Medium	Flat, wavy	Medium
EXX16	ac or dc, reverse polarity (electrode positive)	All	Low-hydrogen potassium silicate binder	Medium	Flat, wavy	Medium
EXX20	dc, straight polarity (electrode negative) or ac for H-fillets; dc either polarity or ac for flat position welding	H-fillets and flat	High iron oxide	Medium	Flat or concave, smooth	Heavy
EXX30	dc, either polarity or ac	Flat only	High iron oxide	Shallow	Flat, smooth	Heavy

in accordance with AWS and ASTM specifications.[2] The meaning of the symbols under the column marked "classification," e.g., EXX10 is as follows: the last two digits, i.e., "10," refer to the operating characteristics and the type of coating given in the table to the right of the symbol. The first two digits "XX" refer to the minimum tensile strength of the weld deposit in 1000 psi in the stress relieved condition. Thus an E6010 electrode is one that will produce a weld metal deposit having a minimum tensile strength of 60,000 psi. Also specified by the code, but not shown by the symbols, are minimum yield strength and 2-in. gage length ductility.

It should be mentioned at this point that a manufacturer of coated electrodes has considerable latitude in the kind of materials that he may use in the coating and in the core wire as long as the above general specifications of Table 8.1 are satisfied. It is obvious from this last consideration that electrodes from different manufacturers may produce deposits having different chemical compositions. It is therefore impossible to make a general rule as to what the composition of the weld metal from any specific electrode type might be.

There is good evidence [3] to support the belief that most molecules passing through an arc are at least partly, if not completely, dissociated. This is especially important because gaseous constituents, such as oxygen, nitrogen, and hydrogen, readily enter the molten weld metal when they are in the atomic form. Hydrogen appears to have a particularly potent influence on the low temperature embrittlement of steels because it often causes microcracks to form during cooling.[4,5] Hydrogen is probably present in the atomic state [3] in all open arc welds where shielding is derived from solid coatings. It may enter the arc zone in the form of moisture contained in the atmosphere; it may be derived from the water solutions of sodium and potassium silicates used as binders; or it may come from cellulose present in certain coatings. The detrimental influence of hydrogen on the soundness and ductility of welds has long been recognized; as a consequence, mineral type coatings low in hydrogen have been developed. These are classified under EXX15 and EXX16 designations (see Table 8.1). Such electrodes do not cause hydrogen embrittlement in the form of underbead cracking even though a small amount of hydrogen (coming from the surrounding atmosphere) may not be completely prevented from entering the metal.

About 0.0035% by weight of hydrogen can be dissolved in molten steel at 3500 F.[6] The solubility of this gas decreases rapidly with temperature, and there are abrupt changes during solidifications and during the austenite-ferrite transformation. As a consequence, the dissolved atomic hydrogen diffuses to internal or external surfaces, where it recombines to form the molecular species of the gas. The gas that collects internally in small cavities or around inclusions may develop tremendous pressures before equilibrium conditions are reached. The high local stresses produced by the gas pressure may actually cause cracking in brittle steel such as underbead cracking in a martensitic heat-affected zone. In the more ductile steels external loads may have to be superimposed on those produced by the gas pressure before fracture will occur. Fisheyes,[7] the round bright spots containing a small gas hole or inclusion and surrounded by a fibrous fracture surface, are commonly found on the fracture surface of weld metal tensile specimens that contain hydrogen. The detailed mechanism by which hydrogen induces cracking in the heat-affected zone or weld metal is, however, only partly understood, but the effect of this gas is well established.

Hydrogen can also react with oxygen, sulphur, or carbon to form gaseous products, which can be trapped in the solidifying weld metal and thereby produce gas cavities.[8] These reversible reactions are indicated below:

$$\text{FeO and 2H} \rightleftharpoons \text{Fe and } H_2O$$

$$\text{S and 2H} \rightleftharpoons H_2S$$

$$\text{C and 4H} \rightleftharpoons CH_4$$

Hydrogen compounds, therefore, can cause porosity and thus provide places for molecular hydrogen to collect.

The effects of hydrogen absorption are illustrated by the test results reproduced in Fig. 8.2.[9] The two electrodes used were E6010, cellulose type, and the E6016, low hydrogen type. Since the chemical compositions of the weldments were practically identical, except for slightly higher Mn and Si content in the E6010 deposits, it may be presumed that the low hydrogen content of the E6016 deposit is responsible for its lower transition temperature. However, this is not a certainty, because other variables are also involved.

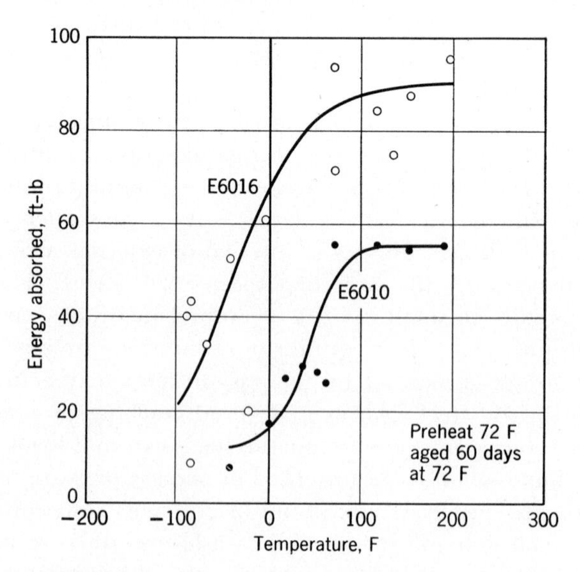

Fig. 8.2 Impact-temperature relation for weld deposits made with E6010 (cellulose) and E6016 (low-hydrogen) coated electrodes.[9]

Nitrogen can contribute to porosity in a manner similar to hydrogen; [10] as much as 0.04% nitrogen may be present in liquid steel at equilibrium conditions,[6] whereas the solid solubility of nitrogen in steel at 890 C is only 0.004%. Therefore it is possible for molecular nitrogen to be trapped in the weld metal and form gas cavities. It is possible, although not proved, that nitrogen may diffuse in the solid metal and collect in cavities to create regions of high local pressure. In addition to causing gas cavities to form, nitrogen can enter into chemical combination with iron and form nitride needles. Andrews [10] noted further that the weld metal was greatly embrittled when iron nitride precipitated in the form of thin plates.

Oxygen also contributes to the embrittlement of steel because it forms gas cavities and nonmetallic inclusions. Gas cavities are produced by the carbon monoxide formed as a result of the oxidation of the carbon in the molten steel by the excess oxygen dissolved in the metal. As the temperature drops, oxygen becomes available to react with the dissolved carbon; gas bubbles form, some of which may be trapped during solidification. Similarly, the nonmetallic inclusions (produced by the oxidation of various elements such as silicon and manganese in the liquid steel) often remain in suspension and become entrapped during solidification.

The effects of other elements found in welds are similar to those described for the base plate in the preceding chapter. Aluminum and manganese are deoxidizers, and aluminum is believed to aid in rendering nitrogen harmless. Additions of these elements help to eliminate the deleterious effects caused by both oxygen and nitrogen absorption. High carbon and high silicon embrittle the weld metal, whereas nickel and manganese lower its ductility transition and fracture appearance transition temperatures. Carbon in ordinary steel weld deposits should be limited to approximately 0.1%. Greater amounts raise the transition temperatures and also promote cracking of the weld metal during cooling.

It may be generally concluded that for good ductility hydrogen should be kept at a minimum in the electrode coating, and carbon, silicon, sulphur, and phosphorus should be kept low in the core wire; manganese and nickel should be as high as is practicable; oxygen and nitrogen should be reduced to a minimum in the arc zone.

THE HEAT-AFFECTED ZONE AND BASE PLATE

In arc welding the weld metal and the adjacent base plate are subjected to severe temperature changes. A bead deposited on a plate will produce large transient temperature gradients in the weld zone.[11] The base metal immediately adjacent to the weld is heated from atmospheric temperature to the melting point in a few seconds; the temperature may decrease from this maximum to slightly below 600 F in less than one minute. The unfused metal near the weld in the base plate is subjected to a variety of temperatures and cooling rates; the magnitudes of these vary with the distance from the weld. As a consequence of the variety of thermal histories, a single heat-affected zone contains a variety of microstructures, and each structure has its own characteristic mechanical properties.

A typical microstructure of the heat-affected zone is shown in Fig. 8.3. The microstructure of this region varies depending upon the welding conditions and the composition and size of the base plate. In fully deoxidized steels the grain structure is finer than in semikilled steels. In the case of multiple pass welds, the structure is altered by the heat from the succeeding passes, and hence the heat-affected zone differs in width and structure from that obtained with a single bead.

Near the fusion zone the structure is generally coarse and bainitic. The maximum temperature in this region greatly exceeds the transformation temperature, and therefore the grains are large. Farther away from the weld metal, where the steel was heated to just above the A_1 transformation temperature, the grain size is small. In the portion of the zone that was heated approximately to the A_1 transformation temperature, the carbides tend to coalesce to form spheroidal par-

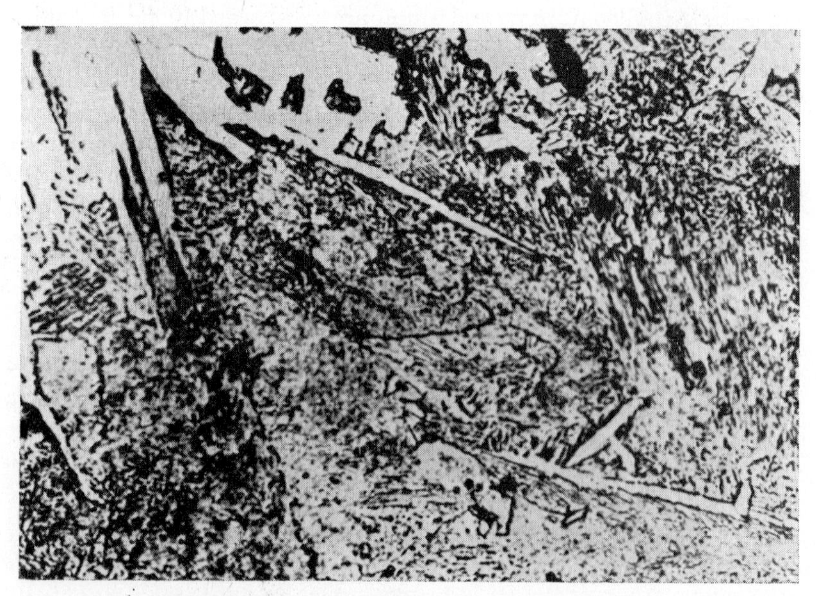

Fig. 8.3 Typical microstructure of heat-affected zone.

ticles. The width and nature of the heat-affected zone vary with the composition of the steel, the plate thickness, and with the welding conditions. Its properties may be a determining factor in the mechanical behavior of a weldment.

The heat-affected zone may be embrittled by hydrogen during welding in a way similar to that of the weld metal itself. Hydrogen can diffuse from the weld metal into the heat-affected zone, precipitate as molecular hydrogen, and thereby set up high aerostatic pressure. Some hydrogen may be held in solid solution in the austenite, which would be rejected when the austenite transformed. This hydrogen could then diffuse into voids and embrittle the metal. Mallett and Rieppel [12] found that the degree of underbead cracking depended on the amount of retained austenite that underwent an austenite-martensite transformation at low temperature. This type of cracking requires the presence of hydrogen but, apparently, is partly due to the stresses generated by the austenite-martensite transformation. (A high hydrogen concentration in stable austenite does not cause cracking because austenite is tough and ductile.) Stewart and Urban [13] found that the presence of carbide-forming elements such as titanium, zirconium, columbium (niobium), and vanadium considerably reduced the underbead cracking. This is probably due to the fact that these elements form carbides that are insoluble or that dissolve slowly and only at high temperatures. Thus the carbon content of the austenite is effectively reduced, and therefore the amount of retained austenite is decreased. The foregoing result strongly supports the findings of Mallett and Rieppel that the amount of underbead cracking is related to the amount of retained austenite.

Mixtures of martensite, pearlite, and bainite are known to have poor notch-toughness characteristics. Another complication is involved because the rapid cooling may cause the ferrite in the heat-affected zone to contain more than the equilibrium amount of carbon in solution. The excess carbon may precipitate during aging and thus cause additional embrittlement.[14]

Nippes and Savage,[15] using sharply notched specimens, investigated the notch brittleness of various zones in welded medium carbon structural steel. The heat-affected zone was subdivided into three areas, namely, (1) the coarse-grained zone immediately adjacent to the outer edge of the weld metal, (2) the fine-grained zone in the region heated just above the critical temperature, and (3) the spheroidized zone in the region where the temperature reached a value slightly below the critical temperature. They used different combinations of welding current and travel rate. The experimental curves are shown in Figs. 8.4 to 8.6. The chemical composition (%) of their steel was:

C	Mn	Si	S	P	Ni	Cr	Cu	Al
0.24	0.42	0.046	0.062	0.014	0.13	0.035	0.22	0.007

They used an electrode of the E6020 type having an iron oxide coating. Their results indicated that above room temperature the weld metal was markedly inferior to the base metal in terms of impact energy absorbed, and to a lesser extent it was inferior to the spheroidized region. Below room temperature, however, the weld metal exhibited somewhat better impact energy than either of the other regions. The spheroidized region had the poorest impact characteristics of the heat-affected zone, but variations in welding conditions could make this zone either better or poorer than the base plate.

Luther et al.[16] used V-notch Charpy specimens to measure the difference in transition temperatures between the base metal (of a high-tensile, low-alloy steel) and the heat-affected zone of bead welded specimens. Since their bead weld specimen was designed so that the root of the notch extended into the heat-affected zone, it may be

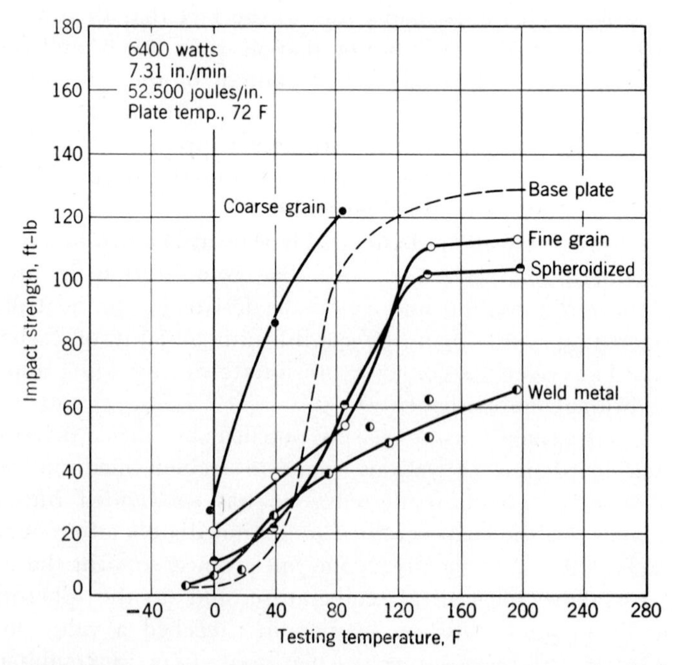

Fig. 8.4 Notch brittleness of various zones in sharply notched specimens of welded medium carbon structural steel, using a controlled combination of welding current and travel rate.[15]

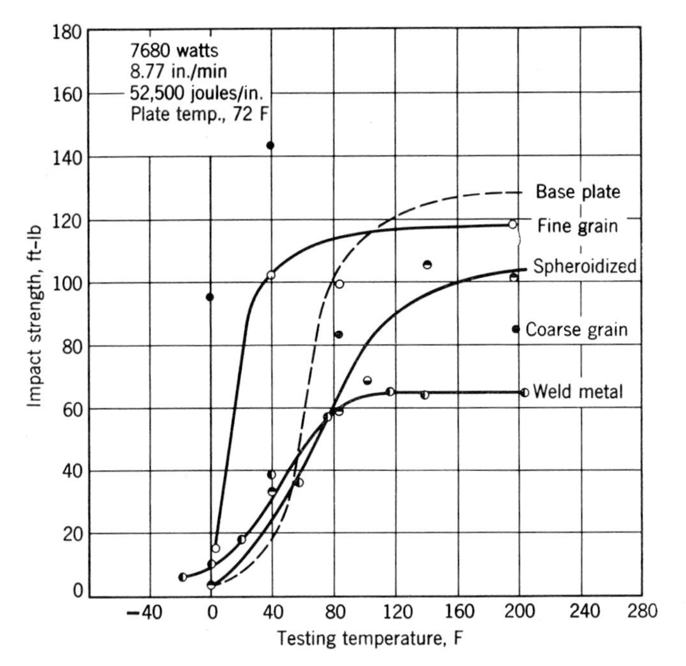

Fig. 8.5 Notch brittleness of various zones in sharply notched specimens of welded medium carbon structural steel, using a controlled combination of welding current and travel rate greater than for the case shown in Fig. 8.4.

assumed that their results can be interpreted as giving results characteristic of the material in this region. The chemical composition of the four steels tested by these investigators is shown in Table 8.2.

TABLE 8.2 [16]

CHEMICAL COMPOSITION (%)

Steel:	454	488	490	503
C	0.20	0.14	0.17	0.14
Mn	0.34	0.54	1.27	1.23
Si	0.01	0.22	0.30	0.30
S	0.019	0.030	0.020	0.022
P	0.009	0.025	0.028	0.025
Ni	0.34	1.64	0.10	0.15
Cu	0.17	0.91	0.17	0.26
Mo	0.05	0.03	0.02	0.03
Cr	0.04	0.04	0.09	0.11
Al	0.010	0.036	0.025	0.036
V	.....	0.005	0.005	0.005
Ti	.....	0.005	0.017	0.010

NOTE: All steels 40.8-lb gage (1 in. thick).

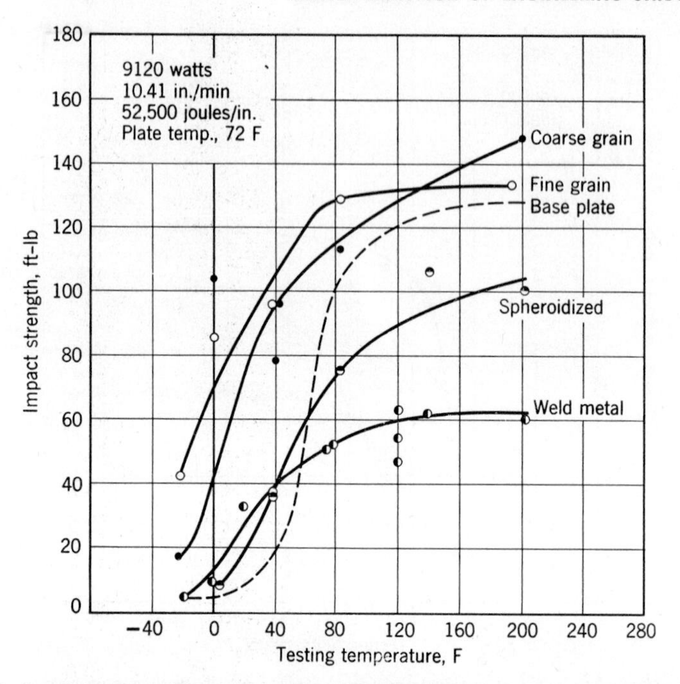

Fig. 8.6 Notch brittleness of various zones in sharply notched specimens of welded medium carbon structural steel, using a controlled combination of welding current and travel rate greater than for the case shown in Fig. 8.5.

The experimental results of Luther and co-workers are shown in Fig. 8.7. The results shown in these figures indicate that the ductility temperature of the original base metal may be either higher or lower than that of the heat-affected zone, depending on the type of the steel.

Brown, Ebert, and Sachs [17] found that zones of low ductility and of high ductility transition temperature are present in the subcritically heated parent metal. They employed notch bars in eccentrically loaded static tensile steel. Their results are shown in Fig. 8.8 for a steel with the following composition (%):

C	Mn	P	S	Si
0.2	0.54	0.016	0.033	0.045

Grossman and MacGregor [18] obtained similar results by conducting notch bar bend tests on a series of steels and showed that the weld was in all cases more ductile than the best base plate material. The region having the highest ductility transition temperature was located one inch from the weld centerline, or one half inch from the edge of

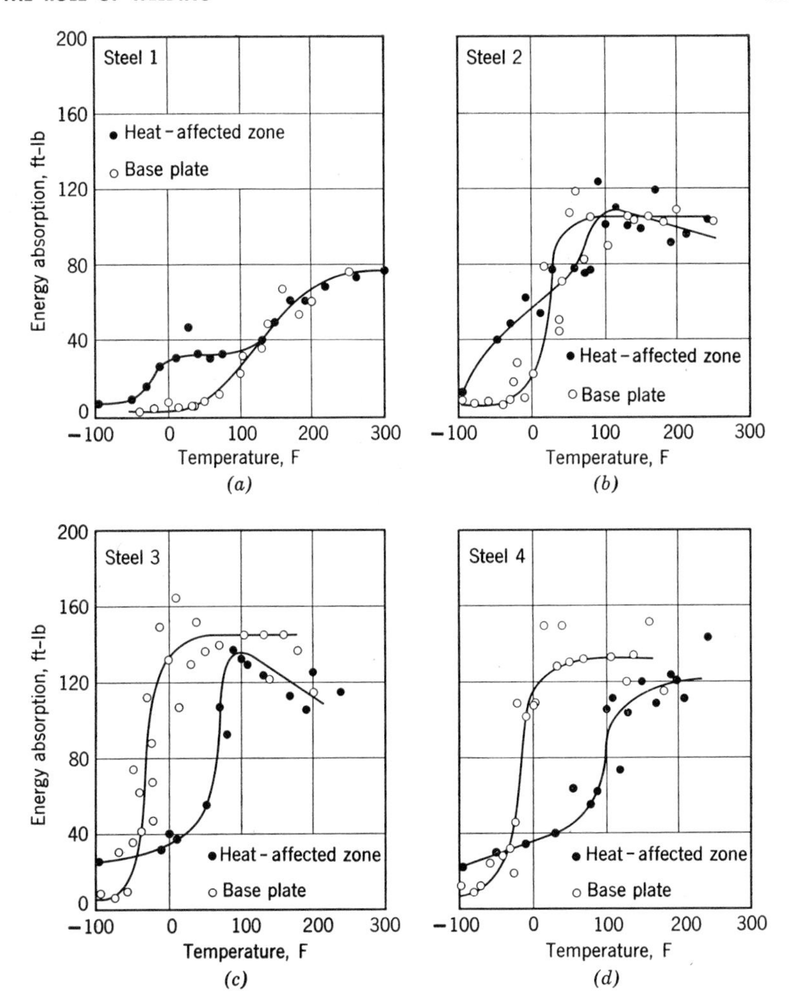

Fig. 8.7 Comparison of transition temperatures between base plate and heat-affected zone of four bead welded steels.[16]

the heat-affected zone. It should be noted, however, that *service failures never seem to originate in the spheroidized zone,* even though this region frequently has inferior notch ductility. The reason for this probably lies in the fact that this zone rarely contains any notches or cracks, whereas the weld metal and the adjacent material frequently have such defects.

Rieppel and Voldrich,[19] using Kinzel type specimens (with the notch crossing the weld metal, heat-affected zone, and base plate) found that in "Br" and "C" project steels (medium carbon structural

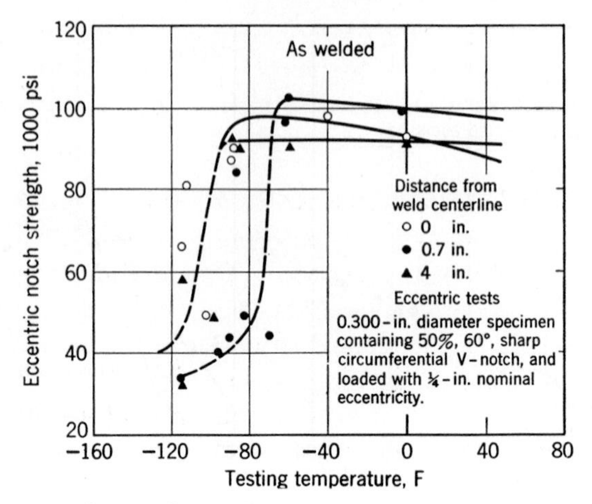

Fig. 8.8 Eccentric notch strength as a function of the testing temperature for longitudinal tensile specimens cut at two distances from the weld centerline.[17] (Hand welded 1-in. thick plate.)

steels) the fractures initiated and propagated in the weld metal. The absorbed energy and fracture appearance curves for welded and unwelded plates of these two steels are shown in Fig. 8.9.

From the wide variations observed in behavior, it is apparent that there can be no universal simple characterization of weldments. Under certain conditions the weld metal may be more notch brittle than either the heat-affected zone or the base plate, while under other

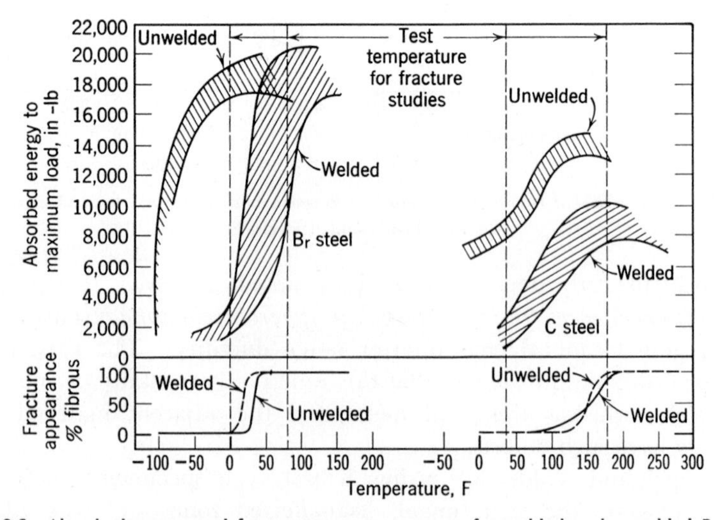

Fig. 8.9 Absorbed-energy and fracture-appearance curves for welded and unwelded B_r and C project steel plates, using Kinzel type specimens.[19]

circumstances the heat-affected zone may have inferior properties; at times the base plate may be the poorer. In order to help clarify this situation, a more detailed discussion of the factors that affect notch brittleness of weldments is next presented.

PREHEAT, POSTHEAT, AND MECHANICAL STRESS RELIEF

It has been shown that fusion welding without preheat subjects the base plate and the weld metals to an unfavorable thermal cycle, causing the formation of a rapidly cooled cast structure in the weld metal as well as a rapidly cooled structure in the heat-affected zone. Rapid cooling tends to produce structures having higher ductility transition temperatures. Hence the question arises: What can be done to minimize the embrittling effect associated with this rapid cooling?

Both thermal and mechanical treatments are used to modify the properties of welded joints. The mechanical treatments do not change the microstructure but may relieve the residual stresses introduced during welding; they are classified as stress relieving treatments. Postheating above about 1000 F alters the microstructure of the metal and also reduces the residual stresses. Whether or not a thermal treatment is used in any specific case is determined by economic or safety considerations; in some instances such a treatment is specified by an engineering code.

Two of the methods employed for mechanical stress relieving are peening and proof stressing. Peening is the process of hammering the weld metal to make it flow plastically, thus reducing to some extent the residual tensile stresses. This method of stress relieving is permitted under the 1942 API-ASME codes for unfired pressure vessels.[20] The code prescribed that peening of multilayer beads in joints must be closely controlled; overpeening may be harmful because cold work raises both types of transition temperatures. The code further provides that the top bead must be left unpeened. DeGarmo and co-workers [21] have shown, however, that peening of welds in ¾-in. plate does not reduce local stresses substantially unless the final pass is also peened. On the basis of this evidence, the method of peening all but the final pass would seem to be of value principally for controlling distortion and for minimizing cracking during welding. Proof stressing is another practice employed for the stress relieving of welds. This method consists in stretching the weld metal so that it flows plastically. Stretching of this kind can be done in pressure vessels by hydrostatic loading. In the fabrication of large welded pipe, the proof stressing operation is frequently combined with a final sizing operation in which the pipe is expanded with jacks or with hydrostatic pressure. Meriam and co-workers [22] showed that the longitudinal stress in a longitudinal submerged arc weld in a 1-in. thick plate 6 ft wide could be lowered substantially by the application of axial loading. It is doubtful, however, that equal reductions are possible in longitudinal welds in tubular sections loaded internally because of the low axial stress acting in such vessels. The "low-temperature stress relief treatment" [23] described in Chapters I and IX has been used rather extensively for stress relieving of large structures that cannot be postheated (and for economic reasons were not preheated), such as ships, penstocks, and large storage tanks. Figs. 8.10 and 8.11 show comparisons between the properties of notched welded plates subjected to bending.[24, 25] They had been given various treatments including low-temperature stress relieving and a high-temperature furnace treating. Statistics have not as yet been accumulated in sufficient quantities to evaluate the merits of this process for stress relieving actual structures. Furthermore, it is sometimes difficult to apply this method of stress relieving to complex portions of a structure.

Preheating usually consists of heating the plates to be welded to a temperature several hundred degrees above atmospheric temperature before welding is commenced. It reduces the cooling rate and thus improves the notch-toughness characteristics of the weld metal and heat-affected zone. Postheating is the process of heating the welded plates to a fairly high temperature after welding. Since postheating is commonly done at temperatures above 1000 F, it is almost always necessary to place the whole welded structure in a furnace—a procedure that is obviously not feasible for large structures such as ships, bridges, and large storage tanks. The benefits of postheating are great, however, and it is highly desirable to employ this treatment whenever possible.

Some defects are introduced during welding, such as porosity, inclusions, excessive increase in embrittling alloying elements such as silicon, hot or cold cracks, underbead cracks, poor penetration, and undercutting along the sides of the weld. These, of course, cannot be corrected by heat treatment. The improvement that results from a postheat treatment is due to favorable metallurgical changes in the weld metal and heat-affected zone and to a diminution of residual welding stresses.

When postheating is carried out above the transformation temperature, as during a normalizing treatment, the microstructure is

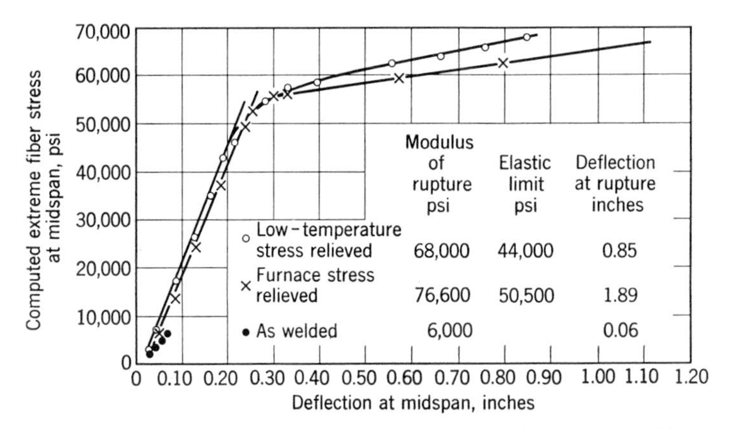

Fig. 8.10 Comparison of notch bend tests for various heat treatments.[24]

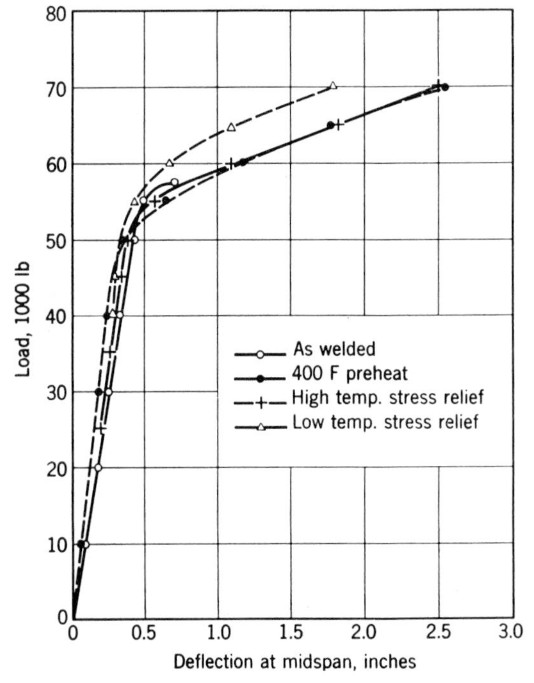

Fig. 8.11 Comparison of notch bend tests for various heat treatments.[25]

generally refined, and the residual stresses are reduced to zero. Postheating just below the critical temperature causes some spheroidization of carbides and reduces the residual stresses to nearly zero. Normal "stress relief" treatments involve heating to 1100 to 1200 F, wherein the residual stresses are reduced to unimportant values and the fast cooled structures are tempered. Low-temperature postheating (e.g., below 700 F) causes no noticeable microstructural changes in ordinary mild steel welds, and the residual stresses are not reduced substantially. However, it is known that even low-temperature postheating drives out appreciable quantities of the absorbed hydrogen, as is shown in Fig. 8.12,[26] and this may have a beneficial effect on the notch ductility.

A great deal of experimental work has been done in an attempt to evaluate the effects of preheating and postheating. Since few of the experiments appear to have a common factor, such as an identical test material, it is difficult to evaluate the conclusions, although each worker has, of course, contributed definite findings to the extant knowledge. Klingler and Ebert [14] compared the transition temperatures of a ¾-in. plate of a project steel "C" when subjected to several heat treatments. They used an eccentric notch tension test for evaluating the behavior of hand-welded double-V joints made with a controlled sequence of six passes using $^{3}/_{16}$-in. E6010 electrodes on

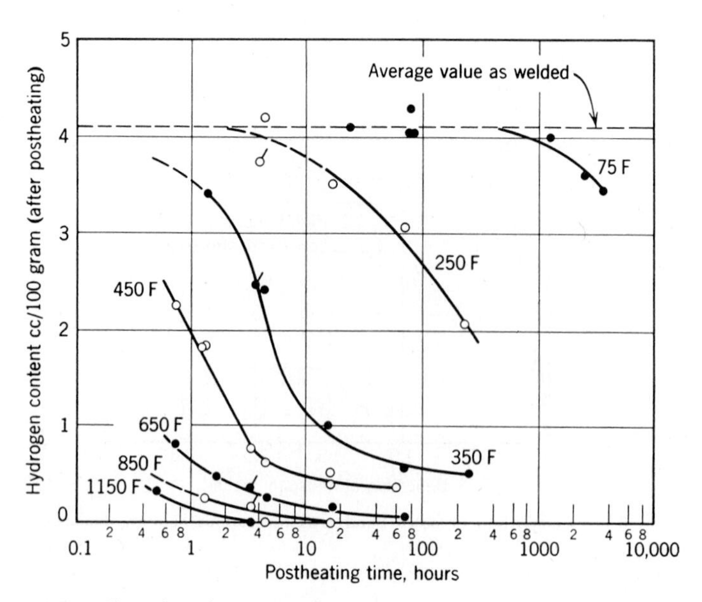

Fig. 8.12 Effect of postheating on the hydrogen content of E6010 weld metal.[26]

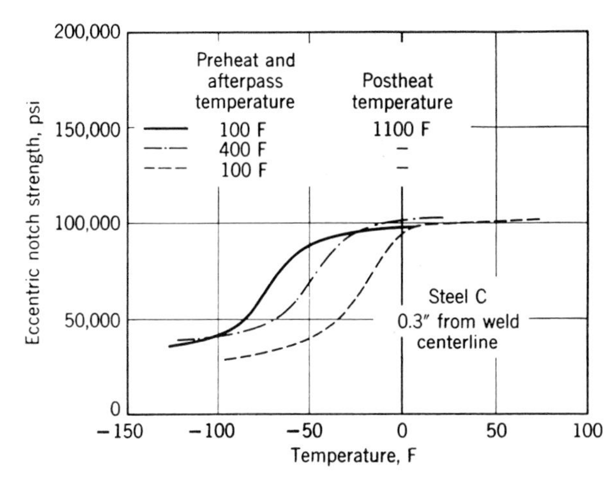

Fig. 8.13 Transition curve of the region of lowest ductility in the heat-affected zone of the base plate for ¾-in. project steel "C" plate.[14]

reverse polarity. The results are given in Fig. 8.13; they show that preheating to 400 F was definitely beneficial in lowering the transition temperatures but that 1100 F postheat following 100 F preheat was superior. From these and other test results it appears that a significant improvement in the ductility transition temperature can be attained by preheating structures that cannot be readily postheated. It should be kept in mind, however, that preheating does not cause any significant change in the residual stress introduced by welding, whereas postheating substantially removes such stress.

BEHAVIOR OF WELDMENTS

Tests on small specimens cut from large welded sections, while revealing insofar as they disclose the properties of the various zones in and near the weld, are often misleading. As was pointed out earlier, both ductility and fracture transition temperatures are highest for the base plate material that has been heated in the temperature range 1100 to 1400 F. For some reason as yet unknown, heating to a temperature within this range has an unusually strong influence in raising the transition temperature. It is possible that this effect is related to the increased carbon solubility in alpha iron in this range of temperature. Air cooling may cause the ferrite to be supersaturated with respect to carbon, which in turn might cause the observed increase in transition temperature. The effect of such heating was strikingly demonstrated by Stout and McGeady,[27] who investigated the effect of heating the base plate to various temperatures and air cooling. They determined both fracture and ductility transition temperatures with longitudinal weld bead notch bend test specimens of the type shown in Fig. 8.14 (unwelded plates were also tested for comparison). The transverse notch employed was 0.08 in. deep and had a root radius of about 0.04 in.* Their data, replotted in Figs. 8.15 and 8.16,[28] show very clearly the large difference that welding can make on the ductility transition temperature. In contrast, welding had practically no effect on the fracture appearance transition. The reason for the different behaviors is relatively simple. The fracture appearance transition reflects properties of the base plate because

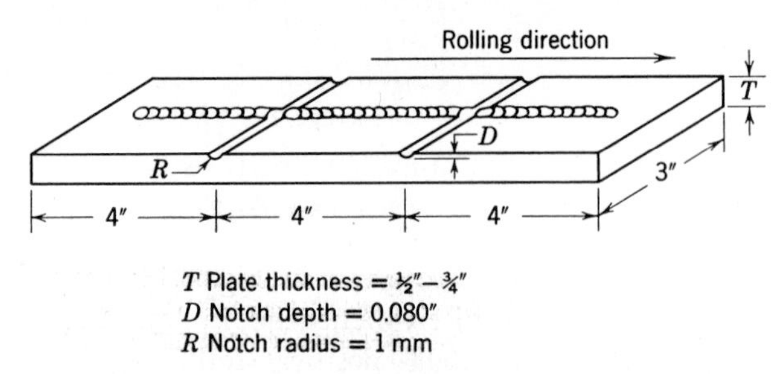

Fig. 8.14 Longitudinal weld bead notch bend test specimen (Lehigh test specimen).[27]

it is based upon the appearance of the entire fracture cross section—over 90 per cent of which is base plate. This criterion merely tells whether or not a crack, once started, will propagate as a cleavage fracture. It tells nothing about how much strain was necessary to form a crack that would propagate spontaneously. The unwelded base plate, as indicated by the ductility transition temperature, must be strained much more than the welded plate in order to form a crack large enough to propagate as a cleavage fracture. The effect of the welding is to foster the formation of a crack at a low strain. The ductility transition temperature is thus a measure of the ability of a material to undergo a significant amount of plastic flow at the bottom of a sharp notch (e.g., enough flow to cause a one per cent lateral contraction) before a crack forms. Welding introduces notch brittle zones of material, the presence of which can be detected by the ductility transition temperature measurement and not by the fracture appearance transition.†

The type of specimen used by Stout and co-workers, i.e., transverse notch and longitudinal bead or weld, has the advantage that the notch

* This specimen is frequently called the Lehigh bend test specimen.

† More extensive discussions of this subject may be found in the book by Stout and Doty [28] and in a paper by Pellini and Eschbacher.[29]

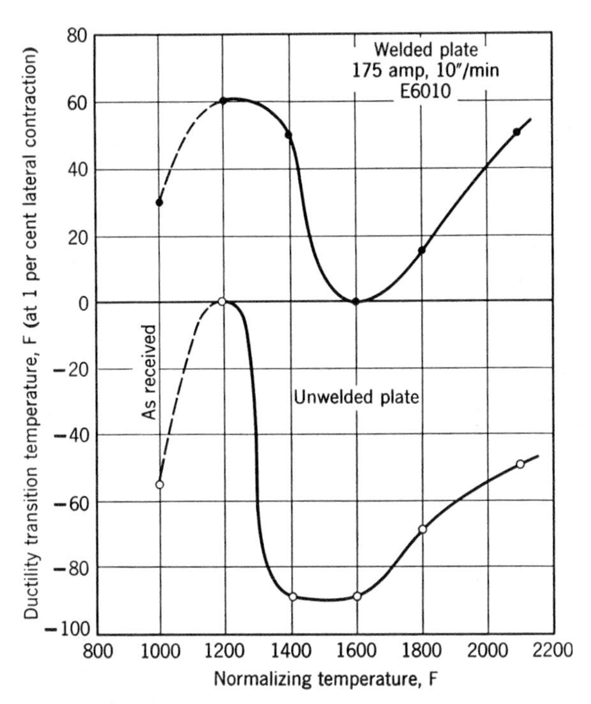

Fig. 8.15 Effect of normalizing before welding on the ductility transition temperature of ½-in. thick, 0.25% carbon steel plate (Lehigh bend test specimen).[28]

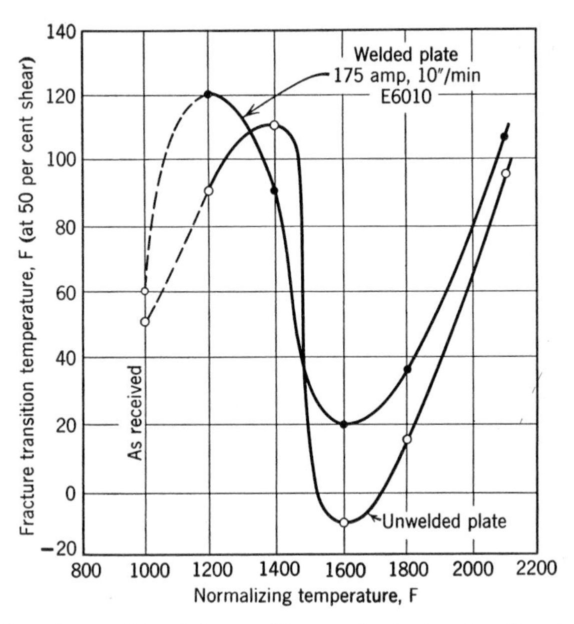

Fig. 8.16 Effect of normalizing before welding on the fracture transition temperature of ½-in. thick 0.25% carbon steel plate (Lehigh bend test specimen).[28]

traverses every zone of the weld and base plate. Consequently, if there is *any* region of low notch ductility, a crack will be encouraged to form at a low strain, and the composite specimen will have higher ductility transition than it would have had if the low ductility zone had not been present. Such a test will reveal the beneficial effect of preheating and postheating, as illustrated by the results from Stout and McGeady [30] shown in Fig. 8.17. The fracture transition temperature was substantially unaffected by the rate of electrode travel, preheat, or postheat treatment, whereas the ductility transition varied over a range of 150 F. The results are not always as striking as those presented in Fig. 8.17, as has been pointed out by Stout and Doty.[28] Nevertheless, the ductility transition is invariably the better criterion for evaluating the performance of a weldment.

Several other examples illustrative of the value of using specimens

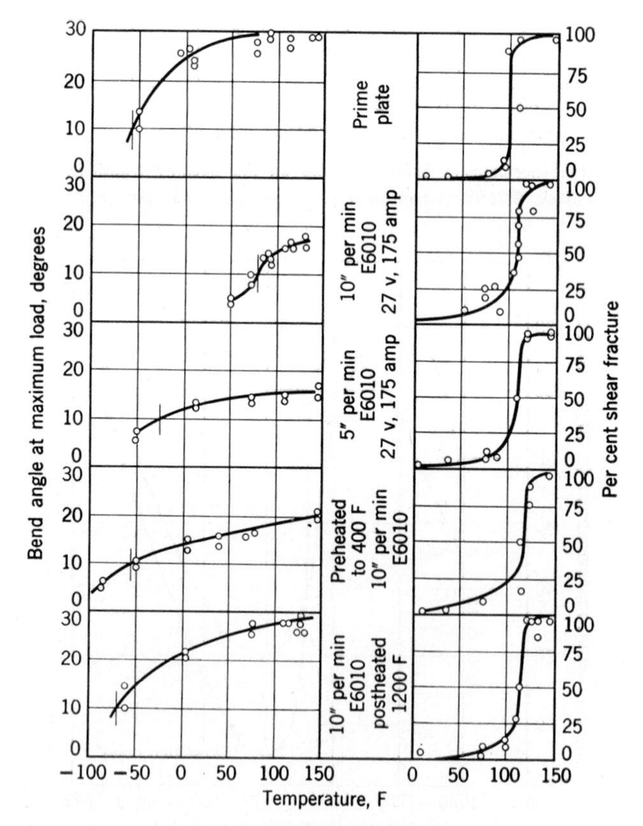

Fig. 8.17 Effect of heat treatment and electrode travel rate on fracture transition temperature and ductility transition temperature (Lehigh bend test specimen).[30]

in which the notch intersects all of the important regions in a weldment have been previously discussed in the work of Greene [24] and of DeGarmo.[25] Their results, given in Figs. 8.10 and 8.11, serve to illustrate the value of such a notch in large specimens.

When the notch is made to run parallel with the direction of the weld, the results are likely to be much different. Pellini and coworkers [29, 31, 32] have made extensive tests on welded specimens using both explosive charges and dropping weights to load the specimens. Pellini and Eschbacher [29] used both types of Charpy specimens and transverse weld bend test specimens to investigate the behavior of weld metal. Their bend specimen shown in Fig. 8.18 had a small

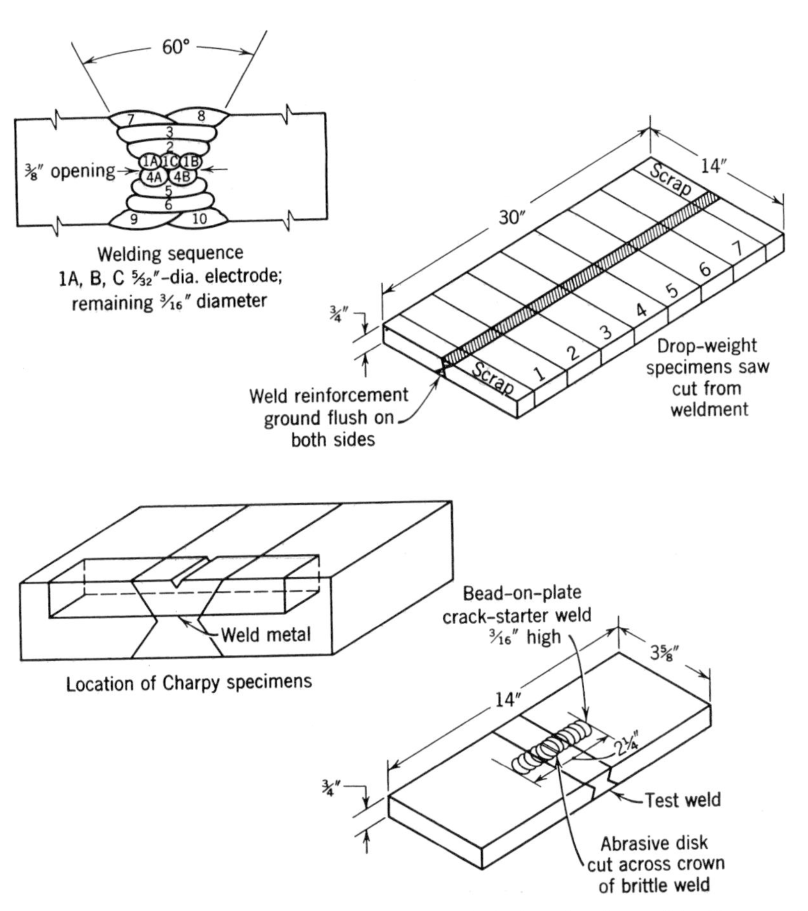

Fig. 8.18 Test specimen preparation for determining behavior of weld metal in Charpy and drop-weight transverse test specimens.[29]

bead of brittle hard facing alloy crossing the portion of the specimen to be tested. This hard bead was notched transversely and placed on the tension side during the test. The notched bead developed a cleavage crack when the specimen had bent three degrees; only two additional degrees of bend were permitted before the deforming specimen encountered a stop that arrested its motion. This test provided a check on the ability of the metal to deform at the root of a very sharp crack. The highest temperature at which a specimen fractured was called the drop weight ductility transition temperature. The fracture was confined entirely to the weld metal; the base plate played no role other than to assist in loading the weld metal. The location in the plate and weld metal of the Charpy specimens used for comparison is also shown in Fig. 8.18.

Results of their tests are shown in Figs. 8.19, 8.20, and 8.21. The first of this series shows the drop-weight ductility transition temperatures obtained with various brands and batches of E6010 electrodes and those obtained for E6012, E6020, E7016, E8016, and E10016 electrodes. A preheat and interpass temperature of 200 F were used in all cases. Most of the weld deposits had transition temperatures around 0 to 20 F; peening made the metal worse. The low hydrogen deposit made with E7016 electrodes was no better than deposits from other types of mild steel electrodes. The higher alloy low hydrogen weld deposits were significantly better, however, with the E10016 deposit having a transition below −50 F.

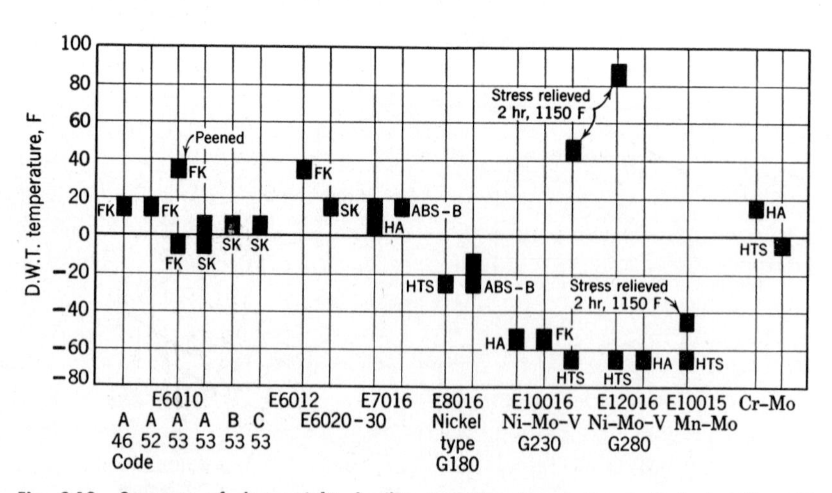

Fig. 8.19 Summary of drop-weight ductility transition temperatures obtained with weld metal from a variety of electrodes.[29]

Fig. 8.20 shows the drop-weight ductility transition temperature superimposed upon the V-notch Charpy curves for the various weld metals. A range from 15 to 25 ft-lb in the Charpy test seems to provide the proper correlation in transition temperatures. The corresponding correlation for rimmed and semikilled steel base plate was found by Pellini to be 5 to 8 ft-lb with V-notch Charpy specimens. This discrepancy again illustrates the futility of attempting to obtain perfect correlations between all types of tests, particularly when the composition and microstructure vary considerably among the steels being examined. Evaluation of weld metal on the basis of the 10 ft-lb energy level for V-notch Charpy specimens would yield conservative estimates of the ductility transition temperature; the same criterion applied to medium carbon structural base plate would be about right for judging service performance.[33]

Fig. 8.21 shows the general relation between the ductility transitions obtained by Pellini for E8016 weld metal with keyhole and V-notch Charpy specimens. The drop-weight transitions are indicated on the curves by the short heavy lines.

Pellini's results show that the ductility transition temperatures for weld metal are lower than those for medium carbon structural steel base plate, which they found had drop weight ductility transformation temperatures in the range of 20 to 40 F. These results, which have in general been substantiated by others, present a seemingly contradictory state of affairs. It has long been recognized that failures in service have almost invariably started at or very near welds. The reason for this seems fairly clear. Cracks or flaws (such as incomplete penetration) are common in the weld zone but rare in the base plate. Since brittle behavior requires that the steel must be below its ductility transition temperature (e.g., below 10 ft-lb for the V-notch Charpy specimen) and that *there must be a notch or crack present* to initiate a brittle crack, the incidence of failures must necessarily be greater where the defects are abundant. The types of defects that can initiate brittle fracture and the conditions under which they will function are somewhat obscure. More will be said about the kinds of defects that were responsible for actual service failures in Chapters XI and XII. However, one phase of this subject is discussed here. It deals with the brittle behavior of apparently sound weld metal. Hartbower and Pellini[34] found that unnotched E6010 weld deposits in ¾-in. thick plate of ASTM A-201 steel (0.14% carbon, 0.60% manganese, fully killed) had a much higher ductility transition temperature when tested in an explosive bulge test; failures initiated in the weld metal.

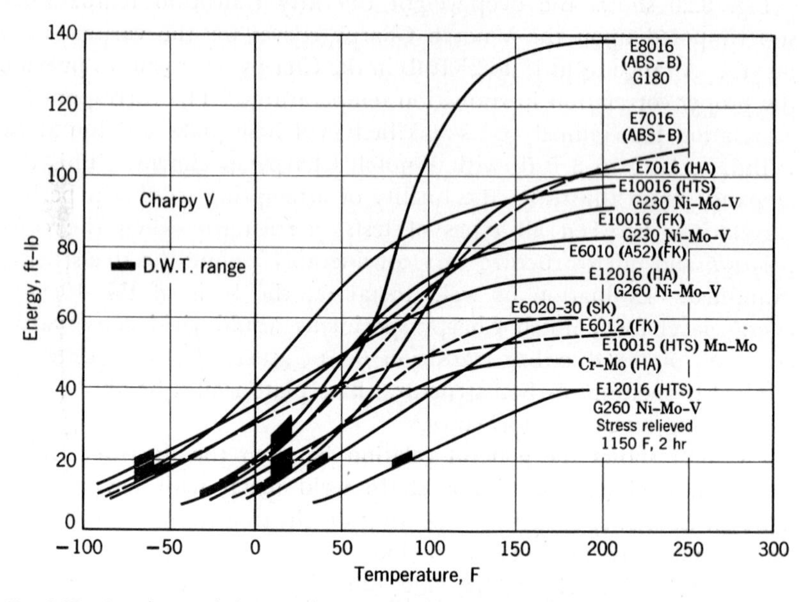

Fig. 8.20 Correlation of drop-weight transition temperature with V-notch Charpy curves for various weld metals.[29]

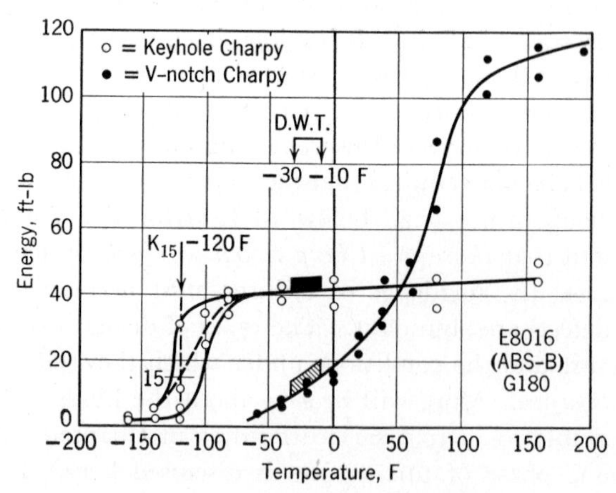

Fig. 8.21 General relation between V-notch Charpy, keyhole Charpy, and drop-weight transition data for weld metal deposited with E8016 electrode.[29]

The V-notch Charpy ductility transition temperature was found to be −50 F, however, in comparison with a corresponding value of 0°F for the base plate. The Charpy data indicated that the failure should have initiated in the base plate in the bulge test. To explain this discrepancy, Pellini suggested that the weld metal failed in the bulge test because of weld metal flaws not present in sufficient quantities to be detected by Charpy specimens.

Similar results are frequently obtained with static bend tests on unnotched specimens that can be bent 180° wthout cracking even at a temperature of −40 F. A longitudinal weld bead made with an E6010 electrode will develop cracks at a relatively small bend angle even at room temperature. Flanigan [4,5] has done an excellent job in contributing to the understanding of this behavior. He found a correlation between bend test performance and the presence of microcracks. (Such defects are difficult to detect; their discovery requires special metallographic techniques.) The defects form in weld metal at temperatures below 212 F and can be eliminated by slow cooling from above this temperature. A preheat of 150 to 200 F was sufficient to eliminate microcracks in the weld metal; when no microcracks were present, the bend angle was high even at low temperatures. It will be recalled that the tests by Pellini reported in Figs. 8.19, 8.20, and 8.21 were conducted on welds made with a 200 F preheat. These welds should have had few if any microcracks—a fact that could account for their apparent superior performance.

SUMMARY

Defective welding has been largely responsible for most of the recent structural failures in service. Almost without exception the origins of cleavage cracks in welded ships have been at weld defects. Very rarely have cracks been observed to start in sound welds in any type of engineering structure.

The transition temperatures of weld metal vary over a wide range of temperature depending upon the welding conditions, the type of electrode used, and the design of the specimen employed for the test. Fast cooling leads to poor notch ductility. Consequently, small fast stringer beads or fillet welds should be avoided. Preheating retards cooling and hence generally lowers the ductility transition temperature. Postheating to 1100 to 1200 F generally produces a substantial improvement in the notch ductility of weld metal or in weldments made without preheat. Deposits made with low hydrogen (E6015 or E6016) electrode or by the submerged arc process generally have lower ductility transition temperatures than E6010 deposits made without preheat. Preheat and postheat treatments have little effect upon the (already good) notch toughness of E6016 deposits. The rather poor notched bar properties of E6010 weld metal are due in large part to microcracks that form at temperatures below 212 F in rapidly cooled weld metal. Preheating even to 200 F retards the cooling sufficiently to prevent microcracks from forming.

The fracture appearance transition temperature has been shown to be relatively insensitive to variations in the welding condition. This criterion reflects the propensity of the base plate to fail by cleavage but does not indicate whether or not the fracture was preceded by extensive plastic flow. The amount that a metal can flow before forming a crack that will propagate through the base plate is best indicated by the ductility transition temperature. This criterion seems to be satisfactory for evaluating the performance of weldments, whereas the fracture transition is not.

The performance of a weldment is best indicated by specimens that contain the entire weld zone as well as a portion of the base plate. Furthermore, the specimens should be notched so that the notch extends across the weld, the heat-affected zone, and the base plate. Specimens having notches parallel to the direction of the weld reflect only the properties of the particular zone of the weldment containing the notch. Such tests, however, are particularly useful for disclosing which zone has the highest ductility transition temperature.

REFERENCES

1. *Welding Handbook,* p. 23. American Welding Society, 3d ed., 1950.
2. *Welding Handbook,* pp. 843–851. American Welding Society, 3d ed., 1950.
3. F. Rapatz and W. Hummitzsch, "Coated Electrodes" (Umhüllungsmasse bei elektroschweissdrähten), *Stahl u. Eisen, 65*:9–10, 109–118 (March 1945).
4. A. E. Flanigan, S. I. Bocarsky, and G. B. McGuire, "Effect of Low-Temperature Cooling Rate on the Ductility of Arc Welds in Mild Steel," *Welding J.,* Res. Suppl., pp. 459-s–466-s (September 1950).
5. A. E. Flanigan and T. Micleu, "Relation of Preheating to Embrittlement and Microcracking in Mild Steel Welds," *Welding J.,* Res. Suppl., pp. 99-s–106-s (February 1953).
6. *Basic Open Hearth Steel Making,* p. 469. New York: American Institute of Mining and Metallurgical Engineers, 1944.
7. A. L. Schaeffler, H. C. Campbell, and H. Thielsch, "Hydrogen in Mild-Steel Weld Metal," *Welding J.,* Res. Suppl., pp. 283-s–309-s (June 1952).
8. D. Warren and R. D. Stout, "Porosity in Mild Steel Weld Metal," *Welding J.,* Res. Suppl., pp. 381-s–386-s (August 1952).
9. F. W. Daniels, F. S. Gardner, and R. M. Rood, "The Comparative Behavior of Mild Steel Welds Made with E6010 and E6016 Electrodes," *Welding J.,* Res. Suppl., pp. 436-s–440-s (September 1948).

10. W. Andrews, "Constitution of Weld Metal," *Trans. Inst. Welding (London)*, *8*:3, 119–132 (1945).
11. *Welding Handbook*, p. 79. American Welding Society, 3d ed., 1950.
12. M. W. Mallett and P. J. Rieppel, "Underbead Cracking of Welds Cathodically Charged with Hydrogen," *Welding J.*, Res. Suppl., pp. 343-s–347-s (July 1950).
13. R. S. Stewart and S. F. Urban, "Influence of Carbide-Forming Elements on Underbead Cracking of Low-Alloy Steels," *Trans. Am. Soc. Metals, 42*, 653–665 (1950).
14. L. J. Klingler and L. J. Ebert, "Distribution of Relative Ductility in Steel Weldments," *Welding J.*, Res. Suppl., pp. 59-s–73-s (February 1950).
15. E. F. Nippes and W. F. Savage, "The Weldability of Ship Steels," *Welding J.*, Res. Suppl., pp. 776-s–788-s (November 1946).
16. G. G. Luther, C. E. Hartbower, R. E. Metius, and F. H. Laxar, "An Investigation of the Effect of Welding on the Transition Temperature of Navy High-Tensile, Low-Alloy Steels," *Welding J.*, Res. Suppl., pp. 634-s–645-s (October 1946).
17. W. F. Brown, Jr., L. J. Ebert, and G. Sachs, "Distribution of Strength and Ductility in Welded Steel Plate as Revealed by the Static Notch Bar Tensile Test," *Welding J.*, Res. Suppl., pp. 545-s–554-s (October 1947).
18. N. Grossman and C. W. MacGregor, "The Brittle Transition Temperatures of Various Low-Carbon Steels Welded by the Same Method," *Welding J.*, Res. Suppl., pp. 267-s–272-s (May 1948).
19. P. J. Rieppel and C. B. Voldrich, "Fracture Initiation and Propagation in Welded Ship Steels," *Welding J.*, Res. Suppl., pp. 188-s–198-s (April 1952).
20. API-ASME Code for Unfired Pressure Vessels, Par. W-463, 1942.
21. E. P. DeGarmo, F. Jonassen, and J. L. Meriam, "The Effect of Peening upon Residual Welding Stresses," *Welding J.*, Res. Suppl., pp. 616-s–623-s (October 1946).
22. J. L. Meriam, E. P. DeGarmo, and F. Jonassen, "Redistribution of Residual Welding Stresses by Tensile Loading along a Unionmelt Weld Joining Two 3-Ft. x 12-Ft. x 1-In. Plates," *Welding J.*, Res. Suppl., pp. 697-s–699-s (October 1946).
23. T. W. Greene and A. A. Holzbaur, "Controlled Low-Temperature Stress Relieving," *Welding J.*, Res. Suppl., pp. 171-s–185-s (March 1946).
24. T. W. Greene, "Evaluation of Effect of Residual Stresses," *Welding J.*, Res. Suppl., pp. 193-s–204-s (May 1949).
25. E. P. DeGarmo, "Preheat vs. Low- and High-Temperature Stress-Relief Treatments," *Welding J.*, Res. Suppl., pp. 233-s–237-s (May 1952).
26. A. E. Flanigan, "An Investigation of the Influence of Hydrogen on the Ductility of Arc Welds in Mild Steel," *Welding J.*, Res. Suppl., pp. 193-s–214-s (March 1947).
27. R. D. Stout and L. J. McGeady, "Notch Sensitivity of Welded Steel Plate," *Welding J.*, Res. Suppl., pp. 1-s–9-s (January 1949).
28. R. D. Stout and W. D. Doty, *Weldability of Steels*, pp. 183, 184. New York: Welding Research Council, 1953.
29. W. S. Pellini and E. W. Eschbacher, "Ductility Transition of Weld Metal," *Welding J.*, Res. Suppl., pp. 16-s–20-s (January 1954).
30. R. D. Stout and L. J. McGeady, "The Meaning and Measurement of Transition Temperature," *Welding J.*, Res. Suppl., pp. 299-s–302-s (June 1948).

31. P. P. Puzak, E. W. Eschbacher, and W. S. Pellini, "Initiation and Propagation of Brittle Fracture in Structural Steels," *Welding J.*, Res. Suppl., pp. 561-s–581-s (December 1952).
32. W. S. Pellini, "Evaluation of the Significance of Charpy Tests," ASTM Symposium on Metallic Materials at Low Temperature, 1953.
33. M. L. Williams, "Brittle Fracture in Ship Plates," *Mechanical Properties of Metals at Low Temperatures*, National Bureau of Standards Circ. 520, pp. 180–206, May 7, 1952.
34. C. E. Hartbower and W. S. Pellini, "Investigation of Factors Which Determine the Performance of Weldments," *Welding J.*, Res. Suppl., pp. 499-s–511-s (October 1951).

CHAPTER

Residual Stresses

INTRODUCTION

Residual stresses are defined as those which are present in a body without any external forces acting. They combine with other stresses in the same way that any stress systems combine.[1] Although there is still much debate as to whether residual stresses contribute to brittle behavior of engineering structures, it is a demonstrated fact that welding produces such stresses and that they may be very large in magnitude. As pointed out in Chapter I, residual stresses due to welding arise primarily from local thermal expansion and contraction. The local regions that attempt to expand upon heating are constrained in one or more directions by the surrounding metal so that upsetting occurs. During the subsequent cooling these regions contract, and since after upsetting they are too small to fit into the original spaces in the plate, tensile stresses develop. Such stresses are frequently equal to the yield strength of the material. Thus, in a longitudinal seam weld as the hot weld zone cools, its contraction is restrained by the adjacent plate, and a longitudinal stress is produced that is equal to the yield strength of the metal.[2] The residual stress pattern that results from such a weld is shown in Fig. 9.1. Simultaneously a transverse stress is developed, the magnitude of which varies with the width of the plate and the geometry of the structure. It should be noted, however, that the transverse stress may also be as high as the yield strength.

It should be clear that the *existence* of residual stresses is not ques-

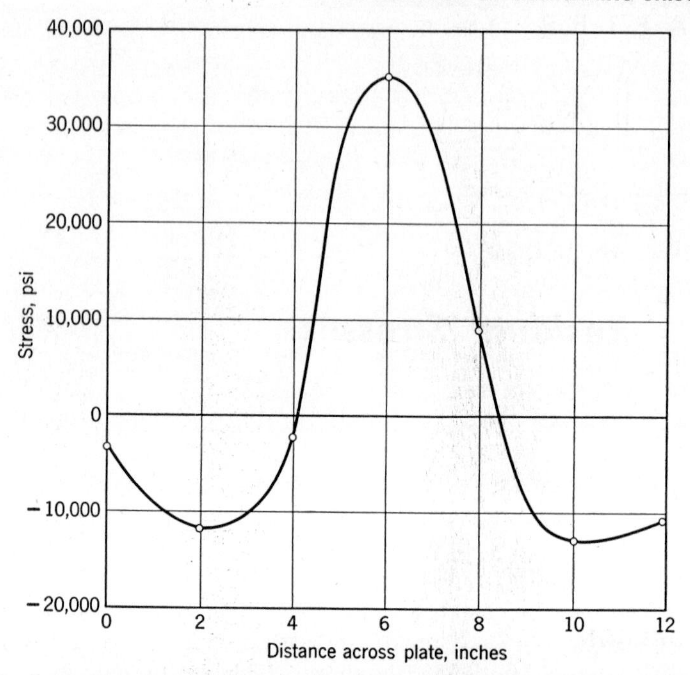

Fig. 9.1 Residual longitudinal stress pattern in a 12-in. plate containing a longitudinal butt weld.[2]

tioned but that the effects they may have on large structures is the subject of much debate. It is argued by many that a slight amount of plastic flow will relieve the residual welding stresses and that therefore they cannot be harmful. This view is supported by experiments which show that a residual stress pattern created by heating a spot in the middle of a plate is altered by subsequently pulling the specimen in tension. If the original residual tension stress is equal to the yield strength, the residual stress is reduced in magnitude by the amount of the tension stress produced by loading.

Similarly, it has been stated [3,4] that the large number of investigations made on structural members containing residual stresses have failed to provide conclusive evidence that the useful carrying life of the structure was impaired by the presence of such stresses. For example, large tensile specimens 40 in. wide and 15 ft long were tested by Wilson and Chao-Chien Hao.[5] These members were fabricated from ¾-in. plate, contained a longitudinal weld, and were tested in both the as-welded condition and after low-temperature stress relieving. Although these specimens contained high residual stresses, no difference in fracture strength was observed. However, as pointed out by Greene,[6] "the welds were free from defects (as shown by perfect X-rays) and the method of testing itself obliterated any effect of residual stresses." These tests were conducted under conditions that favored plastic flow, whereas residual stresses could only be expected to contribute to failure when the testing conditions were such as to encourage brittle behavior.

GENERAL DISCUSSION

Although numerous attempts have been made to demonstrate the effects of residual stresses by means of laboratory tests, most have failed in their objective. This may be attributed to the fact that no satisfactory "critical" test has been devised–the results of most tests performed to date can be explained satisfactorily without considering the influence of residual stresses.

The size of the test specimens is limited by practical considerations, and most laboratory specimens have been relatively small. There is ample evidence to demonstrate that there is a pronounced size effect. As Benson [7] pointed out, residual stresses are less likely to be reduced by yielding (because cracking tends to occur instead) when the dimensions of structures are increased. The effect of size was nicely demonstrated by the experiments of Docherty.[8] He used notched bend specimens of varying size, all of which had been machined from the same piece of steel. He found that the type of failure changed progressively from ductile to brittle as the size of the specimens was increased from 10 mm by 10 mm to 100 mm by 100 mm. A scale effect has also been found in testing notched and unnotched fatigue specimens.[9,10] Very few tests have been conducted at temperatures low enough to induce real brittleness in steel, and it is well known that residual stresses cannot affect the behavior unless the material fails at strains comparable with those observed within the elastic range.

With these objections in mind, it should be pointed out that the study of unnotched welded fatigue specimens, with and without residual stresses, reported by Hall and Parker [11] did not reveal any difference in fatigue limit due to the presence of residual stresses. However, the tests were conducted at room temperature and not in the temperature range where unnotched specimens of steel behave in a brittle manner. In another series of unwelded but notched specimens, they did, however, find a very marked difference in fatigue limit when residual stresses were present. These tests were also conducted at room temperature, but the notches changed the behavior of the steel, so that it was brittle at the test temperature.

In a series of static bend tests, Greene [6] utilized large welded plates (approximately 3 ft square) containing high residual stresses. The plates had sharp notches running across the weld at the midlength of the plate. He found that low-temperature stress relieved plates could carry about four times as much load as the as-welded specimens when tested in the brittle fracture temperature range. Furthermore, one of the as-welded specimens broke spontaneously before any load was applied; this fracture was obviously caused by the residual welding stress. Similar cracking caused by residual stresses in the absence of external loads has been observed by McKinsey [12] when subjecting as-welded mild steel plates to a 70½-hr exposure in a mixed nitrate solution. This stress-corrosion cracking was conspicuously absent when the welds were stress relieved by the low-temperature stress relieving process. Other instances of spontaneous failure will be discussed in Chapter XI, on service failures.

Some discussers have suggested that the beneficial result obtained from the stress relieving treatment may be due to metallurgical changes in the specimens caused by the stress relieving treatment rather than the absence of residual stresses per se. This objection is not supported by the facts; the low-temperature stress relieving process used to reduce the residual stress does not heat the weld zone above 100 F. This low temperature has never been known to cause any metallurgical change except strain aging, which occurs normally in any weld stressed to the yield point. Other discussers have pointed out, however, that the stretching imposed on the weld by the low-temperature stress relieving process enlarges the radius at the root of the crack, a change that favors improved performance.

A number of spontaneous fractures of welded structures have occurred prior to the application of any service load.[13] Consequently, many construction engineers are convinced that residual welding stresses can cause spontaneous failure of large weldments. More will be said about this in Chapter XII. The laboratory counterparts of such failures have not yet been fully developed to a satisfactory state, and so the conditions leading to such failure often are still obscure. However, spontaneous cracking of stressed notched plates has been observed by Weck [14] when cooling the plates to a temperature below their transition temperature as determined from Izod tests. The residual stresses were introduced into the 8-in. by 16-in. by ¾-in. thick test plates by so-called reaction stresses, which were obtained by welding the specimens as windows into a rigid frame under constrained welding conditions. This technique of welding windows into rigid frames had been used by Kennedy [2] as early as 1945; he reported fractures that followed the cooling of variously notched test windows (after reaction stresses had been induced) to temperatures of −60 F or lower. However, he subjected only the "window" to cooling, thereby increasing the reaction stresses in the window as the temperature was lowered. The fractures obtained in the Kennedy experiments resulted, therefore, from simultaneous lowering of the temperature and a slight increasing of the stress. In his experiments Weck improved upon this technique by cooling the whole assembly, i.e., the frame and the specimen, very slowly in an insulated box by circulating cooled CO_2 gas around the heavy sections of the frame, thus keeping the reaction stresses constant. He found that a coarse-grained mild steel plate fractured spontaneously when tested in the manner described. Another plate having finer grains and a lower transition temperature did not break at a temperature below its Izod transition temperature even when struck with hammer blows. Both of these experiments, conducted quite independently of each other, indicate spontaneity of fracture under certain conditions due to residual stresses.

The suggestion has been made by some investigators that residual stresses originally present in a structure are reduced to a negligible quantity after an initial high loading. Ffield [15] pointed out that studies on several Liberty ships failed to reveal any signs of stress relief as a result of one year or more of service. Consequently, it seems rather certain that normal operating loads cannot be depended upon to reduce the magnitude of the internal stresses.

A report of a Board of Investigation to inquire into the design and methods of construction of welded steel merchant vessels contains an analysis of nine ship failures in which cracks originated in structural members having maximum nominal applied stresses between 3,300 and 12,000 psi.[16] Some of the failures occurred in still water, where dynamic loads due to wave action were absent. It is possible, although certainly not proved, that residual welding stresses contributed to the failure.

Arnott [13] described four cases of spontaneous fracturing of ships while under construction. In one of these a welded ship subassembly fractured spontaneously, with the crack extending for a length of 18 ft. There were no external loads except perhaps those due to the weight of the structure itself, and the maximum nominal tensile stress was only 2,000 psi. An appreciable time elapsed between completion of welding on the structures and the time of fracture. No feasible explanation of these failures has been offered except that they were caused by residual stresses arising during fabrication. In this connection, Fig. 9.2 is of more than passing interest; it is a good example of cracking due to residual stresses. The top figure [17] shows a weld bead

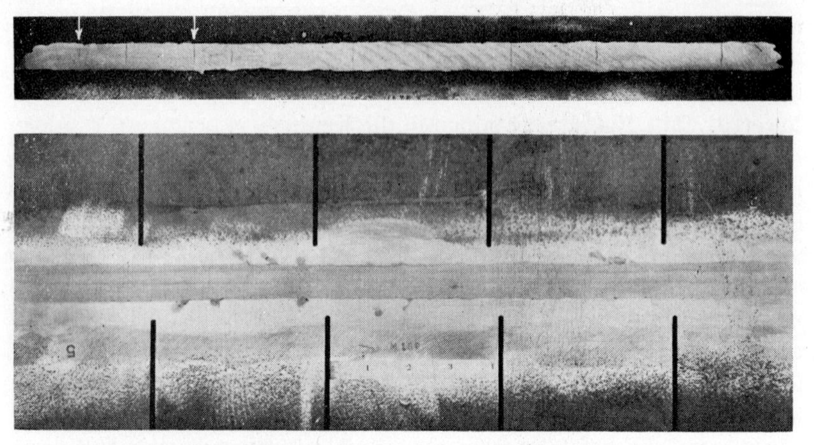

Fig. 9.2 Photographs showing cracks in weld metal due to residual stresses.[17]

that was apparently sound in every respect at the time it was made; yet the cracks indicated by arrows appeared approximately 3 hours after welding, and the other cracks appeared between 6 and 21 hours after welding. A similar weld was made on plates slotted prior to welding in order to minimize the longitudinal restraint so that the residual stress would be reduced. It may be seen that this weld remained sound. The welds in this case were made with a relatively brittle material, but similar cracks are occasionally found in mild steel welds.

Campus [18] has described other examples of fractures in which residual stresses were credited with playing major roles. He made a study of a large number of cases where high residual stresses in combination with fabrication defects (such as notches and/or faulty welds coupled with poor fabrication procedures) caused failures. He also cited several examples of spontaneous fracturing of rolled structural shapes under conditions of zero external load (Fig. 9.3). From the facts presented, it appeared impossible to avoid the conclusion that residual stresses were the primary cause of these failures.

During the past decade a number of techniques have been developed for measuring residual stresses. All methods but one, namely, the utilization of X-rays, are destructive to the specimen and involve some damage to the structure being examined. The most reliable method involves the removal of material, with continuous measurements of the dimensions of the part being made during the process of removal. The development of the electric resistance wire strain gage has been probably the greatest single factor in improving the accuracy of strain measurements. A description of the various techniques used is beyond the scope of the present work; those interested are referred to the existing literature on the subject.[19-22] One word of caution should be noted, however: the method of sampling is very critical. If the stress relieving cuts are made in a certain sequence, the stress values obtained may be erroneous, and they may lead to incorrect conclusions concerning the merits of a specific design or fabricating procedure. In general it is best to sever the compression zone before a test piece is removed from a region in tension. The great interest aroused by the known presence of residual stresses, along with the attendant uncertainty of the role they play in service failures, has led many people to investigate ways of removing them. Basic and detailed designs have been altered to keep inherently adverse long range "locked in" stresses (reaction stresses) at a minimum. Similarly, fabrication procedures and sequences are under continuous scrutiny in an effort to improve the final structure in this respect. These long range stresses are particularly bad in causing warping and distortion; they may occasionally contribute to fracture. An example of this is the cracking that occurs when a patch is welded in a plate.

Fig. 9.3 Photograph of a spontaneously fractured I-beam under conditions of zero external load. At time of fracture beam was lying flat on the ground and the temperature was normal.[18]

In spite of all such preventive measures, large residual stresses cannot be avoided in many welded assemblies. As stated earlier, they are a natural consequence of the welding process, particularly when large components are joined. They can be eliminated only by a post-welding heat treatment at a temperature of 1100 to 1200 F, a temperature which effectively reduces the stresses to unimportantly low values.

Another method for reducing residual stresses has already been suggested, i.e., proof loadings of the welded structure to a stress level that will cause some plastic yielding of the assembly. However, neither this nor the furnace stress relief procedure is feasible on many large structures. Since service loads cannot be relied upon to relieve residual stresses, it is sometimes important to have an alternative method available for use. The "low-temperature stress relieving process" accomplishes this result. This technique has been described in detail by Greene and Holzbaur and consists in progressively heating bands on each side of the weld to about 350 F.[23] Six-inch wide oxyacetylene torches were used for this work. The heating torches were followed by air-water cooling applied about 6 in. behind the advancing flame. This procedure imposes a longitudinal tension strain on the weld that cannot be excessive, since it is due entirely to the thermal expansion of the heated areas. The residual stresses are reduced to a negligible value by this process when it is properly applied. This is illustrated in Fig. 9.4, which is quite typical of the results obtained. In this case the maximum residual stress was reduced from 42,000 to 5,000 psi. Although this process produces rather spectacular results, it must be kept in mind that it is not a cure-all for the residual stress problem because of the relatively limited number of situations to which it can be applied. It is most applicable where the structure contains long butt welds; it would be very difficult to apply to irregular or complicated assemblies, such as hatch corners, a location where many of the ship failures originated.

DeGarmo [24] recently reported results of an investigation carried out to determine the relative merits of preheating, low-temperature stress

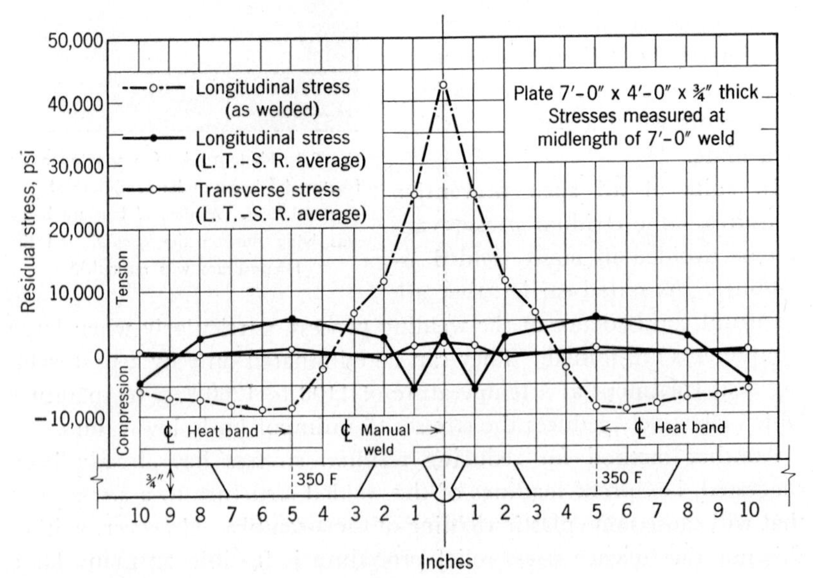

Fig. 9.4 Residual welding stresses before and after low-temperature stress relieving process.[23]

relieving, and high-temperature (1200 F) heat treating after welding. Results of bend tests on specimens prepared by each of these methods are shown in Fig. 9.5. A specimen that was tested in the as-welded condition is also shown for comparison. It may be noted that this is the only one that failed. The preheat treatment and the high-temperature

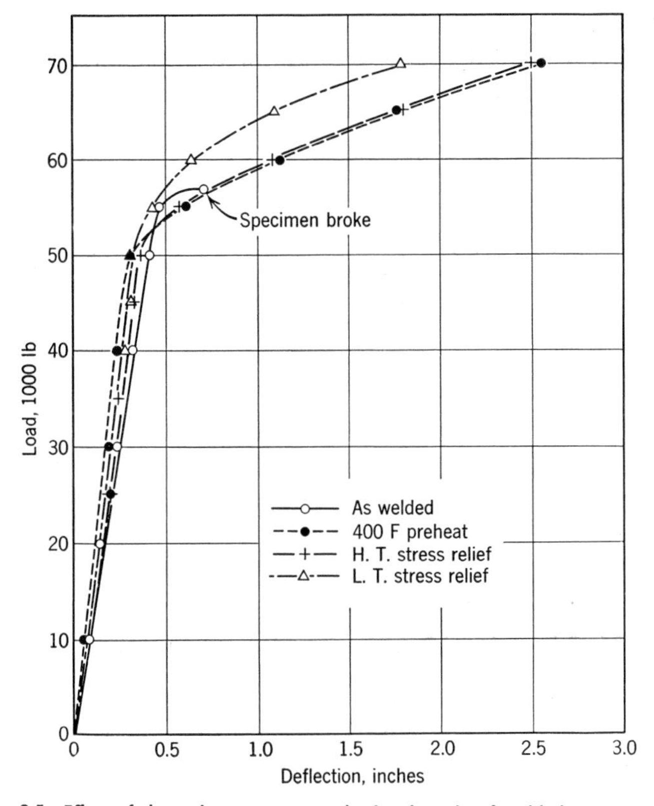

Fig. 9.5 Effect of thermal treatments on the bend angle of welded specimens.[24]

postheating both yielded excellent results; the specimen given the low-temperature stress relieving treatment was even somewhat superior, but the number of specimens tested was too small to warrant definite conclusions. However, Greene [6] had previously conducted similar tests and also had found a similar beneficial effect from low-temperature stress relieving.

INITIATION AND PROPAGATION OF FRACTURES

Some recent investigations have shed considerable light upon the conditions necessary for the spontaneous propagation of brittle fractures. Robertson [25] devised a test with which he could investigate the effect of stress on the propagation of a brittle crack; his specimens had a temperature gradient, and the crack would stop in the warm zone, so that he was able to determine the temperature above which a crack would not propagate at any given stress level. The specimen, shown in Fig. 9.6(*a*) consisted of a short, wide section of the steel being tested, which was welded to long, thin pulling tabs through which the load was applied. The thickness of the end pieces was chosen

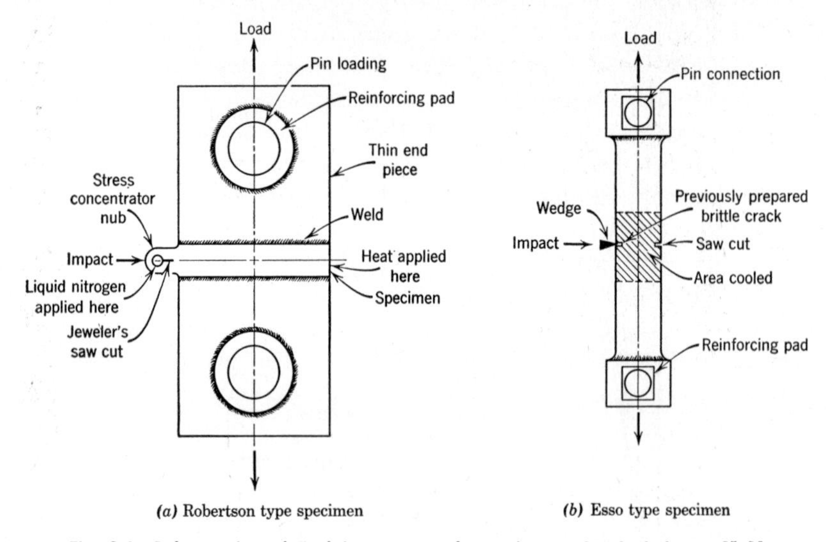

Fig. 9.6 Robertson's and Feely's specimens for evaluating brittle behavior.[25, 26]

so that the desired stress in the test section, e.g., 10,000 psi, would cause yielding in the thin pieces. Thus a fairly uniform distribution of stress in the test section was assured. The temperature gradient modified the stress distribution somewhat, causing it to vary by perhaps ± 10 per cent. Robertson was able to show by this test that below a certain temperature cracks would propagate spontaneously in medium carbon structural steel when the nominal stress was above about 10,000 psi, but that the cracks would stop when the stress was below this value.

Feely and co-workers,[26] investigating the cause of failure of two large oil storage tanks, made a thorough investigation of the Robertson type of specimen. As a result, they devised a specimen and test procedure that was free from most of the objections to the Robertson test. Their specimen, shown in Fig. 9.6(*b*), was uniform in cross section and had a high ratio of length to width, i.e., about 10. A cleavage crack, made at liquid nitrogen temperature, was used for the notch; a saw cut was made on the opposite edge to improve the stress distribution. The entire specimen was uniformly cooled to the desired testing temperature, and a selected load was applied. The cleavage crack would not initiate failure, however, unless a stress approaching the yield point was applied. In order to cause the initial crack to start propagating at stresses between 10,000 and 30,000 psi, the investigators found that an impact load had to be used. This was provided by a wedge driven into the cleavage initial crack by a slug shot from an impact gun. The energy of the slug was insufficient to extend the crack very far but was adequate to provide a running crack that would continue when the stress level was above about 10,000 psi and the temperature was below some critical value, e.g., −35 to +40 F for various steels. Their tests indicated that the steels in the tanks that failed were susceptible to brittle failure at 40 F (the actual temperature at the time of failure) when the stress reached the range of 14,000 to 20,000 psi. The calculated stresses at the time of failure were 14,200 and 15,800 psi. The 10 ft-lb ductility transition temperature for V-notch Charpy specimens was found to be between 45 and 60 F for plates containing the fracture origins. Thus, quantitative correlation between laboratory tests and service failures seems possible. This subject will be developed further in Chapters XI and XII, which deal with service failures.

The foregoing discussion has brought out the fact that below the ductility transition temperature (as measured by V-notch Charpy or the Standard Oil tests), a cleavage crack *once started* will continue to grow at stress levels above about 10,000 to 15,000 psi. However, *static loads would not cause a cleavage crack to grow unless the average stress reached the yield point.* Thus a major question remains yet to be answered—What causes fractures to start in large welded structures when no impact loads are applied? Actually, there may be a number of reasons why cracks suddenly begin to grow spontaneously. Feely and co-workers [26] proposed that incompletely penetrated welds might suddenly fail at moderately low loads and thereby subject the adjacent sound metal to an impact load of sufficient magnitude to cause a crack to propagate. In an actual test where this condition was simulated, failure occurred at a stress of 27,400 psi, 8,000 psi below the yield point.

Some recent work by Kennedy [27] has indicated the possibility of another explanation for crack initiation at low nominal stress levels. He found that certain welding procedures produced *triaxial tension* stresses at the center of the plate in butt-welded joints. The magnitude of the thickness direction stress varied with the welding technique employed but was substantially the same for $\frac{3}{4}$-in. and for 2-in. thick plates of medium carbon structural steel. As indicated in Table 9.1, stringer

TABLE 9.1

TRIAXIAL RESIDUAL WELDING STRESSES AT MID-THICKNESS OF PLATE AND AT CENTERLINE OF DOUBLE-V BUTT WELD [27]

Welding Technique	Plate Thick-ness, in.	Longitudinal Stress, psi	Transverse Stress, psi	Thickness Direction Stress, psi
Hand, stringer bead	$2\frac{1}{2}$	58,000	49,000	37,000
Hand, stringer bead	$\frac{3}{4}$	59,500	47,500	49,000
Submerged arc	$2\frac{1}{2}$	28,000	15,000	−13,000
Hand, weave	$\frac{3}{4}$	12,000	−6,500	−26,400

bead welds had the highest thickness direction stress; submerged arc welds and hand welds made by the weaving technique had compression stresses in this direction. Kennedy used precision dial gages, mounted on a large yoke that spanned the specimen, to measure the thickness direction strains during the machining operations used to relax the welding stresses. Longitudinal and transverse strains were measured with resistance wire strain gages in the conventional manner. Simple trepanning was insufficient to relax all of the thickness direction stresses, so the weld was subjected to a boring operation, with holes centered at the mid-thickness of the weld. Readings were taken after each increment in the boring operation; the final hole left only a thin surface layer of metal.

The presence of a high triaxial tensile component of residual stress changes the conclusions concerning the probable effects of residual stress (previously assumed to be biaxial in nature). Load stresses would *add* to the internal stress in this case, even though the maximum longitudinal stress was already as high as the uniaxial tensile yield point of the weld metal. A small sharp weld crack could have at its root a triaxial tensile stress, presumably large enough to initiate a spontaneous failure when the temperature was lowered below the ductility transition (as observed by Greene [6]), or when a small service load was applied. The investigation is being continued so that the relative merits of various welding techniques can be evaluated and the effects of stress relieving procedures can be appraised.

SUMMARY

The conflicting evidence concerning the effect of residual stresses has led to a great deal of confusion, and it is impossible at the present time to reach unambiguous conclusions concerning the possible effects of residual stresses on the brittle behavior of engineering structures; laboratory test results and theoretical analyses indicate that such stresses are of minor importance to the life of large structures. However, operating field engineers are familiar with an uncomfortably large number of failures that are apparently unexplainable on any other basis. Since it is recognized by all that large residual stresses do exist and a truly critical laboratory test has not yet been devised to determine their effects on the occurrence of brittle failures, it would appear to be advisable at this time to take every possible precaution to minimize such stresses wherever possible.

Designs and fabrication techniques should be refined to minimize residual stresses, and one of the available methods of relieving residual stresses should be used in critical assemblies. Abrupt changes in section should be eliminated, and weld defects should be avoided. Preheating and postheating are very beneficial. There is an impressive amount of evidence to indicate that service life probably *is* affected by residual stresses in structures made of materials that can fail in a brittle manner. Medium carbon structural steels fall in this class only when the temperature is well below the ductility transition temperature. The use of normalized steels (preferably fully deoxidized) welded with low hydrogen electrodes should provide an adequate safeguard against failures due to residual stresses.

It has been established that cleavage cracks can propagate spontaneously in structures subjected to stresses above about 10,000 psi, provided, of course, that the temperature is below the ductility transition of the steel. The conditions necessary for the spontaneous initiation of cracks in structures subjected to low nominal stresses are still obscure. Perhaps several factors can operate to help start cracks—the sudden fracturing of an incompletely penetrated weld being one and the presence of triaxial tensile stresses due to welding being another.

REFERENCES

1. W. Prager and P. G. Hodge, Jr., *Theory of Perfectly Plastic Solids,* p. 42. New York: John Wiley & Sons, 1951.
2. H. E. Kennedy, "Some Causes of Brittle Failures in Welded Mild Steel Structures," *Welding J.,* Res. Suppl., pp. 588-s–598-s (July 1945).
3. W. Spraragen, "Residual Stresses in Welding," *Residual Stresses in Metals and Metal Construction,* W. R. Osgood, ed., pp. 85–102. New York: Reinhold Publishing Corporation, 1954.
4. R. Weck, "Residual Stresses Due to Welding," *Welding J.,* Res. Suppl., pp. 9-s–14-s (January 1949).

5. W. M. Wilson and Chao-Chien Hao, "Residual Stresses in Welded Structures," University of Illinois Engineering Experiment Station Bull. Series No. 361, pp. 3–78, 1946.
6. T. W. Greene, "Evaluation of Effect of Residual Stresses," *Welding J.*, Res. Suppl., pp. 193-s–203-s (May 1949).
7. L. E. Benson, "Some Considerations Regarding the Generation and Importance of Residual Welding Stresses," *Residual Stresses in Metals and Metal Construction,* pp. 75–83. New York: Reinhold Publishing Corporation, 1954.
8. J. G. Docherty, "Slow Bending Tests on Large Notched Bars," *Engineering (London), 139*:3606, 211–213 (1935).
9. C. E. Phillips and R. B. Heywood, "The Size Effect in Fatigue of Plain and Notched Steel Specimens Loaded under Reversed Direct Stress," *Proc. Inst. Mech. Engrs. (London), 165,* 113–124 (1951).
10. R. B. Heywood, "The Relationship between Fatigue and Stress Concentration," *Aircraft Eng. (London), 19*:217, 81–84 (1947).
11. L. D. Hall and E. R. Parker, "Effect of Residual Tension Stress on the Fatigue Strength of Mild Steel," *Welding J.,* Res. Suppl., pp. 421-s–425-s (August 1948).
12. C. R. McKinsey, "Effect of Low-Temperature Stress Relieving on Stress Corrosion Cracking," *Welding J.,* Res. Suppl., pp. 161-s–166-s (April 1954).
13. D. Arnott, "Some Typical Cases Where Residual Stresses Set Up by Welding Appear to Have Contributed to Ship Structural Failures," *Residual Stresses in Metals and Metal Construction,* W. R. Osgood, ed., pp. 33–39. New York: Reinhold Publishing Corporation, 1954.
14. R. Weck, "Experiments on Brittle Fracture of Steel," *Welding Research.* London: British Welding Research Association, *6*:4, 70-r–82-r (1952).
15. P. Ffield, "Some Notes on Typical Residual Stresses Encountered in Welded Ships," *Residual Stresses in Metals and Metal Construction,* W. R. Osgood, ed., pp. 45–74. New York: Reinhold Publishing Corporation, 1954.
16. *Final Report of a Board of Investigation to Inquire into the Design and Methods of Construction of Welded Steel Merchant Vessels.* Washington, D. C.: Government Printing Office, 1946.
17. A. W. Steinberger and J. Stoop, "Studies of the Crack Sensitivity of Aircraft Steels," *Welding J.,* Res. Suppl., pp. 527-s–542-s (November 1952).
18. F. Campus, "Effects of Residual Stresses on the Behavior of Structures," *Residual Stresses in Metals and Metal Construction*, W. R. Osgood, ed., pp. 1–21. New York: Reinhold Publishing Corporation, 1954.
19. W. V. Bassett, H. Cromwell, and W. E. Wooster, "Improved Techniques and Devices for Stress Analysis with Resistance Wire Gages," *Proc. Soc. Exp. Stress Anal., III*:2, 76–88 (1946).
20. C. S. Barrett, "A Critical Review of Various Methods of Residual Stress Measurement," *Proc. Soc. Exp. Stress Anal., II*:1, 147–156 (1944).
21. A. J. Durelli, H. Ekstein, R. H. Jacobson, and C. H. Tsao, "Residual Stress Survey," Armour Research Foundation, Project #2-937 J, 1951.
22. D. Rosenthal, "Measurement of Residual Stress," *Residual Stresses in Metals and Metal Construction,* W. R. Osgood, ed., pp. 271–283. New York: Reinhold Publishing Corporation, 1954.
23. T. W. Greene and A. A. Holzbaur, "Controlled Low-Temperature Stress Relieving," *Welding J.,* Res. Suppl., pp. 171-s–185-s (March 1946).

24. E. P. DeGarmo, "Preheat vs. Low- and High-Temperature Stress Relief Treatments," *Welding J.*, Res. Suppl., pp. 233-s–237-s (May 1952).
25. T. S. Robertson, "Brittle Fracture of Mild Steel," *Engineering* (*London*), *172:* 4471, 445–448 (1951).
26. F. J. Feely, Jr., D. Hrtko, S. R. Kleppe, and M. S. Northup, "Report on Brittle Fracture Studies," *Welding J.*, Res. Suppl., pp. 99-s–111-s (February 1954).
27. H. E. Kennedy, Private communication.

CHAPTER

Design and Workmanship

INTRODUCTION

The design of welded structures involves complex problems that vary in nature from one structure to another. A discussion of design details and fabrication procedures is beyond the scope of this book and, since these problems have been adequately treated in a number of texts,[1-5] only a brief discussion of the importance of proper design will be presented here. The discussion will be illustrated with a series of test results on full-scale specimens representing a corner of a hatch opening in a ship. This series of tests illustrates the principles involved in designing to avoid the occurrence of brittle fractures.

A study of service failures reveals that not all brittle failures are caused by inappropriate designs. In the majority of the cases the failure could be attributed to imperfections in the structure, such as incompletely penetrated welds, tack welds, arc strikes, mechanical gouges, and similar defects, which provide structural discontinuities inadvertently introduced during fabrication or installation. Such defects have caused numerous failures of simple tubular structures such as penstocks and natural gas transmission lines. Obviously, then, attention to design details alone is not sufficient to ensure against brittle failure. Careful workmanship is essential if dangerous structural defects are to be eliminated. Also, it has become increasingly evident that defects introduced through poor workmanship or by accident must be detected by diligent and well trained inspectors prior to the time that the structure is put into service. Experience has shown that if this is not done serious service failures may occur. It is unfortunately true, however, that in spite of all attempts to detect defects, some escape observation. The practice of proof loading prior to service use is an excellent safeguard for preventing service failures. Such testing singles out weak areas and induces failures under controlled test conditions, thus preventing later service failures, which could be disastrous.

A factual report on service failures is presented in Chapters XI and XII; some conditions leading to such failures are discussed herein.

DESIGN

The influence of design on the performance of welded structures was investigated with a comprehensive series of full-scale tests on specimens shaped like the corner of a ship hatch opening. The results of this series were reported by DeGarmo [6] and reviewed by Jonassen [7] and by the Ship Structure Committee.[8] The same steel, electrode type, and welding conditions were employed for the various designs. A glance at Fig. 10.1 shows how important design can be in a critical case. All 11 of the design variations tested were improvements over the basic design. The 3 best designs from the standpoint of strength and energy to failure were (1) the Kennedy, (2) the American Bureau of Shipping, and (3) the Coast Guard, Code 1. Some of the details of construction are shown in Figs. 10.2, 10.3, and 10.4; these may be compared with the basic design shown in Fig. 10.5.

All specimens were tested to fracture in a large tensile testing machine. The performance was evaluated in terms of maximum load and energy absorbed to failure. It is important to note the tremendous improvement achieved by the Kennedy design. This construction introduces flexibility, which allows the load to become more uniformly distributed. The ABS design, on the other hand, achieved the objective of distributing the load in a different manner. The deck plate was rounded, with an 18-in. radius, to reduce the stress concentration at the corner; the longitudinal coaming was extended beyond the corner for about 2 ft to carry the stress away from this critical region. An additional safety feature was provided by the use of "snipes" (openings cut through plate) to avoid a concentration of welding at the intersection of three plates.

The Coast Guard design, U.S.C.G. Code 1, had been used on a large number of later Liberty ships. This design was also of rigid construction. It had a large doubler plate, a 12-in. radius at the

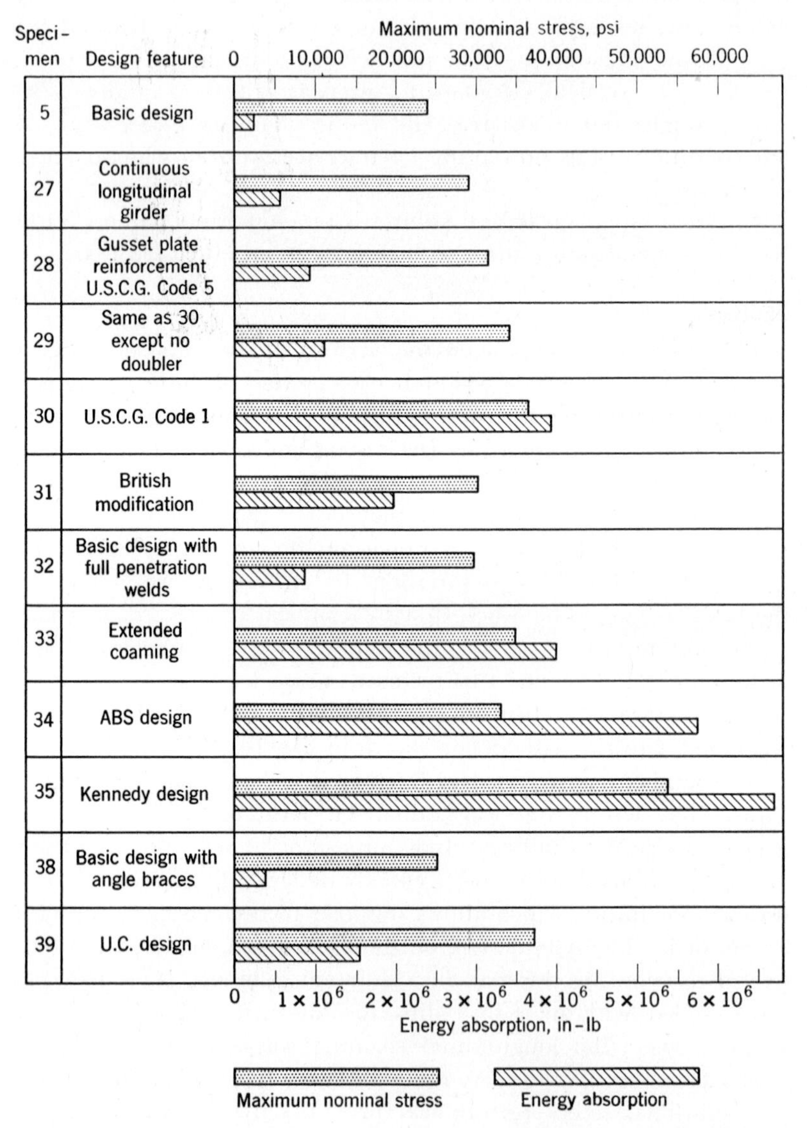

Fig. 10.1 Results of tension tests on hatch corners with 11 design modifications.[6]

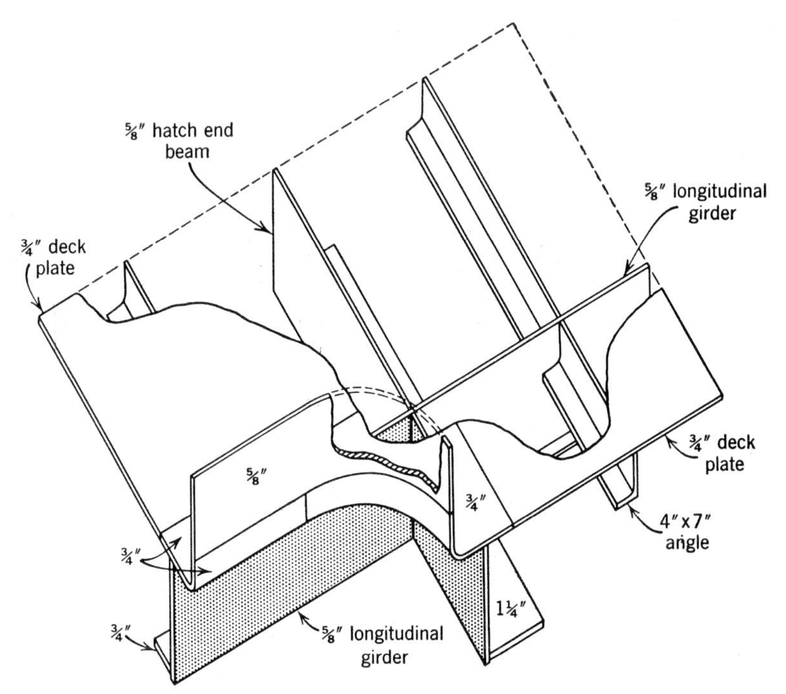

Fig. 10.2 Isometric view of Kennedy hatch corner specimen No. 35.[6]

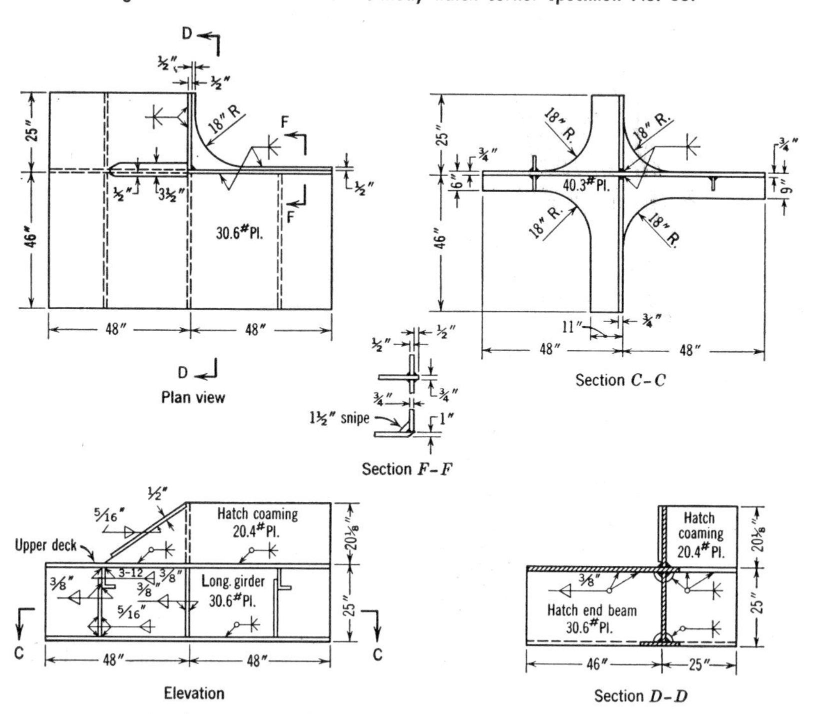

Fig. 10.3 Full-scale asymmetric hatch corner specimen No. 34 (modified ABS design).[6]

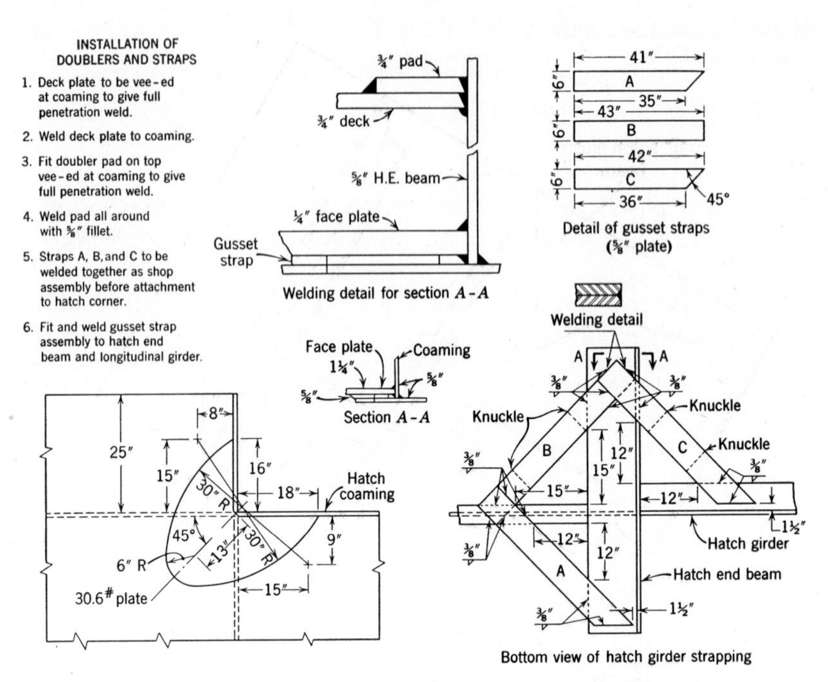

Fig. 10.4 Hatch corner reinforcement specimen No. 31 (British Modification Code 1-A).[6]

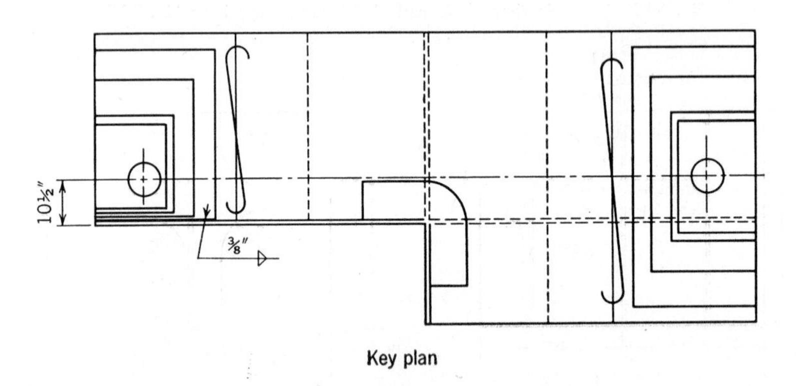

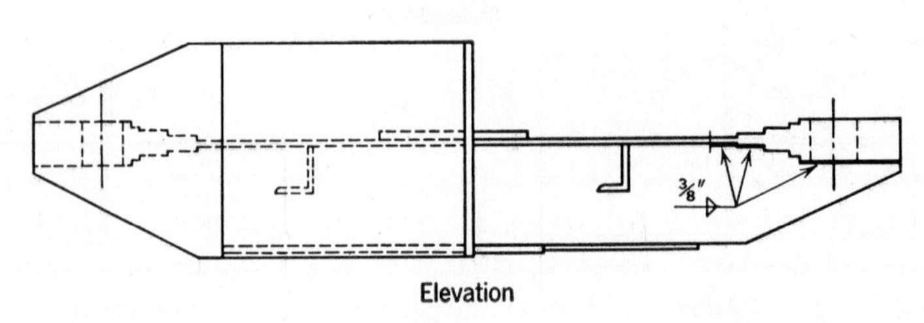

Fig. 10.5 Basic design of the full-scale hatch corner specimen.[6]

corner, and a diagonal corner bracket. This design was proved by laboratory test and by service record to be very satisfactory.

It is evident that brittle fracture can be discouraged by reducing high local stress concentrations. Two means are available for accomplishing this objective: (1) introduce flexibility at the discontinuity or (2) increase the stiffness by reinforcements so that deflections, and hence stresses, in the critical region are reduced.

The following quotation, taken from a Ship Structure Committee Report,[8] summarizes hatch corner design principles:

A. GENERAL PRINCIPLES

(1) Ease notches in all members and especially those carrying main longitudinal stresses.
(2) Avoid coincidences of notches.
(3) Avoid the intersection of welded joints as far as possible, especially at points of stress concentration.
(4) Minimize welding defects by proper design for welding.

B. SPECIFIC SUGGESTIONS

Selection of specific suggestions listed below must depend upon the ship design. Effective hatch corner reinforcement need not incorporate all of the features listed below. The judgment of the designer must prevail.

(1) At the corner provide a heavier deck plate with a generous radius. (For main hatches in typical cargo ships such as the Liberty a radius = 1/20 of the transverse dimension of the opening was satisfactory.)
(2) Taper hatch side coaming beyond hatch end.
(3) Ease longitudinal girder to hatch end beam connection at flange level as by radiused gusset.
(4) Specify full penetration welds for joining deck to coaming in way of the hatch corner and for such joints as are subject to direct loading, in order to avoid cavities or piping in such welds, especially those perpendicular to the principal tensile stresses.

Other tests on ship components have also been undertaken.[9,10] Static experiments on ships in still water have been made with the primary objective of checking the accuracy of the simple beam theory for the calculation of stress in ships of complex design. Measurements have been made of longitudinal ship deflection and transverse strains in the region of maximum bending moment and for known conditions of loading. From these data the effective section modulus and moment of inertia have been calculated. Measured values of section moduli did not agree with those calculated from the geometry, and it was necessary to assume a lower value of modulus of elasticity than that normally assigned to steel in order to reconcile the calculated with the measured values. The lower effective modulus of elasticity was presumed to be due to rivet slip and structural hysteresis. More recent evidence, however, indicates that the calculated values of section modulus were erroneous because some of the material included for the purpose of calculations was not carrying the amount of load assigned to it in the calculations. In spite of the discrepancy between measured and calculated deflections, the stress distribution found experimentally has been in fairly good agreement with that calculated from classical beam theory. This has been true for vessels with one or many full-width decks as well as for ships with corrugated, plane, or no longitudinal bulkheads. This agreement was also found to be independent of the type of framing and held for welded as well as for riveted ships.

Irwin and Campbell [10] tested a number of large specimens representing the intersection of a bottom longitudinal girder with a transverse bulkhead in a welded tanker. They tested three basic designs of a longitudinal girder connection. One of these was a through longitudinal, another was an interrupted longitudinal, and the third was a through-bracket type. The through longitudinal was of experimental design; the interrupted longitudinal was of the type used in the basic T-2 tanker design; the through-bracket type was characteristic of that used in a Navy oiler design.

Elastic stress distributions were determined at critical sections for each design. The maximum stress concentrations found on the sections adjacent to the transverse bulkhead were 1.2 for the through longitudinal, 2.8 for the interrupted longitudinal, and 1.9 for the through-bracket design. These stress concentrations correlated fairly well with the measured ability of the longitudinals to absorb energy when tested to failure.

All specimens were made of yard stock ship plate. Tests were made at various temperatures ranging from −20 to 38 F; all specimens failed by cleavage after various amounts of deformation. Generally the energy to fracture increased with test temperature. A comparison of maximum load, over-all elongation, and energy to fracture showed that qualitatively the designs could be rated as follows: (1) through longitudinal, (2) through-bracket longitudinal, (3) interrupted longitudinal.

CAUSES OF FAILURES

As has been pointed out, regions of high stress concentration introduced as part of the design can be a primary cause of trouble. Corrective measures, as the history of ship failures shows, can eliminate such difficulties and reduce to zero the incidence of failure due to such

Fig. 10.6 Photograph of T-2 tanker that broke in two in Boston Harbor December 1947.[7]

cause. Unfortunately, many of the failures have been caused by structural defects not anticipated by the design engineer. For example, the tanker *Ponagansett* broke in two in Boston Harbor in December 1947 [7] because a small clip was tack-welded to the deck. The fractured tanker is shown in Fig. 10.6, and the harmless looking clip responsible for the disaster is shown in Fig. 10.7.

The case just cited is unfortunately not exceptional. There are many other similar examples among the case histories available. The numerous failures of natural gas transmission lines during test provide an additional simple illustration. They were due to defective welds not detected during fabrication and to deep scratches in the pipe caused by bulldozer cleats, which dug into the pipe during field installation.

Fig. 10.7 Photograph of T-2 tanker showing fractured section of deck, looking forward. Clip for degaussing cables, the origin of the failure, designated by arrow.[7]

Similarly, large oil storage tanks in England were caused to fail by incompletely penetrated welds and by defective or poor welds. No matter how well a structure is designed on the drafting board, it cannot be safe unless the construction and inspection crews cooperate to the fullest extent in eliminating structural discontinuities, no matter how unimportant they may appear to be.

A manual for shipyard welders has been prepared by the U.S. Coast Guard.[11] It contains recommendations for welders and welding leadermen concerning the relation between workmanship and the service performance of welded vessels. The booklet contains photographs and descriptions of structural failures that illustrate the important role played by workmanship. The remainder of the figures in this chapter are taken from that booklet.

There is ample evidence to prove that poor workmanship has in many cases been responsible for fractures that have occurred in welded vessels. Weld defects have provided the notches responsible for initiating brittle fractures. A defective weld at which a crack encircling a T-2 tanker originated is shown in Figs. 10.8 and 10.9. The cost of repairs in this case was $426,626.

An interesting phenomenon is shown in Fig. 10.10. The formation of a herringbone pattern is a common characteristic of brittle fracture surfaces. It is very useful because the origin of the fracture can be determined merely by following the herringbone pattern, which points toward the origin of the fracture. Boyd [12] has presented an excellent analysis of the herringbone formation. The crack apparently starts at the midplane of the plate and advances stepwise in the forward direction, developing the herringbone pattern as it moves along. A close-up view of the fracture origin shown in the preceding figure is presented in Fig. 10.11, and a macrograph of a nearby section of the same weld is shown in Fig. 10.12. Repairs to this T-2 tanker cost $265,450.

Fig. 10.8 Defective weld at which a crack encircling a T-2 tanker originated.[11]

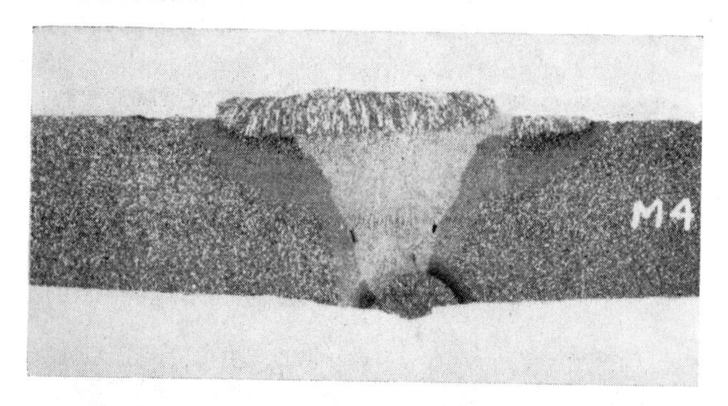

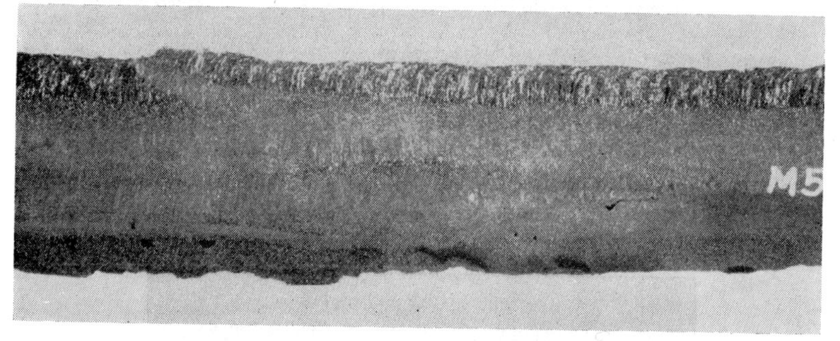

Fig. 10.9 Macrospecimen taken from weld shown in Fig. 10.8, approximately 15 in. from source of defective weld. Note porosity, slag inclusion, incomplete penetration in specimen M-4. In specimen M-5, note small longitudinal crack and considerable amounts of slag in overhead pass at bottom of joint.[11]

Examination of fractured structures, about which more will be said in Chapters XI and XII, has demonstrated conclusively the need for completely sound welds. It is the responsibility of the welder and of the welding supervisor to guard against defective welds. The welder can be shown the serious consequences of producing defective welds but, being subject to human failings, cannot be relied upon entirely to produce sound welds. Nearly all welders reach a stage when they believe that they know a lot more about welding than they actually do. Consequently, they often resent offers of help or advice and do not question their own ability to make sound welds regardless of the circumstances. Cooperation by the welders in pointing out to the supervisor poor setups likely to cause trouble is highly desirable. If this were done, the adverse conditions could be corrected and welding defects minimized. Some of the common defects are shown in Figs. 10.13 through 10.20. All of these were actual defects found on welded ships. They are, however, characteristic of weld defects found in all

Fig. 10.10 Characteristic herringbone pattern common to brittle fracture surfaces. Arrow points to origin of fracture in weld.[11]

Fig. 10.11 Close-up view of fracture origin shown in Fig. 10.10.[11]

Fig. 10.12 Macrograph of a nearby section of weld shown in Fig. 10.10.[11]

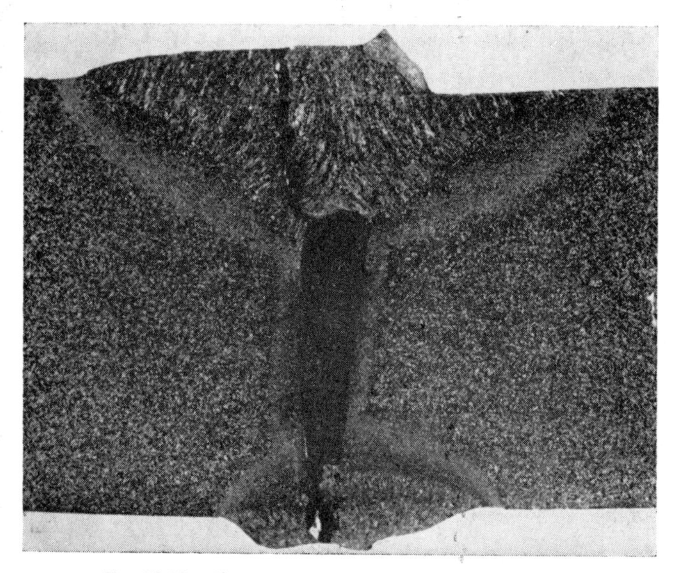

Fig. 10.13 Characteristic weld defect—saddle weld.[11]

Fig. 10.14 Characteristic weld defect—saddle weld.[11]

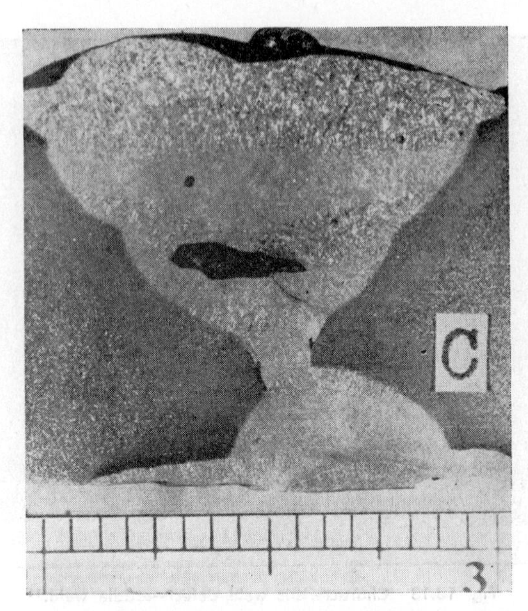

Fig. 10.15 Characteristic weld defect—cavities in weld.[11]

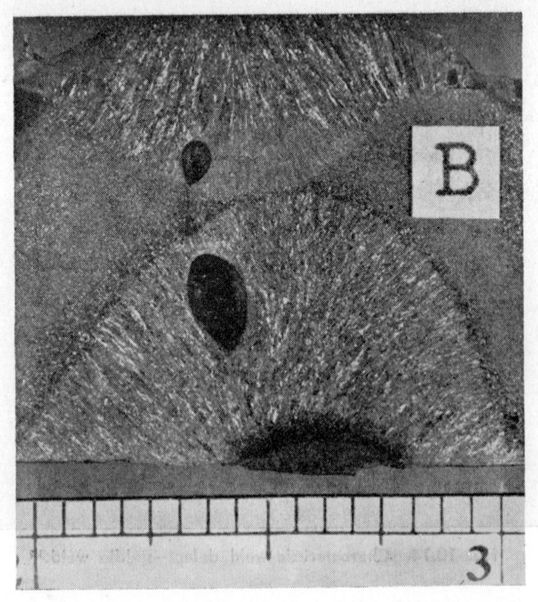

Fig. 10.16 Characteristic weld defect—slag and dirt in weld.[11]

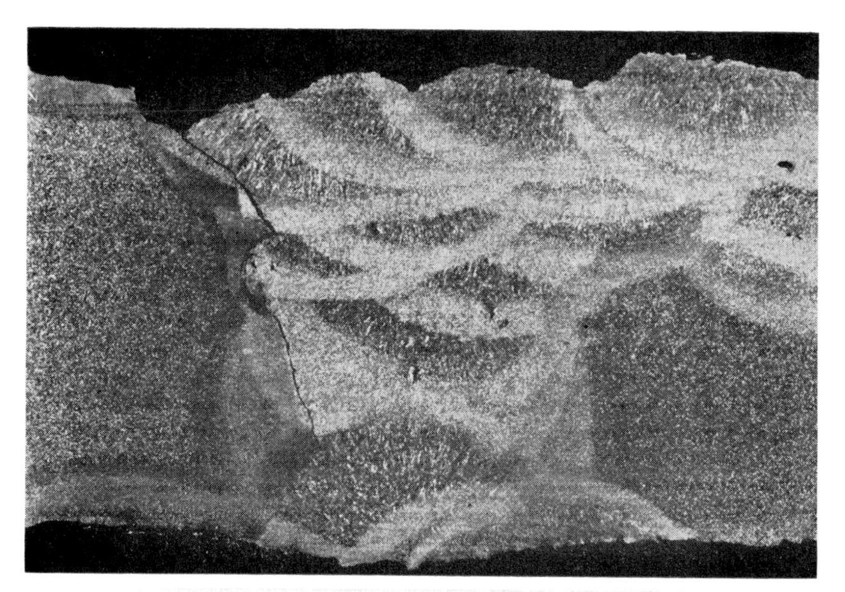

Fig. 10.17 Characteristic weld defect—shrinkage crack in weld.[11]

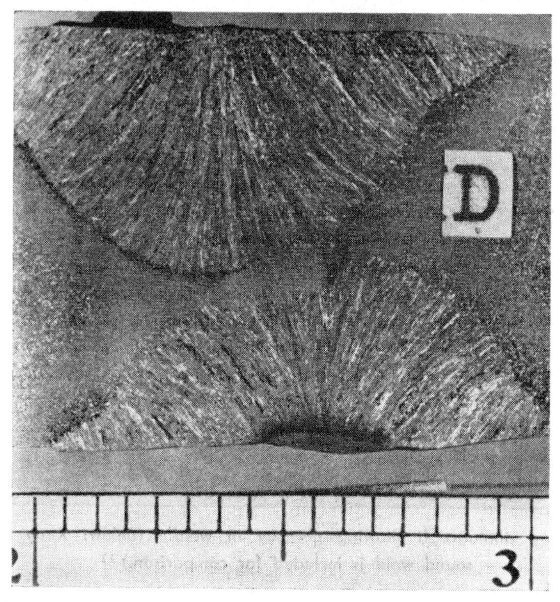

Fig. 10.18 Characteristic weld defect—other nicks and cracks in weld.[11]

Fig. 10.19 Characteristic weld defect—buried crack in weld.[11]

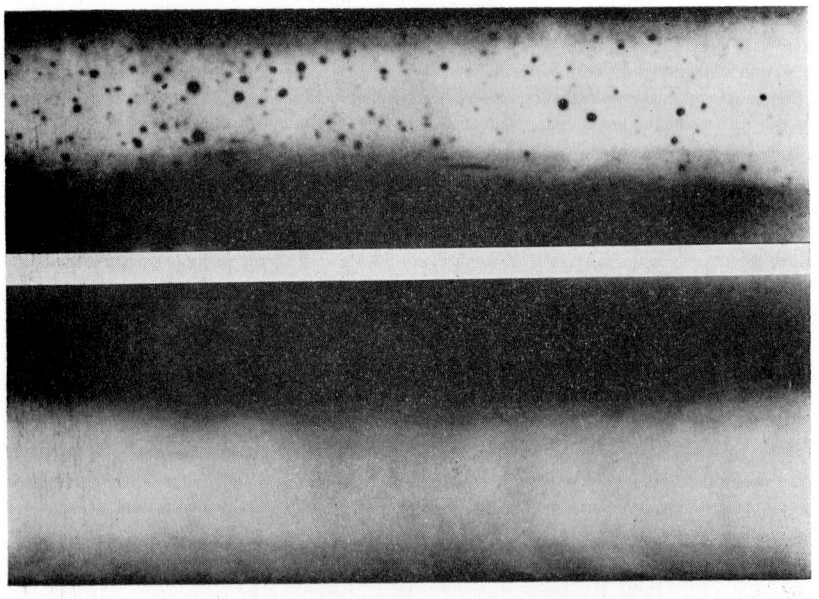

Fig. 10.20 X-ray photograph showing porosity in weld. (Below: X-ray photograph of sound weld is included for comparison.)[11]

kinds of welded structures. Table 10.1 lists the defects resulting from various kinds of faulty welding practice.[11] Two examples of fractures originating at defects immediately adjacent to welds are shown in Figs. 10.21 and 10.22.

TABLE 10.1 [11]

FAULTY WELDING PRACTICES AND THEIR RESULTS

Type of Practice	Saddle Welds	Cavities or Poor Penetration	Slag and Dirt	Shrinkage Cracks	Other Nicks and Cracks in Weld Metal	Buried Cracks and Cavities	Porosity	Nicks and Notches Not in Weld
1. Fit-up—improper fit-up resulting in too wide or too narrow a welding groove	X	X	X	X	X	..	X	..
2. Plate edge preparation—beveled edge too shallow, ragged edges, uneven weld groove, etc.	X	X	..	..	X	..	..	..
3. Electrode—use of wrong size or type	X	X	..	X	X	..	X	..
4. Electrode—too dry or too damp	..	..	X	..	..	..	X	..
5. Welding arc—too long or too short	..	..	X	..	..	..	X	..
6. Machine setting incorrect	X	X	X	X	X	..	X	..
7. Speed—excess	..	X	X	..	..	..	X	..
8. Sequence—failure to follow proper sequence	..	..	..	X	X	..	..	..
9. Preheating—failure to preheat when required	..	..	..	X	X	..	..	..
10. Chipping—improper chipping of weld groove at weld intersection	X	X	X	..	X	..	..	..
11. Chipping—improper chipping, use of diamond-pointed tool	X	X	X	..	X	..	..	..
12. Chipping—failure to back chip	X	X	X	..	X	..	..	..
13. Chipping—careless chipping; knocking off clips instead of chipping them off	..	..	..	..	..	..	..	X
14. Craters—failure to chip craters out, or fill them in at end of welds	..	..	..	X	..	..	..	..
15. Cleaning—failure to clean welding groove properly or to clean beads between passes	..	X	X	..	..	..	X	..
16. Peening first pass	..	..	..	..	X	..	..	..
17. Bobbing or caulking of weld defects to stop leaks—welding over cracked tacks	..	..	..	..	..	X	..	..
18. Use of slugs	..	X	..	..	..	..	..	..
19. Striking of arc—careless striking on plating	..	..	..	..	..	..	..	X

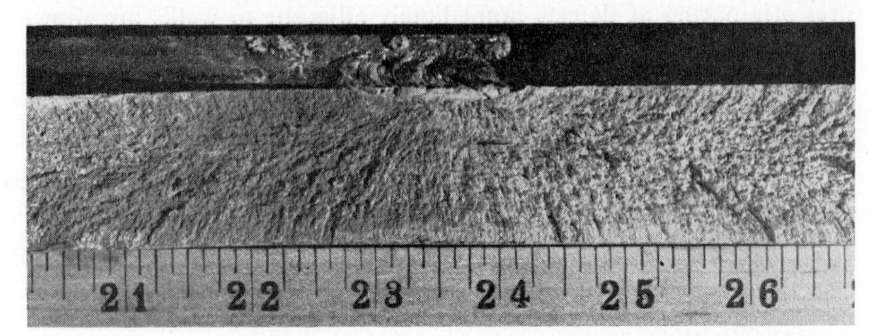

Fig. 10.21 Nicks and notches not in weld. Note clip attached to shell plating.[11]

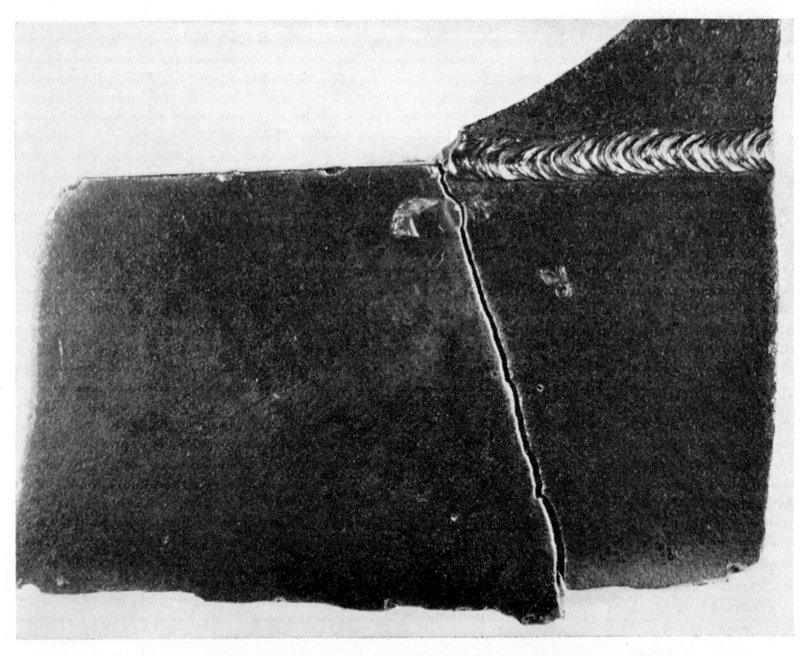

Fig. 10.22 Nicks and notches not in weld.[11]

NONDESTRUCTIVE TEST METHODS FOR INSPECTING WELDED JOINTS

The methods presently available for detecting defects in welds are: (1) radiography, (2) magnetic particles, (3) ultrasonics, and (4) fluid penetrants. Radiography is the most widely used, although the magnetic-particle method has found considerable use. The fluid-penetrant method is used occasionally; ultrasonic methods are currently under development and are already being used for some applications.

Radiography, though unsatisfactory for detecting microscopic cracks, is excellent for detecting slag inclusions, porosity, incomplete penetration, and macroscopic cracks. Radiographic methods can be relied upon to give a 2 per cent sensitivity (ratio of smallest thickness difference visible on radiograph to thickness of plate being X-rayed) for the types of defects listed above. Portability is an important factor in the radiographing of large welded structures. Gamma-ray sources are sometimes more desirable from this point of view, but the sensitivity obtainable from gamma rays is generally lower than that available from X rays. The difference is not great, however, and the selection of a radiation source is usually governed by other factors, such as accessibility, thickness of specimen, setup time, and availability of various sources.

The magnetic-particle method is best suited for revealing discontinuities such as cracks that terminate at the surface. This method is much less reliable for detecting subsurface defects, although fairly large defects, such as gas holes located within a tenth of an inch or so of the surface, may be revealed. Where it can be applied, the magnetic-particle method is a rapid and relatively inexpensive method of inspection.

Ultrasonic flaw detection offers more potentialities than any other known nondestructive test method. This inspection method is still in an early stage of development and does not yet have the required degree of simplicity and reliability.

The liquid-penetrant method is simple and reliable, although it will only reveal cracks that are open to the surface. The penetrants are safe to use and portable kits are commercially available.

REFERENCES

1. *Welding Handbook,* 3d ed. New York: American Welding Society, 1950.
2. *Procedure Handbook of Arc Welding Design and Practice.* Cleveland: Lincoln Electric Co., 1945.
3. *Manual of Design for Arc Welding Steel Structures.* New York: Air Reduction Co., 1947.

4. *Standard Welding Terms and Their Definition.* New York: American Welding Society, 1949.
5. J. L. Morris, *Welding Principles for Engineers.* New York: Prentice-Hall, 1951.
6. E. P. DeGarmo, "Tests of Various Designs of Welded Hatch Corners for Ships," *Welding J.*, Res. Suppl., pp. 50-s–68-s (February 1948).
7. F. Jonassen, "Brittle Fracture and Fatigue in Ships," *Fatigue and Fracture of Metals,* pp. 52–73. Massachusetts Institute of Technology: Technology Press, and New York: John Wiley & Sons, 1952.
8. "Considerations of Welded Hatch Corner Design," Ship Structure Committee Report, Serial No. SSC-37, October 1, 1952.
9. J. H. Evans, "Past Structural Studies Related to the Ship and Ship Components and for Determining Loads and Strains on Ships at Sea," Ship Structure Committee Report, Serial No. SSC-62, December 15, 1953.
10. L. K. Irwin and W. R. Campbell, "Tensile Tests of Large Specimens Representing Intersection of a Bottom Longitudinal with a Transverse Bulkhead in Welded Tankers," Ship Structure Committee Report, Serial No. SSC-68, January 18, 1954.
11. "Shipyard Welding Workmanship," *Publication NAVCG 137* (*Ship Construction Manual No. 1*). Prepared by the U.S. Coast Guard, Bureau of Ships, U.S. Navy, U.S. Maritime Commission, American Bureau of Shipping, June 1945.
12. G. M. Boyd, "The Propagation of Fractures in Mild-Steel Plates," *Engineering* (*London*), *175*:4538, 65–69 (January 16, 1953) and *175*:4539, 100–102 (January 23, 1953).

CHAPTER

Service Failures in Structures Other Than Ships

INTRODUCTION

Brittle fractures in large structures made of medium carbon structural steel are far from uncommon. Shank [1] has made an extensive survey of brittle fractures in structures other than ships. He analyzed 64 structural failures in both riveted and welded structures, including tanks, bridges, pressure vessels, power shovels, gas transmission lines, a smoke stack, and a penstock. These failures will be discussed first, and then the story of the fractured steel ships will be reviewed. The information presented in this chapter is based upon the excellent summary prepared by Shank.[1]

Brittle fractures of mild steel have been a plague to engineers ever since 1856, when steel first became available in quantities large enough for structural use.* For example, the *Journal of the British Iron and Steel Institute* in 1879 contained a paper by Nathaniel Barnaby entitled "The Use of Steel in Naval Construction." The author commented that "Recent cases have occurred of fracture in Bessemer bars . . . from some trifling blow or strain—they nearly all took place during the late severe weather at Chatham." In a discussion of this paper, Kirk reported cases of steel plates that "when cold, on being thrown down, split right up. Pieces cut from each side of the split stood all the Admiralty tests."

* The Bessemer steel making process was first introduced in 1856; the open-hearth process became available in 1861.

Shank found 39 failures of nonship structures reported in the literature; letters sent to various industrial people, technical organizations, and government agencies revealed another 19 failures. These figures did not include cases of transcontinental gas transmission pipelines, nor did they contain reports on fractures of unassembled structural components. Literally hundreds of brittle fractures have occurred in subassemblies (and even in completed structures) that have not been reported for various reasons.

FAILURES IN RIVETED STRUCTURES

Brittle behavior is not uniquely associated with welded construction. Serious failures are, however, more likely to occur in welded structures because there are no structural discontinuities, such as riveted joints, which can effectively interrupt the progress of a brittle crack. Nevertheless, many serious failures have occurred in riveted structures, as demonstrated by the following reports:

Water Standpipe, Gravesend, Long Island, New York, October 7, 1886.[2] This standpipe was 250 ft high and had a diameter of 16 ft up to a height of 59 ft; above this height the diameter decreased conically until at 84 ft it reached a value of 8 ft, which remained constant from there to the top. The structure was steadied by guy wires. Plates 5 ft by 7 ft and 5 ft by 9 ft were used; the thicknesses ranged from 1 in. at the bottom to ¼ in. at the top. The plates were joined with three rows of rivets. Failure occurred during the hydrostatic test required for acceptance. The water level had risen to 227 ft when a vertical crack about 20 ft long appeared at the bottom; the tower immediately collapsed. A report[2] of the account states that

> Some plates are bent almost double, and others are actually rolled up, showing a very tough metal. . . . The utter destruction of the lower parts of the tower and the appearance of the fallen tower, which broke in two just above the cone and presents an almost clean square cut just below this cone, can be likened to nothing better in effect than the sudden smashing of the lower part of a high glass cylinder and the vertical drop and then fall of the upper part. . . . In summing up on the general evidence, we should say that the plates were amply thick enough to stand the stress put upon them, even were they a good wrought iron; . . . we should say that the main cause of failure lay in the presence of defective steel plates in the lower part of the tower. These plates certainly varied very much in quality, and the wreck shows plates which could not possibly have stood any considerable test for tensile stress. Only a brittle material could have brought the utter destruction there exhibited and it would seem as if this brittle material had unfortunately been concentrated in the portion of the tower exposed to the greatest strain.

The effect of plate thickness, apparent even in this early failure, was not to be understood for over half a century.

Gasholder, Brooklyn, New York, December 23, 1898.[3] This tank, which failed during the hydrostatic acceptance test, was 178 ft in diameter and 42 ft high; 25 ft of the tank was underground. The plates involved ranged from 1¼ in. thick at the bottom to 7/16 in. at the top. The fracture followed a path through the body of the plates and not through the rivet holes. According to a witness [3]

> . . . the fracture in some cases taking a curved form similar to that seen in the fracture of a pane of glass. . . . An examination of these fractures shows metal of a rather coarse crystalline structure at the center of the surface, with here and there splintered edges much like a broken case-hardened material.

Water Standpipe, Sanford, Maine, November 17, 1904.[4] This tank was 40 ft in diameter and 80 ft high. The plate thickness ranged from ⅝ in. at the bottom to ⅜ in. at the top. The tank had been in service for about seven years and was nearly full of water when it broke. The fracture passed through the rivet holes; many small cracks radiated from these holes. The report stated that

> . . . enough clean fractures were found to indicate that the steel was hard and brittle, showing a crystalline structure. Apparently no rivets were sheared; many plates were torn through the rivet holes. . . . A number of rivet holes were found where there were one or more cracks radiating from the hole. . . . It seems probable that the rupture started in the crack radiating from a rivet hole; and that these radiating cracks may have been caused in the brittle steel . . . due to cutting out the rivet (holes). It is not evident, however, why failure did not take place immediately upon the initial application of full pressure.

This failure, as well as many of the subsequent ones, may have been influenced by thermal stresses. The tank was nearly full of water at the time it failed, and consequently the temperature inside the tank was above freezing. Although the ambient temperature was not reported, it may have been relatively low because the failure occurred at 3 A.M. in the middle of November in a part of the country that frequently experiences cold weather. Substantial temperature gradients may thus have existed in the structure.

Molasses Tank, Boston, Massachusetts, January 15, 1919.[5–10] One of the most spectacular brittle fractures that has ever occurred was that of the Boston molasses tank. As a result of this failure, 12 persons were drowned in molasses or died of injuries incurred at the time of the accident; 40 others were injured; many horses drowned; houses were damaged and a portion of the Boston Elevated Railway structure was destroyed.

The calculated stresses were reported [6,7] as being 26,400 psi in the thicker plates and 36,000 psi in the thinner ones. When allowances were made for the increase in stress at the riveted joint, the calculated stresses became 40,000 to 50,000 psi. This was about twice the stress permitted by the current building laws and was too close to the 55,000 psi measured tensile strength of the steel. During the extensive lawsuit that followed, many experts testified. Some of these insisted that the failure was due to a bomb explosion; others contended that the tank was underdesigned. One of the interesting sidelights of the case, however, was the report of some test results by G. G. Lutts of the Boston Navy Yard. He tested notched plates in the laboratory and produced brittle fractures having a herringbone appearance like those found on steel from the tank. Furthermore, he associated the direction of the chevrons with the direction of propagation of the fracture. Unbeknown to Lutts was the fact that de Fremenville [11] had established the significance of the herringbone pattern by laboratory tests reported in 1914.

Crude Oil Storage Tank, Ponca City, Oklahoma, December 19, 1925.[12] This tank, which was 117 ft in diameter and 41 ft 10 in. high, was made with plates ranging in thickness from 1 in. at the bottom to ¼ in. at the top. The shell was riveted and the bottom course of plates was welded to an angle iron base ring.

The tank was full of crude oil at the time of the failure. The fracture followed a sudden drop in temperature. During the day the temperature had been 60 F, but it suddenly dropped to −4 F during the night. Light, muffled, explosion-like sounds were heard, followed by the appearance of flames. After the fire was extinguished, the pieces of the steel tank were examined. It was found that the second course of plates had broken away from the first along an irregular line. No evidence was found that the failure was caused by either riveting or welding. The fracture was thought to be due to secondary stresses introduced by the sudden temperature drop.

Eight Riveted Crude Oil Tanks, South and Midwest United States, 1930–1940. According to Shank,[1] data concerning the failures were collected from industrial records. A brief history of each tank follows:

Tank No. 1, whose dimensions were not available, was believed to be a secondhand tank when it was put into service for oil storage in 1917. Its history is beclouded with five recorded failures, the first of which occurred in January of 1918. The temperature was below zero when a crack occurred in the lower course of plates. The tank was patched by welding and returned to service, where it performed well until November 1924, when another crack appeared in the lower course of plates just below the manhole. This crack was repaired, and again the tank performed well until January 1929, when a new crack formed in a lower plate. The temperature was −15 F at the time of this failure. In December of the same year the temperature dropped to −2 F and another crack appeared. The entire lower course of plates was replaced during the ensuing repair.

Another failure occurred in February 1933 on a day when the temperature had dropped to −10 F. The tank contained only 14 ft of oil at the time of the failure. Subsequent inspection revealed that the bottom sheets had been welded to the 3-in. by 3-in. by ⅝-in. angle at the base of the tank and that this angle contained 34 serious vertical cracks, 12 of which had been repaired by welding.

Tank No. 2 had a 55,000 barrel capacity and was erected in 1917. It failed February 7, 1933, when the ambient temperature was −4 F, with a vertical fracture passing entirely through a sheet in the bottom course of plates. The break passed between rivet holes at both top and bottom edges of the plate. Three years prior to the failure a new butt welded bottom angle had been welded to the tank wall and new bottom was welded to the angle iron. The vertical leg in the angle was also broken, and the crack extended through the weld. The origin of the fracture was uncertain, but it was thought that the butt weld in the angle iron was the first part to fail.

Tank No. 3 was erected in 1923; it was 171 ft in diameter and 42 ft high. The bottom course of plates was ⅝ in. thick; the plate thickness was less for the upper courses. Four rows of rivets were used to join the plates. This tank failed December 7, 1932, when the temperature had dropped to −18 F. It was filled with crude oil at the time of failure. The crack presumably originated at the bottom ring. It ran vertically through two courses of plate where it apparently stopped momentarily. The tank then bulged until a horizontal split formed. In this final stage of failure, the vertical crack was extended to the top of the tank.

Tank No. 4 was exactly like Tank No. 3 and had been erected at the same time. It failed February 8, 1933, when the air temperature was below −30 F. This tank was nearly full of oil at the time of failure. The fracture pattern was similar to that of the sister tank. Chemical analyses revealed that the steel in Tank No. 3 had 0.29% carbon and 0.42% manganese, whereas that in Tank No. 4 had 0.17% carbon and 0.51% manganese. Charpy tests were made on steel samples from each tank. The values for the steel from Tank No. 3 ranged from 3 to 11 ft-lb at 25 F, 5 ft-lb at 0°F, and only 1 to 2 ft-lb below −25 F. Similar results were obtained with steel from Tank No. 4 except that the Charpy energy at 25 F was 21 ft-lb. The superior notch toughness of steel in Tank No. 4 could account for its survival during the −18 F weather that cracked Tank No. 3.

Tank No. 5 was 120 ft in diameter and 40 ft high. It had been in service for about 14 years before it failed. On January 9, 1937, although the tank was only half full, a crack was detected in one of the bottom plates. The crack had apparently formed during the preceding night, when the temperature had been below −11 F. This crack apparently did not originate in a weld, even though the tank contained some welded patches.

Tank No. 6 had the same dimensions as Tank No. 5, but it failed about a year later. The oil level was 36 ft. The crack extended through the bottom sheet and into a plate in the second course. The crack passed through a rivet hole but did not intersect a nearby welded patch.

Tank No. 7 was 117 ft in diameter and had a height of 42 ft. During 1933 a crack was detected in the bottom angle iron. One year later cracks were found in three of the lower plates and in the angle adjacent to two of the three plates. These cracks were repaired, but in January of 1935 a failure occurred in one of the previously repaired plates. However, this crack did not start in the repair weld but in a section of the plate 6 ft away. At the time of the failure, the oil level was 32 ft.

Tank No. 8 was also 120 ft in diameter and 40 ft high. Complete failure occurred during the night of February 25, 1934, when the temperature dropped to −20 F. The oil level was 37 ft at the time of failure.

It is of interest to note that all tanks were primarily of riveted construction, and in all cases the rivet holes had been punched or subpunched and reamed. All failures occurred at temperatures of 0°F or lower.

Oil Storage Tank, Middle West United States, December 14, 1943.[1] This tank was 114 ft in diameter and 30 ft high. The bottom plates were ½ in. thick and were joined to the second course by a single row of rivets. The vertical seams were joined with four rows of rivets. The fifth and top course of plates was ¼ in. thick. A triangular hole about 55 in. on a side had been cut in one of the bottom course plates to permit access for workers who repaired a leak in the tank bottom. The patch had been arc welded back in place, with the welding being done from the outside only. The repair work was done seven months before the tank failed. It was full of oil at the time. The temperature had dropped to 12 F above zero when a crack formed that appeared to start in the horizontal portion of the repair weld; it crossed the entire width of the plate.

FAILURES IN WELDED STRUCTURES

Vierendeel Truss Bridge, Albert Canal, Hasselt, Belgium, March 14, 1938. This bridge [13,14,15] had a span of 245 ft and was made of welded plate. The upper and lower chords were each made of two I-beams, with flange plates welded across the top and bottom, forming a box girder. These chords had a depth of 40 in. or more, and the plate thicknesses ranged from ¾ to 2³⁄₁₆ in. The vertical members were welded I-beams and were constructed of lighter material than the chords. The gussets joining the chords and the vertical members were steel castings having a tensile strength of about 58,000 psi.

The bridge was lightly loaded when it failed during a cold spell about a year after construction. The bottom chord parted with a loud bang, between the third and fourth verticals (about one fourth of the length from the center). The top chord supported the weight of the bridge for only six minutes before the bridge finally broke into three pieces and fell into the canal. All fractures were cleavage; some passed through welds, others through plates only.

Vierendeel Truss Bridge, Albert Canal, Herenthals-Oolen, Belgium, January 19, 1940. [15,16,17] The span of this bridge was 200 ft; it had single welded I-beam chords. Plate thickness dimensions were not available. When the failure occurred (about three years after the bridge had been put into service), three loud reports were heard. The bridge did not collapse, and five hours later a locomotive passed over it without causing failure. The temperature at the time was about 7 F. A subsequent inspection revealed a number of cracks, all of which had originated at welded junctions.

Vierendeel Truss Bridge, Albert Canal, Kaulille, Belgium, January 25, 1940. [15,16,17,18] This bridge was erected about 1935. It has a span of 160 ft and was constructed of I-beam chords. The temperature was 7 F when the failure occurred. The bridge did not collapse, but six cracks were found in the lower chord.

The steel in these bridges had a normal chemical composition except that some of the plates and beams had apparently been made of Bessemer steel; the phosphorus and sulphur were higher than is normally found in open-hearth steels. Mechanical tests on steel from the bridges were apparently satisfactory, except perhaps for somewhat low Izod and Charpy values, especially on the thick plates. The 10 ft-lb keyhole Charpy transition temperatures ranged from −60 to −40 F for the thinner plates and were somewhat higher for the thicker plates. Bend tests were also made on pieces of plate on which had been placed longitudinal weld beads. These plates broke after being bent through only a small angle.

Duplessis Bridge, Three Rivers, Quebec, Canada, January 31, 1951.[19, 20] This deck construction type of bridge was 1380 ft long; it consisted of six 180-ft spans and two 150-ft spans. The girders were 32 ft apart and were made of continuous welded plate 12 ft deep at the piers and 8 ft deep at the midspan. The flange plates were 2½ in. thick. In February 1950, when the bridge was only 27 months old, two fractures were found in the girders. Both cracks originated in the top flange plates and extended part way across the girder. The cracks apparently started in the welds. Examinations revealed that the cracks, which were partly rusted, had advanced in two or more steps. Paint found in the cracks indicated that the initial fractures had existed before the girders had been erected. Repairs were made by riveting, and all tension joints were thereafter reinforced with riveted plates.

Almost a year had elapsed after the repairs when the west half of the west crossing suddenly collapsed and fell into the river, as shown in Fig. 11.1. At the time of the failure there was practically no traffic

Fig. 11.1 **Photograph of the collapsed portion of the Duplessis Bridge at Three Rivers, Quebec. Four spans of an eight-span continuous girder bridge rest in the ice of the shallow St. Maurice River.[19] *(Wide World Photo)***

on the bridge, but the temperature was −30 F. Lack of attention could not be blamed for the trouble. A continuous 10-day inspection had been made of all of the bridge components only two weeks before the disaster.

Investigations following the original detection of cracks had revealed that steel for the flange plates had been ordered on ASTM A-7 specifications. Thick structural plate to meet this specification is usually rolled from semikilled or fully killed steel, but in this case the plates had been made of rimming steel. Analyses of this steel revealed extensive segregation. The carbon ranged from 0.23 to 0.40%; the sulphur from 0.04 to 0.116%; the manganese from 0.30 to 0.33%. Test bars cut from various portions had yield strengths between 27,800 and 57,800 psi; the average tensile strength was 58,000 psi. V-notch Charpy tests showed energy values of only 3 to 6 ft-lb at 100 F. The welds were generally of satisfactory quality, but the higher carbon regions of the plate were definitely unsatisfactory for welding. It is likely that the welds contained some undetected cracks, which helped initiate the failure, since 17 other welded continuous girder deck bridges are still in operation in Quebec. The failure in this case is very likely due to the use of unsuitable steel.

Spherical Hydrogen Storage Tank, Schenectady, New York, February 1943.[21,22,23] This tank was 38.5 ft in diameter and was made of semikilled steel plate 0.66 in. thick. It had been welded in accordance with Paragraph U-69, ASME Code for Unfired Pressure Vessels. The working pressure was 50 psi, which produced a nominal stress of 11,000 psi. The tank had been proof-tested in 1942 with a pressure of 62.5 psi; no leaks were found. The manhole at the bottom of the tank, at which the fracture started, was made of ¾-in. plate that had been sheared and cold formed. No stress relieving was required, and none was performed. The manhole cover had been made in two pieces—the bolt flange of the neck and the collar and sphere plate. These two pieces had been welded together; a picture of the fractured manhole assembly is shown in Fig. 11.2.

The temperature had been below zero but had risen 27 F in seven hours and was 10 F above zero at the time of the failure. The sphere fractured with terrific violence, breaking into 20 pieces. The fracture, originating in an old weld crack in the manhole, generated 650 linear ft of fracture surface.

Subsequent investigations established that the failure was not due to an internal explosion. The difficulty was attributed to: (1) high stresses at the manhole neck due to the design of this portion of the sphere, (2) high residual stresses in the manhole welds (several old

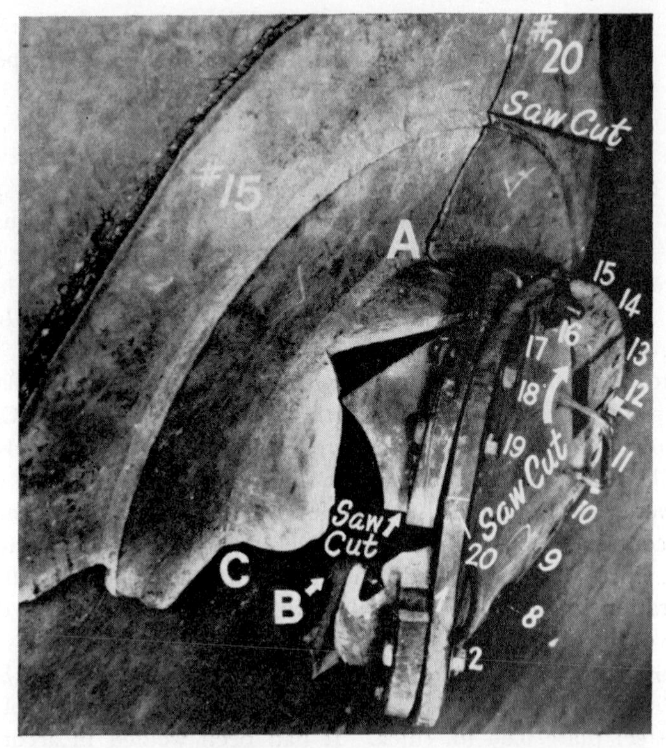

Fig. 11.2 Photograph of the reassembled manhole cover taken from the fractured spherical hydrogen storage tank at Schenectady, New York. An old weld in the manhole assembly was considered to be the source of fracture.[21]

weld cracks were found), (3) notch brittleness of the steel at the temperature of failure, and (4) thermal stresses due to the sudden rise in temperature.

The investigators recommended that in the future such gas storage tanks should be subjected to proof tests at twice the working load and that water instead of gas should be employed for such tests. Furthermore, they recommended that subassemblies, such as manholes, should be shop welded and given a furnace stress relief.

Spherical Ammonia Tank, Pennsylvania, March 1943.[23] This tank was designed to contain liquid ammonia at a pressure of 75 psi. The sphere was 40 ft in diameter and was made of ⅞-in thick steel plate; both semikilled and rimmed steel plates had been used. Seven columns were used to support the vessel.

The 1940 ASME Code for Unfired Pressure Vessels required that the tank be filled with water, the pressure increased to 115 psi, and welded seams then struck with an 8-lb sledge hammer. A brittle fracture running across the weld in the horizontal direction occurred when one of the vertical seams was struck with the hammer. Examination failed to reveal any serious defects in the remaining welds; they were considered to be of good commercial quality. The fracture had initiated in a portion of the weld where there was a slight overlap and some slight weld metal porosity, but the weld was otherwise sound. A previously built twin sphere was tested at 75 psi water pressure to check the adequacy of the design. Resistance wire strain gages were placed at various locations to measure the local load stresses. The design was considered to be satisfactory.

Spherical Pressure Vessel, Morgantown, West Virginia, January 1944.[1,23] This tank was one of a group of six spheres in an ordnance plant at Morgantown, West Virginia. They had been in service for some time and were used to store a liquefied gas at a pressure of 50 psi; the design stress was 11,000 psi. The recent failures of spherical storage tanks had indicated the desirability of checking the six tanks at Morgantown. Magnaflux examination of the manholes indicated the need for some repairs. Subsequently, the tanks were tested with water at a pressure of 100 psi. The second tank failed at 98 psi while being tested. The bottom dropped out and the remainder of the tank fell on top of it. The wrecked tank is shown in Fig. 11.3. There were 350 linear ft of cleavage fracture, only 4 ft of which went along a weld. The fracture apparently started in a supporting column just below the point where it was attached to the shell. Strain gage read-

Fig. 11.3 Photograph of a collapsed spherical pressure vessel designed to hold liquefied gas, Morgantown, West Virginia, that failed during hydrostatic testing.[1]

ings taken later on an identical sphere showed high local stresses at column attachments. The welding was generally of good commercial quality.

The temperature was 30 F at the time of failure; the water temperature was about 38 F. The keyhole Charpy impact energy for the steel was below 15 ft-lb at 32 F. The steel was ASTM A-7, firebox quality and contained 0.20% carbon and 0.47% manganese.

Recommendations were made that in the future all subassemblies should be furnace stress relieved and that thicker plates should be used at the column connections to reduce the bending stresses.

Cylindrical Gas Pressure Vessel, Cleveland, Ohio, October 1944.[1, 23, 24, 25] This was one of the most disastrous brittle fractures in history. It took the lives of 128 persons, and the damages amounted to almost $7,000,000. The tank was cylindrical-toroidal, a shape felt by the designer to be safer than the spherical tanks already in use for gas storage in the plant. A 3.5% nickel steel (0.09% carbon), fully killed and presumably normalized, was used for the shell. The seams were welded with Type 310 electrodes (25% nickel, 20% chromium). Charpy specimens machined from weld metal and heat-affected zones (removed from various locations in an earlier tank built to the same specifications) all had more than 15 ft-lb at −260 F.[24] The design stress in the tank that failed was 12,496 psi, and the operating temperature was −260 F, the temperature required to maintain natural gas in the liquid state at a pressure of 5 psi. The inner shell was 70 ft in diameter and 42 ft high; the outer shell was 76 ft in diameter and 51 ft high. The space between the shells was filled with rock wool.

The tank was given a hydrostatic test by filling it half full of water and then raising the pressure in the space above the water to 5 lb per sq in. The tank was filled with liquefied gas in June 1943, and a crack formed in the bottom. The cracked section was chipped out, and a patch was welded in. The patch plate was cooled with dry ice prior to welding to minimize residual stresses. After retesting, the tank was slowly cooled and filled with liquid natural gas. This tank remained in service without incident until October 20, 1944, when it failed as the plant was being shut down. A witness saw vapor coming from the tank at a point about halfway up the side. (The ambient temperature was 51 F.) Immediately after this observation there was an explosion, and a disastrous fire followed, which destroyed an adjacent spherical tank also filled with liquefied natural gas. The gas flowed over the surrounding area and into the sewer system, causing great damage to life and property.

A number of investigations were made. One report [23] indicated that the fracture started at the center of the roof and ran outward through the shell and back across the bottom. There was no evidence that the fracture had been initiated by an explosion. Another investigation [1] revealed that fractures had started at many places almost simultaneously and that the origin of the first crack could not be definitely established.

The plate from the failed tank was found to be in the as-rolled condition—it had not been normalized as required. Charpy tests on specimens machined from the tank plates showed less than 5 ft-lb energy absorption at −248 F. Similar tests on Charpy specimens made from steel cut from one of the spherical tanks that had not failed showed only 1 to 6 ft-lb energy absorption at −248 F. These results were at variance with the 15 ft-lb results quoted earlier.[24] The lack of adherence to the 15 ft-lb minimum at the service temperature was thought to be primarily responsible for the disastrous failure.

Five Oil Storage Tanks in Russia, December 1947.[26] No construction details were available for these five tanks except that they were of 160,000 cu ft capacity and that they were built somewhere in Russia. The steel presumably contained about 0.18% carbon, 0.45% manganese, a trace of silicon, and less than 0.05% phosphorus and sulphur. The electrodes were of a primitive nature, being bare wire with a thin chalk coating.

The tanks had been in service since 1941–1943, and there had been no previous trouble. Much of the welding had been done in the winter, when the temperature was considerably below freezing. At the time of the failure, the weather had been mild and there was no snow on the ground. The contents of the tank were relatively warm when a sudden cold spell dropped the ambient temperature to −47 F. Innumerable cracks formed on the windward side, where the cold wind dropped the temperature suddenly. No tanks burst but all developed leaks. In one tank cracks started in the weld that joined the angle iron base to the lower plates. In another the crack started at a crater. All cracks apparently started in welds.

Crude Oil Storage Tank, Midwest Area, United States, February 1947.[1] This tank had been built in 1944, but its height had been increased from 40 ft to 48 ft 4¾ in.; the diameter was 120 ft. There was a steel shortage at the time this tank was constructed, and so it was built of steel plates 0.66 in. thick that had been reclaimed from dismantled riveted tanks. The tank had a square cornered cleanout door in the first course of plates. The shell plates had 0.11% carbon, 0.44% manganese, 0.002% silicon; it was apparently made to ASTM Specification A-70 or A-10. The reinforcing plate over the cleanout opening had 0.28% carbon, 0.49% manganese, and 0.002% silicon; this plate was presumably ASTM grade A-7.

The tank was being filled with oil at the time of failure. The oil height had risen to about 45 ft. The oil temperature was 43 F, and the air temperature was about 0°F. The calculated nominal stress was 19,000 psi. Failure originated at the square upper corner of the cleanout door. It spread upward at 45° until it reached the horizontal weld joining the cover plate to the shell plate; then it extended vertically for the full height of the tank.

Keyhole Charpy tests were made on samples removed from the shell plate and cover plate. The shell plate absorbed only 5 to 8 ft-lb at 0°F, and the reinforcing cover plate only 3.5 ft-lb.

Two Oil Storage Tanks, Fawley, England, February and March 1952.[27] One of these tanks was 140 ft in diameter and 54 ft high. The plate thickness ranged from 1 1/32 in. to 1/4 in. This tank failed during the hydrostatic acceptance test when the water level had reached 48 ft. The water temperature was 40 F, and the air temperature was 30 F. There had been a previous failure in this tank during an earlier hydrostatic test. A 24-in. long crack, originating at a repair weld made where material had been removed for a test coupon, had formed when the water height had reached 35 ft. The tank was drained and repaired. The final failure, which occurred about two weeks later, did not pass through the repaired area.

The final failure also originated in a patch weld where another test plug had been removed. This crack, which extended for the full height of the tank, was about 180° from the first one and started at the first horizontal junction. The weld plug had been cut from the outside with a cylindrical saw. The cut barely went through the shell plate. The opening was filled with weld metal which did not penetrate through the plate. A void was left unwelded which was about 2 in. long and extended about one fourth of the way through the plate.

The second tank was 150 ft in diameter and 48 ft high. The plates ranged in thickness from a maximum of 1 1/32 in. to 1/4 in. This tank also failed during the hydrostatic test. The water level had reached about 39 ft. The water temperature was 40 F, and the air temperature was 47 F. The fatal crack started at an imperfectly repaired crack near the top of the first course of plates. The original crack had been about 12 in. long and had extended about 2 in. into the second course plate. This crack had been improperly repaired; it had not been completely chipped out before welding, and only a cover bead had been placed over the 2-in. portion in the second course plate. When parts of the failed tank were examined, the old oxidized crack was discovered.

Plates in these tanks had a carbon range from 0.16 to 0.24%; the manganese ranged from 0.54 to 0.62. The tensile properties were normal. V-notch Charpy tests showed that plates in the first and second courses had energy values of 10 to 15 ft-lb at the temperature of failure.

Following the procedure as required for the sectioning method (specified by the API Code, Section 120) was actually responsible for one of the failures and did not reveal the defect causing the other failure. Radiographs provide a better means for checking the soundness of weld joints and have been used at Fawley since the tank failures.

The steel used had a 10 ft-lb V-notch Charpy transition temperature around 40 F; a better steel such as ABS (American Bureau of Shipping) Class C steel or material meeting Lloyd's Register of Shipping Specification P-403 would have provided greater security.

Failures of Three Empty Oil Storage Tanks in Europe During 1952.[28] These tanks were 144 ft in diameter and 45 ft high. The plates ranged from 7/8 in. for the lower course to 1/4 in. at the top. The tensile strength of the steel was about 60,000 psi, and the elongation was 20 per cent in 8 in.

The welds had been chipped flush on the inside of the tank, and extensive heavy hammering had been done to correct distortion. The tanks had been completed for about three weeks and were still empty when the temperature fell to 25 F. The next morning a large number of cracks extending across the welds were discovered. These cracks extended for about 3 in. into the plates. V-notch Charpy tests on plate and weld metal showed that the 15 ft-lb transition temperature was about 32 F.

The brittle behavior of these tanks was shown to be due at least in part to the cold working and notches introduced by the chipping; residual and thermal stresses provided the energy necessary to crack the steel. Specimens cut from the tanks were bent at 32 F, with the chipped surface on the tension side of the specimen; fracture occurred without measurable deformation. Similar specimens were ground to remove the cold worked metal and to eliminate the notches introduced by the chipping. These specimens bent 45° at 32 F without cracking.

Penstock at the Anderson Ranch Dam, Boise, Idaho, January 1950.[29] This penstock was a 15-ft diameter pipe laid inside a 20-ft diameter concrete-lined tunnel. The plates were 1 5/16 to 1 9/16 in. thick. The steel was ASTM A-285 and had 0.22% carbon, 0.80% manganese. The specified yield point was 27,000 psi, and the tensile strength was 50,000 psi. The design stress was 13,500 psi. The sections were fabricated in the field under the general regulations of the 1943 API-ASME Code for Unfired Pressure Vessels; this code requires thermal stress relieving for welds in plates over 1¼ in. thick; but stress relieving by peening, while not the best procedure, is permitted by the code for field installations.

A crack 50 ft long formed during the hydrostatic pressure test. The test pressure was 225 psi, but the third section tested failed when the pressure had reached only 200 psi. The crack traversed three pipe sections and broke two stiffener rings. The crack started at the heavy repair weld shown in Fig. 11.4. The crack shown in Fig. 11.5 did not

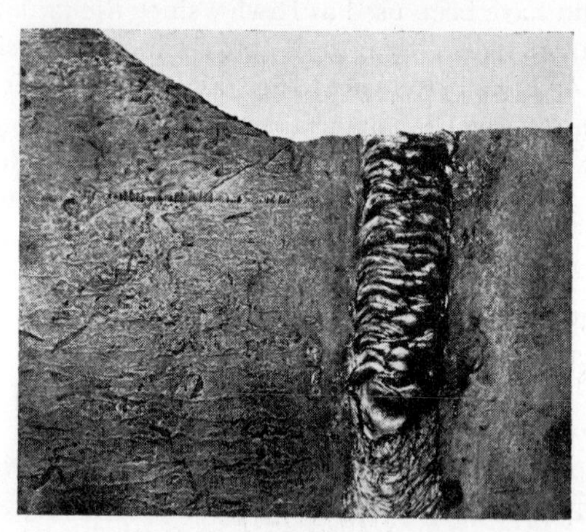

Fig. 11.4 Photograph of repair weld in Anderson Ranch Dam penstock, Boise, Idaho, believed to be the origin of failure during hydrostatic testing.[29]

follow the weld; it was substantially parallel to it but never closer than 5 in. The temperature at the time of failure was 41 F. The fractured plates were replaced; the penstock was low-temperature stress relieved, and then it was retested at 275 psi water pressure. No other cracks formed.

Transcontinental Natural Gas Transmission Pipelines, United States, 1948–1951.[30,31,32] Quite a large number of failures have been reported for transcontinental natural gas transmission lines.[30,32] These failures have almost invariably occurred during the testing period and were generally due to defective welding. Only a small number of serious failures were not associated with welding defects. For example, bulldozer cleats made gouges that extended in some cases about one third of the way through the pipe wall. These have been responsible for originating some brittle fractures. The cracks ranged in length from 180 to 3200 ft. Fig. 11.6 shows a picture of one of the long breaks. Since the initial installation cost was of the order

Fig. 11.5 Photograph of crack in 15-ft diameter penstock of Anderson Ranch Dam, Boise, Idaho. The 50-ft long crack developed during hydrostatic testing, traversed three pipe sections, and broke two stiffener rings.[29]

Fig. 11.6 Photograph of a natural gas transmission pipeline that failed during field testing. (*Courtesy C. T. Schweitzer*)

of $100,000 per mile, it is easy to visualize the seriousness of the repair problem.

A few of the facts concerning the pipeline problem are of interest. The upper limits allowed on check chemical analyses are 0.34% carbon, 1.30% manganese, 0.065% sulphur, and 0.055 to 0.110% phosphorus (depending on manufacturing method). Three strength levels are used, with the yields being 42,000, 46,000, and 52,000 psi. These minimum yields, however, are defined as the stress at 2 per cent strain in cold expanded pipe because the yield point phenomenon is absent in the cold worked material. The wall thicknesses are in the general range of $\frac{1}{4}$ to $\frac{3}{8}$ in. Large diameter pipes (e.g., 30-in.) are made by cold forming 40-ft lengths of rolled plate into tubes, and the seam is submerged arc welded. In one manufacturing process these pipes are rounded with hydraulic pressure in a die that is sufficiently larger in diameter to provide the necessary amount of cold work required for increasing the yield strength to the specified minimum value. This provides an initial proof test on each section; the assembled pipe is subsequently tested at a pressure somewhat above the operating pressure. Under the American Standards Association Code (Paragraph 807 C, 1) the pipelines may be operated at a stress equal to 72 per cent of the specified minimum yield strength in rural areas and about 50 per cent of the yield in populated areas. Thus the steel may be stressed as high as 37,200 psi, a value considerably above that generally permitted for similar steel in other structures.

SUMMARY

Brittle behavior of steel has been a plague to structural engineers ever since steel came into general use. The first recorded incident of brittle behavior was in 1879, only a short time after the Bessemer process for making steel was introduced. Riveted structures suffered from brittle fractures long before welding was ever used. In riveted structures brittle cracks radiating from punched rivet holes were responsible for several serious failures. The number of fractures in riveted structures, however, was not large. With the introduction of welding the brittle fracture problem assumed greater significance. Not only did the incidence of fractures seem to increase (presumably because of cracks present in imperfect welds and greater rigidity at plate junctions in welded structures), but the consequence of a crack forming became more ominous because a crack, once started, could progress without interruption completely across a structure.

The records of service failures indicate, though not quite conclusively, that residual stresses are not a primary cause of failure but may in some cases act in conjunction with other factors, such as load stress, thermal stresses, excessive cold work, and low temperatures, to promote brittle fracture of a structure.

Test data on steels removed from fractured plates are scarce. In the few cases reported, the V-notch Charpy impact energy was 10 ft-lb or less at the temperature of failure.

The brittle behavior of engineering structures is a phenomenon associated with static loading; other evidence, however, indicates that the probability of fracture is enhanced by impact loading.

Fractures originated at defects introduced during fabrication (except in a few cases, where overloading was involved), such as weld cracks, incomplete penetration, gouges in the plate, and punched rivet holes. Cracks did not follow welds or the heat-affected zone except when gross weld defects were present. Thus defective welds were responsible for originating many cracks, but the propagation of the cracks was associated with the notch brittleness of the plate material.

Some failures originated in regions where the design was such as to introduce stress concentration. These regions did not always contain defects.

REFERENCES

1. M. E. Shank, "A Critical Survey of Brittle Failure in Carbon Plate Steel Structures Other than Ships," Ship Structure Committee Report, Serial No. SSC-65, December 1, 1953. (Also reprinted as Welding Research Council Bull. No. 17.)
2. "The Water Tower Failure at Gravesend, Long Island," *Eng. News, 16,* 264 (October 23, 1886).
3. "The Failure of a Large Gas Holder in New York City," *Eng. News, 40*:25, 406 (December 22, 1898).
4. C. W. Sherman, "A Standpipe Failure at Sanford, Maine," *Eng. News, 52*:22, 507 (December 1, 1904).
5. "Disastrous Explosion of a Tank of Molasses," *Sci. American, 120* (February 1, 1919).
6. "Bursting of Molasses Tank in Boston Charged to Bad Design," *Eng. News-Record, 82*:7, 353 (February 13, 1919).
7. B. S. Brown, "Details of the Failure of a 90 Foot Molasses Tank," *Eng. News-Record, 82*:20, 974 (May 15, 1919).
8. "Boston Molasses Tank Trial: the Case for the Defense," *Eng. News-Record, 85*:9, 691 (October 7, 1920).
9. "Experts Deny Bomb Caused Collapse of Boston Molasses Tank," *Eng. News-Record, 87*:9, 372 (September 1, 1921).
10. "Bursting of Boston Molasses Tank Found Due to Overstress," *Eng. News-Record, 94*:5, 188 (January 29, 1925).
11. Ch. de Freminville, "Recherches sur la fragilité," *Rev. Met., Mem., 11,* 971 (1914).
12. "Oil Tank Fails After Sudden Drop in Temperature," *Eng. News-Record, 94*:16, 638 (April 16, 1925).

13. O. Bondy, "Brittle Steel a Feature of Belgian Bridge Failure," *Eng. News-Record, 121*:7, 204 (August 18, 1938).
14. "Welded Bridge Failure in Belgium," *Eng. News-Record, 120*:18, 654 (May 5, 1938).
15. "Causes of Welded Bridge Failures," *Ry. Gaz., 72*:24, 830 (June 14, 1940).
16. "Welded Bridge Failures in Belgium," *Ry. Gaz., 72*:24, 830 (June 14, 1940).
17. F. Campus, "Questions fondamentales en matiere de constructions soudees," *Schweiz. Arch., 14*:5, 29 (May 1948).
18. H. Louis, "Cas de rupture fragiles constatees dans la construction de ponts," *Rev. soudure (Brussels), 6*:2, 96 (1950).
19. F. S. Merritt, "Bridge Collapse in Quebec Charged to Brittle Steel," *Eng. News-Record, 146*:6, 23 (February 8, 1951).
20. D. B. Armstrong, "Canadian Welded Bridge Practice," *Highway Research Abstract, 21*:24 (June 6, 1951).
21. A. L. Brown and J. B. Smith, "Failure of Spherical Hydrogen Storage Tank," *Welding J.*, pp. 235–240 (March 1945).
22. A. L. Brown and J. B. Smith, "Failure of Spherical Hydrogen Storage Tank," *Mech. Eng., 66*:6, 392–397 (1944).
23. F. L. Plummer, "Field Erected Pressure Vessels," *Welding J.*, pp. 1081–1089 (November 1946).
24. M. A. Elliot, C. W. Seibel, F. A. Brown, R. T. Art, and L. B. Berger, "Report on the Investigation of the Fire at the Liquefaction, Storage and Regassification Plant of the East Ohio Gas Co., Cleveland, Ohio," U.S. Department of the Interior, Bureau of Mines, R. I. 3867, February 1946.
25. J. O. Jackson, "Liquefied Gas Storage Containers," *Gas Age*, p. 37 (April 22, 1943).
26. V. I. Shabalin, "Some Cases of Failure of Welded Tanks at Low Temperature," *Avtogennoe Delo, 19*:6, 29 (1948).
27. F. J. Feely, Jr., and M. S. Northup, "Failure of Two Oil Storage Tanks, Fawley, England," Standard Oil Development Co., Esso Engineering Dept., November 3, 1952. (Report for API Meeting, Chicago, November 11, 1952.)
28. W. Barr, "Failure of Welded Oil Storage Tanks," Colvilles, Ltd., Motherwell, Scotland, March 23, 1953.
29. P. J. Bier, "Anderson Ranch Dam Penstock Test Fracture Repaired by Welding," *Welding J.*, pp. 313–319 (April 1953).
30. *The Congressional Record,* United States of America, 82d Cong., First Sess., App. 97, Part 11, pp. A33, A437–8, January 3–March 15, 1951; Part 15, pp. A6658–9, September 18–October 20, 1951.
31. W. A. Saylor, *Iron Age, 167*:13, 97 (March 29, 1951).
32. "Natural Gas Pipe Line Failures and Causes as Reported to the Federal Power Commission," a report submitted to the Committee of Congress Investigating H. R. 88. *The Congressional Record,* Part 15, September 18–October 20, 1951.

CHAPTER

Welded Ship Failures

INTRODUCTION

Attention in recent years has been directed to the brittle fracture of welded ships; but it should be remembered that riveted ships also failed in a similar manner. According to Acker [1] more than a dozen riveted merchant ships have broken in two since 1900. Most of these were of the tanker type—a type that has also caused a great deal of trouble among welded vessels. Most of the riveted tankers failed when they were less than 10 years old. Also of interest is the fact that large cracks developed in riveted passenger liners such as the *Leviathan* and the *Majestic*. Cracks in these ships started at square openings in the upper decks and extended into the side shell. At least one crack was accompanied by a loud report. The *Europa* had deck cracks that started from square openings; additional cracks starting at airports were found in the sheer strake. In other riveted ships minor cracks have occurred around hatch corners, bulwarks, and other regions of stress concentration. It is not certain that all of the cracks were of the brittle type, but undoubtedly some of them were.

Welding in the shipbuilding industry in the United States was not entirely a World War II development. Brown [2] has pointed out that as early as 1917 the authorities in charge of producing large numbers of ships had appointed a committee to consider the feasibility of building welded ships. Subsequently a contract was given to one of the shipyards for the construction of a full-size experimental welded midsection subassembly, and the work was well along at the time of the signing of the 1918 armistice. Shortly before the armistice was signed, a contract was awarded for the construction of a complete all-welded ship, but contracts for this and the subassembly project were both canceled when the war ended. For a number of years thereafter the use of electric arc welding in shipbuilding was confined to repair work.

Apparently, the first all-welded seagoing merchant vessel was the *Fullagar,* a small vessel only 150 ft long, which was built in England in 1921. She operated in the coasting trade and later crossed the Atlantic and was placed in coasting service in British Columbia. She was sunk in 1937 by a collision.

During the 1920's in the United States several small vessels were constructed by welding. These were mainly small tankers operating in rivers and harbors; most of them were towed barges of simple design. With this small beginning the use of welding gradually grew until it included coastwise types of self-propelled tankers; these vessels were shaped like conventional ships. By 1940 practically all vessels under 300 ft in length were entirely welded. The experience thus gained increased the confidence in welding sufficiently that a large ocean-going tanker was constructed in 1937. This vessel was the *J. W. Van Dyke.* She was 521 ft long by 70 ft across the beam by 40 ft deep and had a dead-weight capacity of 18,105 tons and gross tonnage of 11,650. This was the first vessel using plate thicknesses approaching those currently employed; many of the structural details were similar to those now in use. Also worthy of note is the fact that this was the first ship on which automatic welding was used extensively. The ends beyond the cargo tank spaces were generally of riveted construction in the *Van Dyke,* but in similar vessels constructed later, even this riveting was replaced by welding. Thus the *Van Dyke* can be considered the prototype of modern all-welded tankers.

The Maritime Commission was established in 1937 with the authority to inaugurate a long-range merchant shipbuilding program. Fifty ships per year for a 10-year period were to be constructed. Contracts were assigned to the existing yards with the local option to use riveted or welded construction. The different yards elected to use welding in different amounts, so that construction practice ranged from all-welding to all-riveting. When World War II broke out in Europe the Maritime Commission was granted authority to accelerate the construction program. In order to accomplish the task of making a large number of cargo ships, some of the yards then using a large amount of riveting replanned their designs so that subsequent ships could be made by the subassembly system of construction, which involved extensive use of welding. By the time that the shipbuilding industry became geared to produce the number of ships needed for the wartime emergency, welding had been almost universally adopted.

The rapid expansion of all-welded ship construction was undertaken without adequate experience, and so it was to be expected that certain difficulties would arise that might have been avoided during a period of more gradual growth. The large program had some important advantages, however, because the construction of many ships of identical design made it possible to analyze the various structural difficulties on a statistical basis. Over 2500 Liberty ships, nearly 500 T-2 tankers, and more than 400 Victory ships were constructed. Inherent faults caused trouble in a sufficiently large number of cases to make evident the need for corrective measures on the remainder of like ships.

The expanded program was so great in magnitude that insufficiently trained labor had to be used. The management and supervisory personnel were recruited from existing shipyards, but the demand far exceeded the number of well trained men. Under these circumstances the factor of workmanship might be expected to play an important role in many of the failures of the ships constructed during this period.

EARLY CASUALTIES

The first Liberty ships were placed in service near the end of 1941, and by January of 1943 the number in service had reached 500. By this time 10 fractures in hull structures that were serious enough to endanger the vessel had been reported. Most of these fractures had occurred during the winter of 1942–1943. These failures were under study by the American Bureau of Shipping staff at the time of the spectacular failure of a T-2 tanker on the West Coast. On January 16, 1943, while lying quietly at her outfitting dock, she suddenly broke in two. The extent of the fracture in this vessel, occurring spontaneously with no apparent cause, was without precedent in shipbuilding history. The fracture extended across the deck just aft of the bridge and about midship; the break extended down both sides and around the bilges but did not cross the bottom shell plating. The fracture traversed all girders and plating, except the flat portion of the bottom shell plating, thus almost completely severing the ship (see photograph in Fig. 1.1, Chapter I). In the earlier failures cracking had been associated with specific design details and inferior workmanship. In this case, however, the cause was not so readily apparent; the implications were that there was something more fundamental that resulted in the brittle behavior of large monolithic structures assembled by welding. The calculated stress in the crown of the deck was only

9900 psi at the time of the failure. The American Bureau of Shipping appointed a committee of experts to investigate the failure. As a result of the investigation, it was concluded that no external factors, such as grounding or earthquake shock, were involved and that the principal cause of the failure was "an accumulation of an abnormal amount of internal stress locked into the structure by the process used in construction together with an acute concentration of stress caused by defective welding at the starboard gunwale in a way of the abrupt ending of the bridge fashion plate, augmented by the hogging stress due to the ballasted condition."[2] The validity of this conclusion has since been questioned. There is still considerable disagreement about the role played by residual stresses in the brittle behavior of large welded structures. Lack of experienced welders and supervisors and excessive forcing of poorly fitting subassemblies were considered to be contributory factors. The Committee also brought out for consideration the question of appropriateness of the steel specifications: Should not the specifications for steel going into welded ships be different from those used for steel that is to be riveted?

During the remainder of the 1942–1943 winter, several more serious failures occurred. A large bulk freighter under construction on the Great Lakes suddenly fractured across the deck and part way down the sides. A Liberty ship being loaded at a pier suddenly fractured; the crack extended part way down one side. In March 1943 another T-2 tanker split in two at the entrance to New York Harbor; the sea was calm, and the calculated (still water) stress in the crown of the deck was only 12,200 psi. For the next several years there were frequent reports of fractures in welded ships.

INVESTIGATIONS OF CASUALTIES

It was apparent that a deeper insight into the brittle behavior problem was needed. The U.S. Coast Guard requested the Secretary of the Navy to establish a committee with authority to conduct an investigation into the design and methods of construction of welded steel merchant vessels. In April 1943 the Secretary of the Navy appointed a Board that comprised representatives from the U.S. Coast Guard, the U.S. Navy, the American Bureau of Shipping, and the U.S. Maritime Commission (at that time the owners of all seagoing merchant vessels being built in the United States). This Board was set up to supervise an extensive program of investigation relating to all phases of the ship-failure problem. Ship designs were reviewed, loading and ballasting conditions were checked, sea and weather conditions examined, and statistical analyses of all casualties were made. In addition, a number of research projects were initiated. The Board made its final report to the Secretary of the Navy in July 1946.[3] This report contained facts and conclusions concerning the findings of the Board.

A sub-Board was appointed to act as a working group under the Board. Their job was to assemble and analyze the data relevant to casualties. They established definitions for the classification of failures, which have been generally adopted for use in the United States. These definitions are quoted below: [3]

> *Structural failure.*—A structural failure may consist of either a fracture or a buckle. (Buckles were involved in very few of the casualties and in no case were they responsible for endangering the vessel. They have not been analyzed in this report.)
>
> *Casualty.*—A casualty consists of one or more structural failures which have occurred on the same occasion, on a vessel which is afloat. Unless otherwise stated, the casualty occurred under normal operating conditions.
>
> *Class 1 fractures.*—A Class 1 fracture is a fracture which has weakened the main hull structure so that the vessel is lost or is in a dangerous condition.
>
> *Class 2 fractures.*—A Class 2 fracture is a fracture which does not endanger the ship but which involves the main hull structure at a location which experience has indicated is a potential source of a dangerous failure. Such locations include the strength deck, inner bottom, side and bottom shell and attachments thereto such as bilge keels and bulwarks.
>
> * *Class 3 fractures.*—Class 3 fractures include reported fractures which do not fall in Class 1 or 2.
>
> * *Class 1 casualty.*—A Class 1 casualty is a casualty involving at least one Class 1 fracture.
>
> * *Class 2 casualty.*—A Class 2 casualty is a casualty involving at least one Class 2 fracture and no Class 1 fractures.
>
> * *Class 3 casualty.*—A Class 3 casualty is a casualty involving Class 3 fractures only.
>
> *Ship month.*—A ship month is a measuring unit for ship service experienced. It is equal to the service of 1 ship for 1 month.
>
> Examples:—Ten ship months = 1 ship operating for 10 months
> or—Ten ship months = 2 ships operating for 5 months
> or—Ten ship months = 10 ships operating for 1 month.

When the war ended, the Coast Guard, which had been operating under the Department of the Navy during the war, again became part of the Treasury Department. The Secretary of the Treasury, in order to provide continuity of the research work related to ship structures,

* To avoid confusion, particularly with the classes of ship steel now produced to ABS specifications, the word "Group" is now used in place of "Class" when describing casualties.

appointed as a successor to the Board the present Ship Structure Committee. This group was established July 25, 1946, "for the purpose of prosecuting a research program to improve the hull structures of ships by an extension of knowledge pertaining to design, materials, and methods of fabrication." The duties of the Committee include the following functions:

1. Initiate, arrange for financing, and coordinate research and development pertaining to ship structures.
2. Integrate and interpret results.
3. Disseminate pertinent information to all parties having an interest in the building and operating of ships and to research investigators.

The Committee is a technical and advisory group and has no responsibility for introducing into design or construction any of the findings. Application of the knowledge acquired through research is the responsibility of the individual ship owners, the shipbuilders, the U.S. Coast Guard, and the American Bureau of Shipping.

The Ship Structure Committee established a research program consisting in part of a continuation of projects initiated by the Board. The results of the research are described in the Technical Progress Reports of the Committee,[4,5,6] and the research program has been discussed by Wright, Jonassen, and Acker.[7]

MATERIAL

Not unreasonably, a great deal of attention has been devoted to the steel from which the hulls of welded vessels are constructed; ship steel specifications are still a subject of considerable debate. Better performance of hull plate could be obtained by adding to the existing specifications some type of notched bar requirement or by changing chemical, deoxidation, and heat-treating requirements to obtain a steel with a generally lower transition temperature. However, economic considerations impose limitations upon either of these solutions to the notch-toughness problem. The 1955 ABS specification for Structural Steel for Hulls (*ABS Rules*) is as follows:

Chemical Composition—Ladle Analysis

(*a*) Except as specified in Paragraph (*b*) the material shall conform to the requirements of Class A as to chemical composition.

(*b*) Plates over ½ in. and up to 1 in., inclusive, in thickness shall conform to the requirements of Class B as to chemical composition. Plates over 1 in. in thickness shall conform to the requirements of Class C as to chemical composition.

	Class A	Class B	Class C *
Carbon, maximum, %	....	0.23	0.25
Manganese, %	....	0.60–0.90	0.60–0.90
Phosphorus, maximum, % †	0.04	0.04	0.04
Sulfur, maximum, %	0.05	0.05	0.05
Silicon, %	....	....	0.15–0.30

* Plate steels produced to the requirements of Class C shall be made with fine-grain practice.

† Where steel is made by the acid process the maximum per cent phosphorus permitted may be 0.06.

Tensile Properties

(*a*) The material, except as specified in Paragraph (*b*), shall conform to the following requirements as to tensile properties:

	Structural Steel	Rivet Steel and Steel for Cold Flanging
Tensile strength, psi	58,000–71,000	55,000–65,000
Yield point, minimum, psi	32,000	30,000
Elongation in 8 in., minimum, %	21	23
Elongation in 2 in., minimum, %	22	....

(*b*) Flat-rolled steel 3⁄16 in. and under in thickness, shapes less than 1 sq in. in cross section, and bars, other than flats, less than ½ in. in thickness or diameter, need not be subjected to tension tests.

(*c*) For material over ¾ in. in thickness or diameter, a deduction from the percentage of elongation in 8 in. specified in Paragraph (*a*) of 0.25% shall be made for each increase of 1⁄32 in. of the specified thickness or diameter above ¾ in. to a minimum of 18%.

(*d*) For material under 5⁄16 in. in thickness or diameter, a deduction from the percentage of elongation in 8 in. specified in Paragraph (*a*) of 2.00% shall be made for each decrease of 1⁄32 in. of the specified thickness or diameter below 5⁄16 in.

The current hull specifications of Lloyd's Register of Shipping and of the United States Navy are generally similar to those of ABS, the only variations being those of degree. All three specifications incorporate important changes from those in force during World War II; these changes were in general prompted by the early ship failure studies. For example, current specifications recognize the effect of increasing plate thickness on increasing transition temperature and consequently require one or more of the following (any of which promotes lower transition temperature) as plate thickness increases: higher manganese content and lower carbon content, silicon-aluminum killing with fine grain practice, or normalizing. Standard low alloy and proprietary structural steels are frequently used for the thicker plates.

A comparison of Charpy transition temperatures of wartime and present ABS steel [6] is presented in Fig. 12.1. Particular note should be taken of the fact that the thickness of plate used for test specimens did not in all cases comply with the specification limits. As this figure clearly shows, there has been an improvement in the notch toughness of steels used for hull plate. The improved performance of ships built of steel meeting current specifications is anticipated not only from the test results shown in Fig. 12.1 but also from the improvements in design and workmanship incorporated in these vessels. In

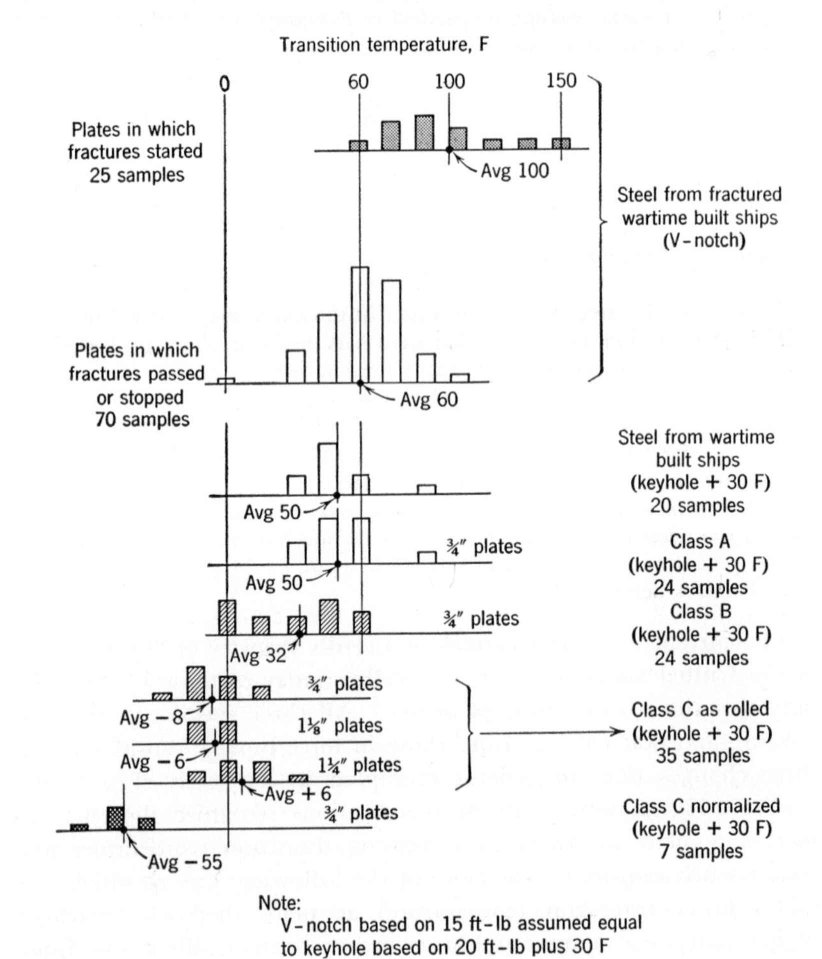

Fig. 12.1 Comparison of Charpy transition temperatures of wartime and present ABS steels.[6]

any event, the ship-fracture problem, although by no means completely solved, no longer appears to be highly critical as long as current practices are followed.

ANALYSIS OF WELDED SHIP FAILURES

Welded ships over 350 ft long have suffered about 250 Group I casualties and about 1200 of the Group II type. Smaller ships have had little trouble. Nineteen of the welded ships broke completely in two or were abandoned after severe cracking. Of these, nine were T-2 tankers and seven were Liberty ships.

A summary of the record of structural performance for various kinds of ships is given in Table 12.1.[6] The performance records for various ships are presented in Figs. 12.2–12.6.[6]

Caution must be exercised in reviewing these data. Fig. 12.2 lists the numbers of casualties each season in the *modified* and *improved* versions of the Liberty ship and T-2 tanker. Therefore, the great number of failures in the original designs of these ships during 1942, 1943, and part of 1944 is not reflected on the chart. An outstanding feature of this summary is the great number of failures that occurred during the severe winter of 1951–1952. Figs. 12.3–12.6 give the *cumulative* record of casualties per 100 ship years of operation; the terminal points of these graphs then average all failures to that date over the total operating time to date, which are the data presented in Table 12.1. It is therefore impossible to obtain an accurate picture of *recent* operating history from these charts without considering the *total* operating history and properly weighting the calculations.

About four times as many welded as riveted (shells or decks) ships have been constructed during the past 15 years. Résumés of the ship fracture problem have been prepared by Jonassen [8] and by Acker.[1] Welded tankers have had much more trouble than welded cargo ships. Also, as shown by Fig. 12.7 taken from the report by Acker, the frequency and severity of fractures (for the same material and equivalent design and workmanship) increased with increasing amounts of welding.

The majority of fractures in Liberty ships started at square hatch corners and at square cutouts at the top of the sheer strake. The frequency of structural failures was greatly reduced by a few structural alterations that involved the rounding and strengthening of square hatch corners and the removal of square sheer strake cutouts. In addition, riveted crack arrester straps were added in the deck and at the gunwales.

TABLE 12.1 [6]

RECORD OF STRUCTURAL PERFORMANCE OF VARIOUS TYPES OF WELDED SHIPS

(From Start * to March 31, 1953)

Type	Ship Years of Service	Group I Casualties	Group I Casualties per 100 Ship Years	Groups I and II Casualties	Groups I and II Casualties per 100 Ship Years
EC-2 (Liberty ships)					
1. All-welded with original details	2100	88	4.18	408	19.45
2. All-welded with improved details	2600	14	0.54	94	3.62
3. All-welded, improved details and some riveting	7303	40	0.55	254	3.48
4. Riveted seams with original details	330	1	0.31	17	5.35
5. Riveted seams with improved details	1833	2	0.11	66	3.60
T-2					
1. All-welded	1483	28	1.89	97	6.53
2. All-welded with riveted straps	2064	25	1.21	119	5.76
VC-2 (Victory ships)	2695	4	0.15	20	0.74
C1-M	1144	2	0.17	2	0.17
C1-A					
1. Riveted seams	120	0	0.00	8	6.67
2. All-welded	203	1	0.49	10	4.93
C1-B					
1. Riveted seams	510	7	1.37	29	5.69
2. All-welded	75	0	0.00	7	9.33
C-2					
1. All-welded, Waterman type	67	2	2.99	6	8.95
2. All-welded with some riveting, Waterman type	188	2	1.06	15	7.98
3. All-welded, North Carolina type	679	4	0.59	25	3.68
4. Riveted seams	887	4	0.45	32	3.61
C-3					
1. Riveted seams	453	0	0.00	4	0.88
2. All-welded	994	7	0.70	63	6.34
C-4					
1. All-welded	243	1	0.41	10	4.12
2. All-welded with riveted gunwale	172	1	0.58	3	1.74
		233		1289	

* Records cover service performance from date at which first vessel of each group was placed in service.

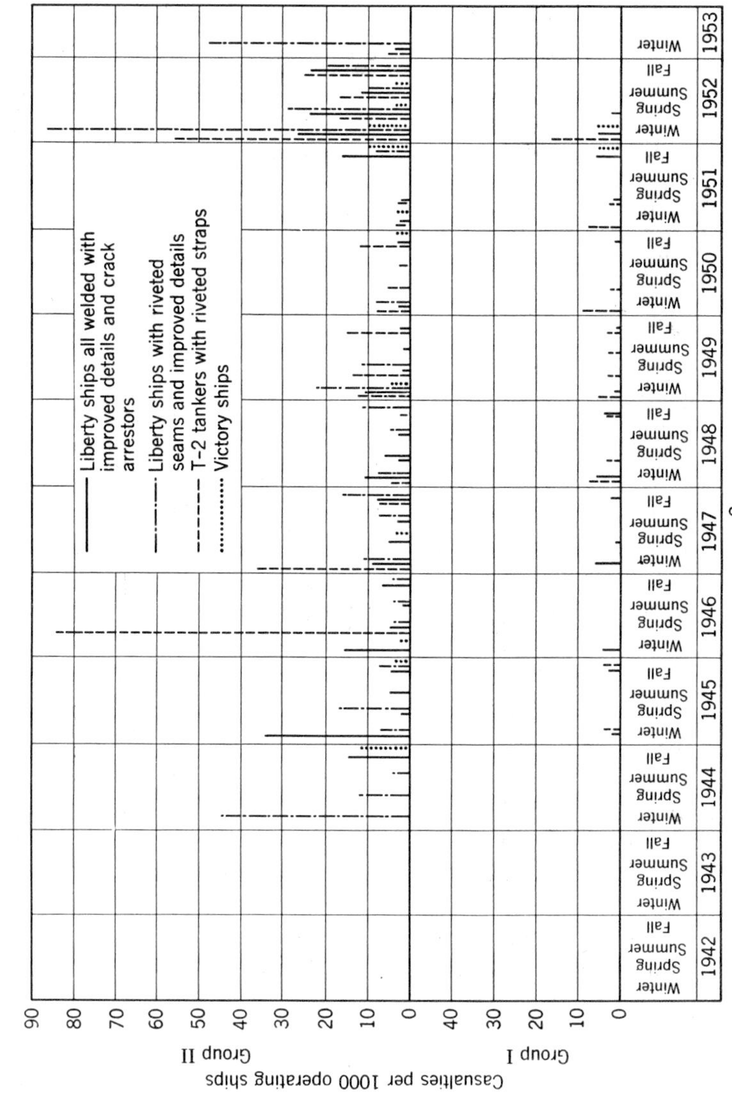

Liberty ships all welded with improved details and crack arrestors

Liberty ships with riveted seams and improved details

T-2 tankers with riveted straps

Victory ships

Casualties per 1000 operating ships

Group II: 0 10 20 30 40 50 60 70 80 90

Group I: 0 10 20 30 40

Year	Seasons
1942	Winter Spring Summer Fall
1943	Winter Spring Summer Fall
1944	Winter Spring Summer Fall
1945	Winter Spring Summer Fall
1946	Winter Spring Summer Fall
1947	Winter Spring Summer Fall
1948	Winter Spring Summer Fall
1949	Winter Spring Summer Fall
1950	Winter Spring Summer Fall
1951	Winter Spring Summer Fall
1952	Winter Spring Summer Fall
1953	Winter

Seasons

Fig. 12.2 Performance record for various ships.[6]

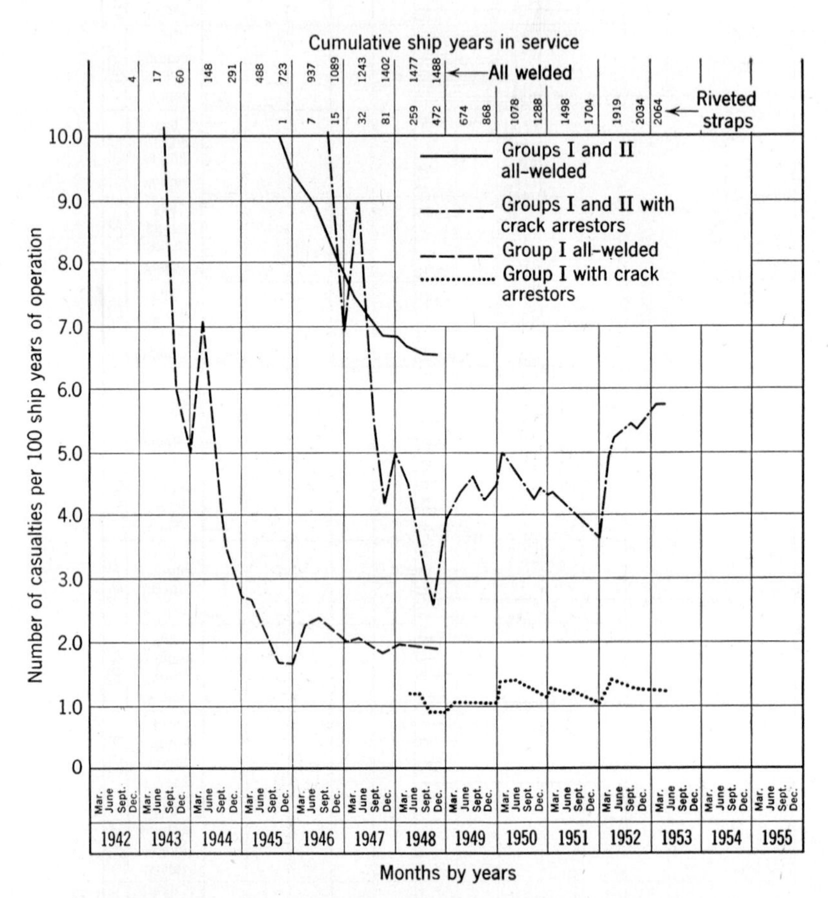

Fig. 12.3 Comparative record of structural performance of T-2 tankers, Group I and Group II structural failures vs. cumulative ship years in service.[6]

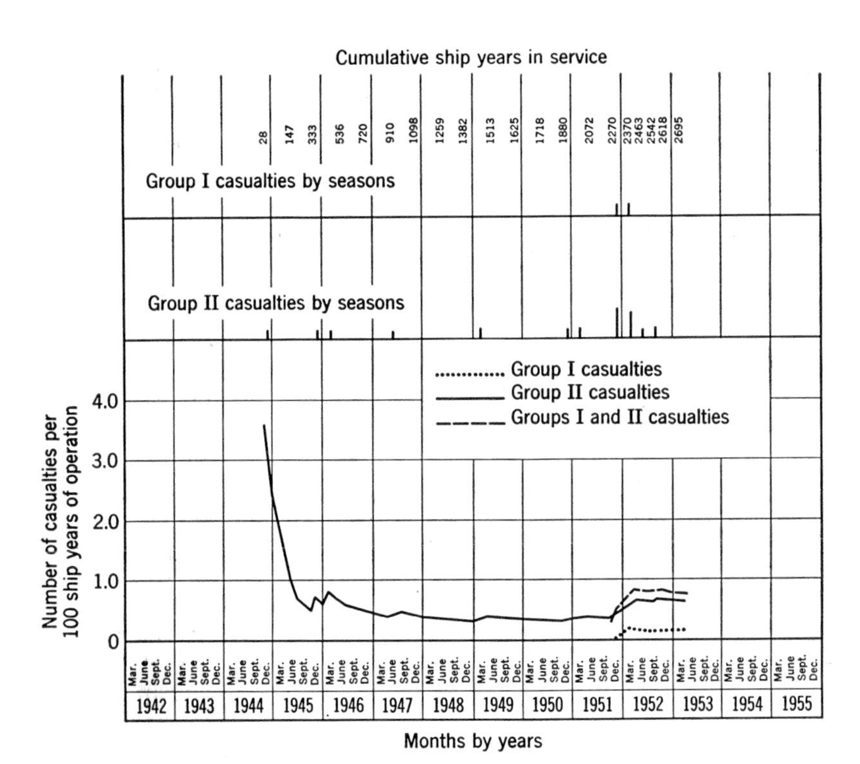

Fig. 12.4 Comparative record of structural performance of Victory ships. Based on monthly percentages of cumulative Group I and Group II structural failures and cumulative ship years in service.[6]

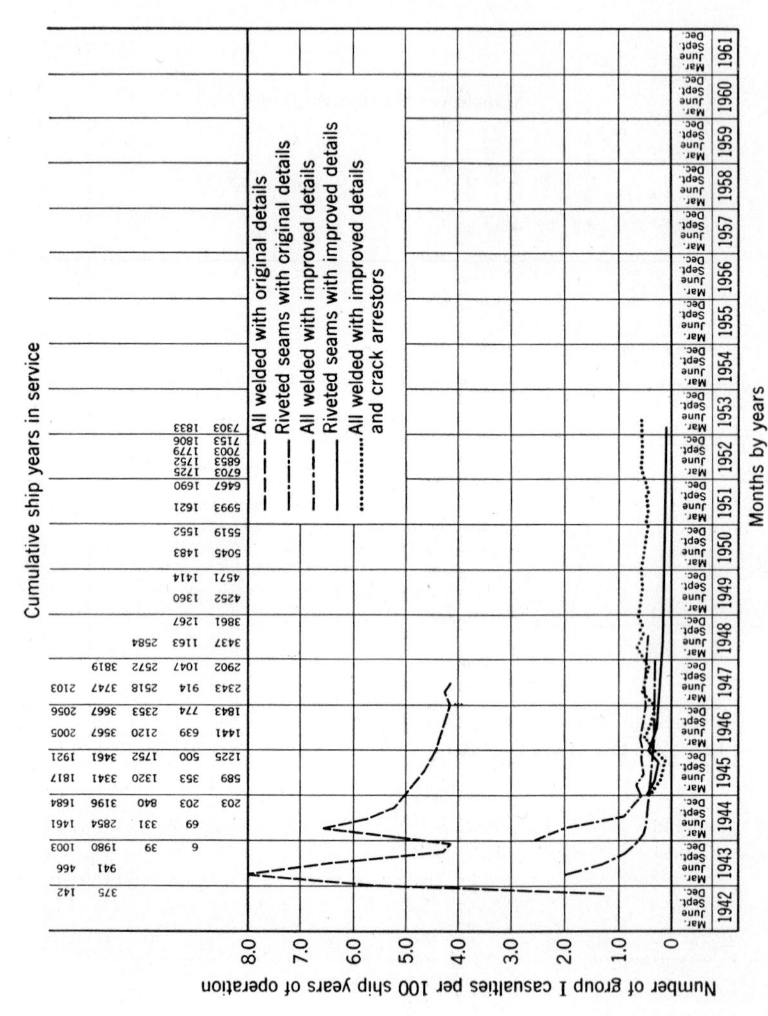

Fig. 12.5 Comparative record of structural performance of Liberty ships. Based on monthly percentages of cumulative Group I casualties to cumulative ship years in service.[6]

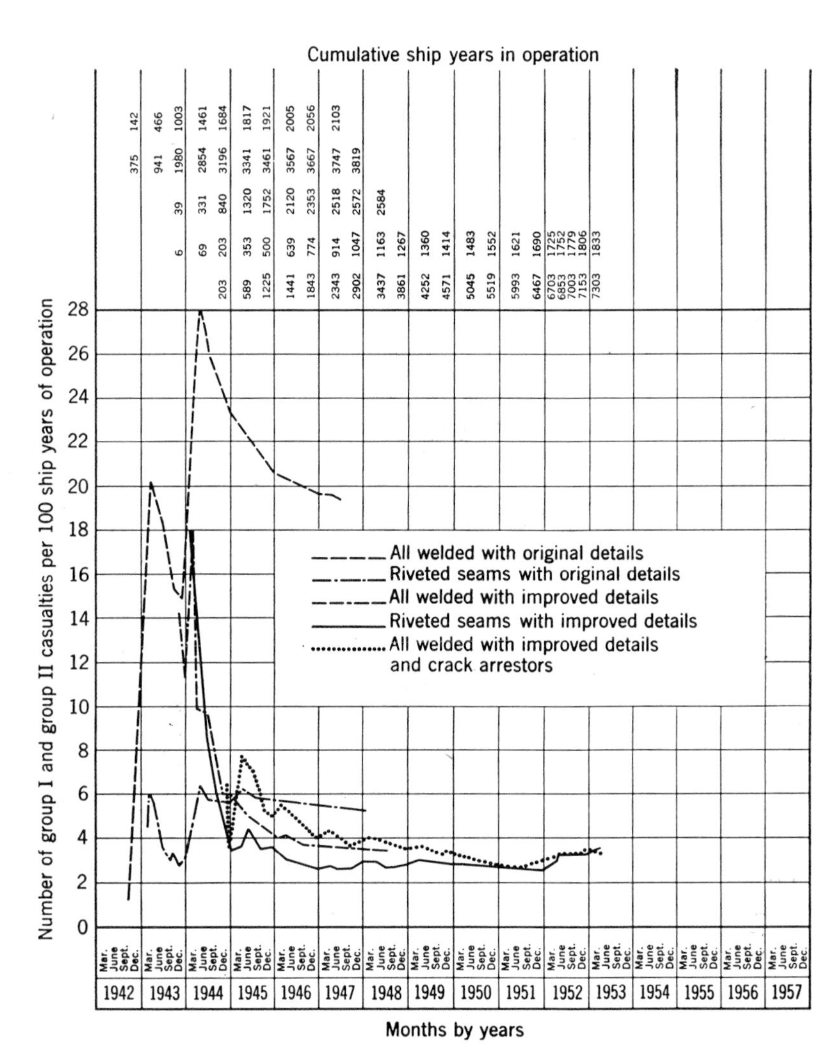

Fig. 12.6 Comparative record of structural performance of Liberty ships. Based on monthly percentages of cumulative Group I and Group II casualties to cumulative ship years in service.[6]

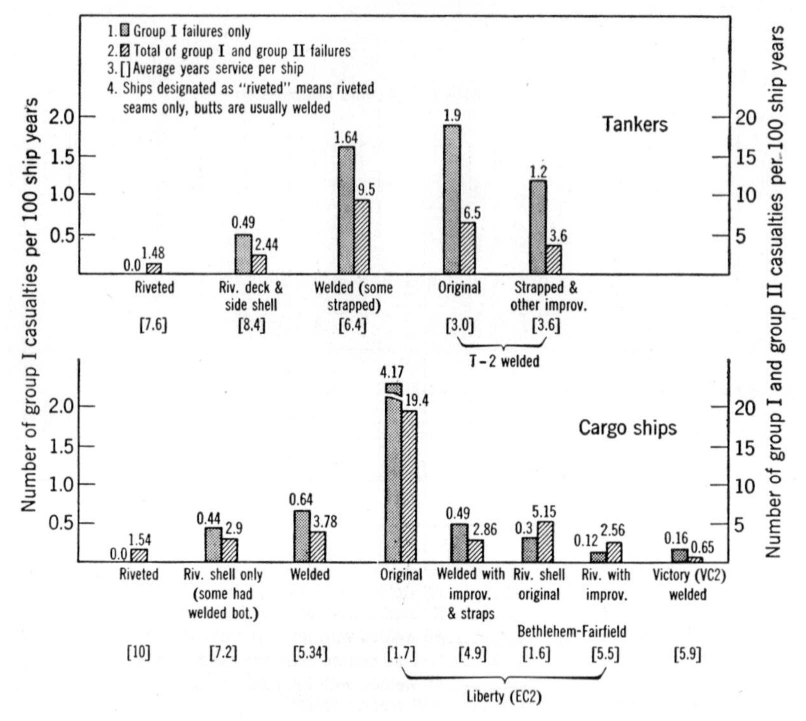

Fig. 12.7 Frequency of casualties for ships built between 1938 and 1953.[1]

Most of the trouble with T-2 tankers originated in defects in bottom shell butt welds. No simple remedies could be applied, but eventually two riveted crack arrester straps were inserted in the deck and two in the bottom plating. These straps were placed in the middle portion of the ship, the region where the serious cracking had occurred. However, in spite of these improvements, fractures in T-2 tankers remained a serious problem. The latest move to improve this situation was the April 1952 American Bureau of Shipping directive to increase the total number of crack arresters to eight and to increase the section modulus of the hull girder by 15 per cent. The ships thus altered have suffered no Group I fractures during the relatively short operational time accumulated to date.

The welded Victory ships that had improved design details have had the lowest percentage of casualties. Even these ships, however, have had four Group I failures. Two of the four failed because of cracks starting at repair welds; in one of the two a crack started at a saddle weld, and in the other the crack originated at a poorly made seam weld that was part of a bottom shell repair made in a foreign

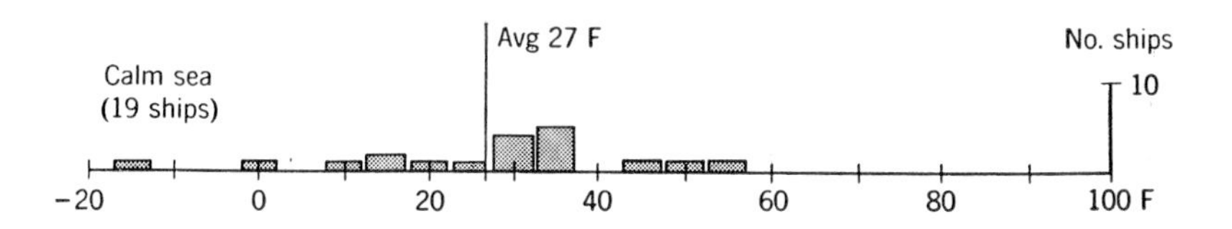

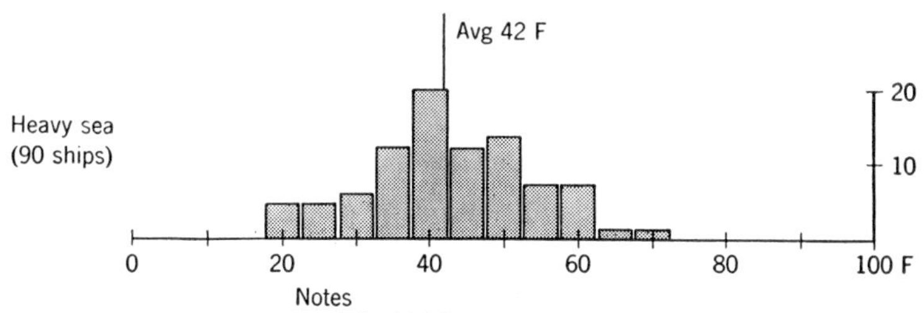

Notes
1. Topside failure - air temperature
2. Bottom failure - water temperature
3. Average of 15 moderate sea casualties was about same as for heavy sea casualties

(a) Plate temperature at time of failure

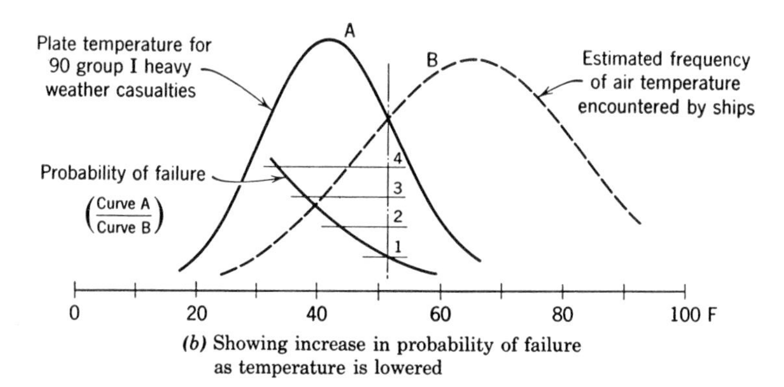

(b) Showing increase in probability of failure as temperature is lowered

Fig. 12.8 Temperature at failure for Group I casualties.[1]

port. The third Group I Victory ship failure occurred when the ship was lightly loaded but was being driven hard in very heavy weather. Two deck cracks running approximately parallel developed and extended from a hatch corner to the shell. The fourth ship was lost, and so nothing is known about the origin and nature of the fracture.

Eighty-three new postwar super tankers of about 28,000 tons dead weight and over have accumulated a total of 220 ship years without a Group I casualty. These tankers were welded except for a number of riveted seams within the 3/5 midship length; all were made of steel that met ABS specifications. Also, welds in many of these ships were checked by radiographic examination. This had a markedly favorable effect upon the quality of workmanship.

CONDITIONS AT TIME OF SHIP FAILURE

Most failures occurred during cold weather and in heavy seas. Fig. 12.8, taken from the report by Acker,[1] shows the distributions of temperatures for Group I casualties and the increasing probability of failure as the temperature is lowered. Fig. 12.9 shows that failure occurred more frequently in dry cargo ships when they were in ballast and in tankers when they were loaded; also shown is the effect of heavy seas. Nominal bending moment stresses of about 10,000 psi are not unusual in tankers. In many cases, however, loads due to heavy seas increased the stresses above the calculated values. Twenty-three (about 10 per cent) of the Group I failures occurred in calm water (10 Liberties, 9 T-2 tankers, and 4 others). These ships were built in 12 differ-

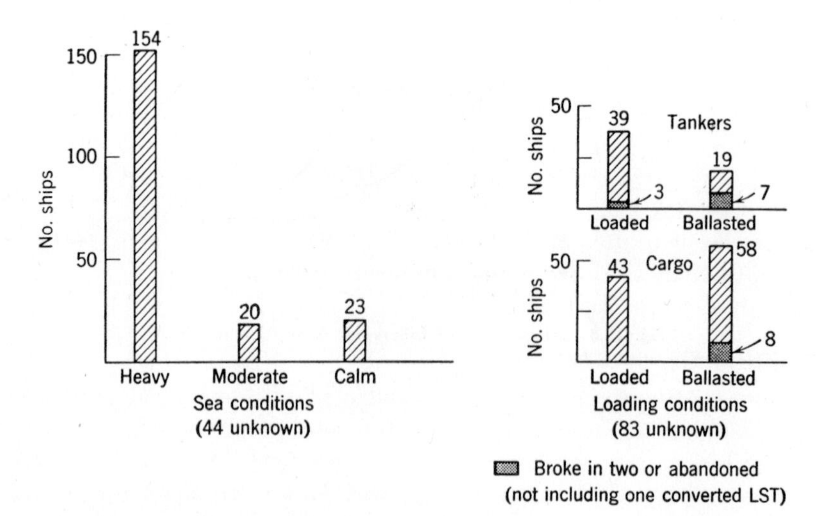

Fig. 12.9 Sea and loading conditions at time of failure for Group I casualties.[1]

ent yards. The average temperature of failure was about 15 F lower than for heavy weather casualties.

Since about 1945 (after the numerous early Liberty failures of 1943–1945), the frequency of failures in both cargo ships and tankers has remained fairly constant. However, failures in the Victory ships be-

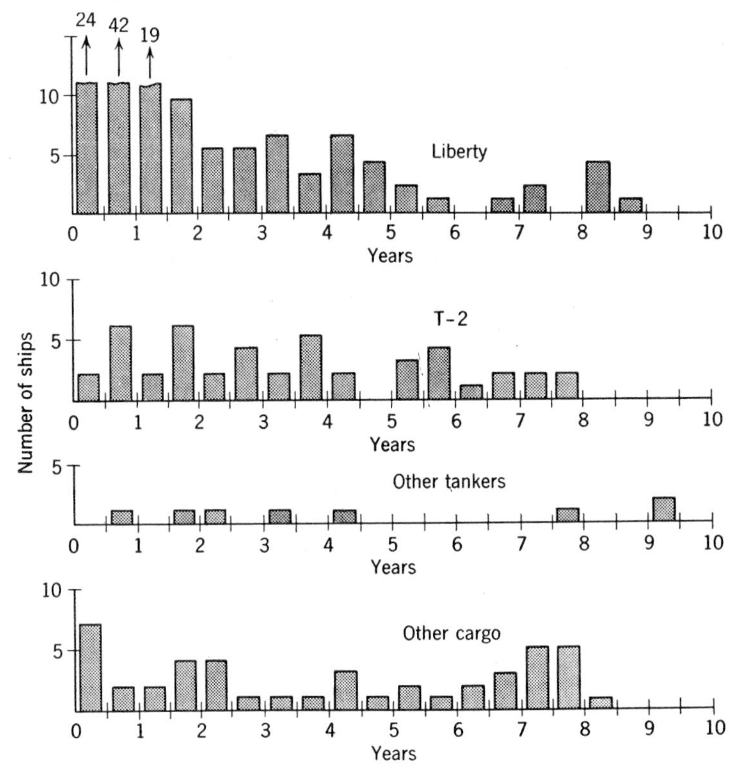

Fig. 12.10 Years in service at time of failure for Group I casualties.[1]

gan to develop after the ships had been in almost trouble-free service for approximately four years. The years in service at the time of failure are shown in Fig. 12.10.[1]

ORIGINS OF FRACTURES

The known origins of fractures have been summarized in Table 12.2[1] and the general locations of fractures of unknown origins, in Table 12.3.[1]

Hatch Corners. The older ships had square hatch openings, and several welded joints were made at each corner. The hatch corners

TABLE 12.2 [1]

KNOWN ORIGINS OF GROUP I FAILURES

	T-2's No.	T-2's %		Others No.
Tankers				
Defective butt welds:				
(*a*) Deck and sheer strake	2	6	47%	1
(*b*) Shell, mostly at bilge	11	32		4
(*c*) Bilge keel	3	9		
End of longitudinal	7	21		2
Bilge keel (scallops, end of keel)	8	23		1
Elsewhere	3	9		1 *
Total	34			9

	Liberties No.	Liberties %		Others No.
Cargo Ships				
Hatch corner	39	54		11
Cutout for accommodating ladder	14	19		4
Defective butt welds:				
(*a*) Shell	7	10	23%	3
(*b*) Bulwark	4	6		1
(*c*) Deck	3	4		1
(*d*) Half-rounds (probably Bessemer steel)	2	3		..
Elsewhere	3	4		2
Total	72			22

* Bessemer steel hot rolled.

in the Liberties were subsequently rounded and reinforced, and the frequency of failures was thus markedly reduced.

Cutouts in Sheer Strake. Cutouts in the way of accommodation ladders were common on early welded ships. To reduce casualties due to cutouts, the cutouts were rounded on the early ships and eliminated on later ships.

Ends of Longitudinals. Fifteen per cent of Groups I and II casualties in T-2 tankers originated in the bottom shell plating at the end of the longitudinals interrupted at transverse bulkheads. About 24 (out of 500) ships were involved in this kind of failure. In tankers of other design but having a similar structural detail, only one failure of this type has been reported for approximately 100 tankers. More recently the design has been altered to provide for a large radius to ease the

TABLE 12.3 [1]

General Location of Group I Fracture Where Origin Not Known

	T-2's No.	T-2's %	Others No.
Tankers			
Bottom shell and bilge	10	59	1
Deck and gunwale	2	12	
Elsewhere	5	29	
Total	17		

	Liberties No.	Liberties %	Others No.
Cargo Ships			
Upper deck and gunwale	57	90	18
Bottom shell and bilge	4		3
Elsewhere	2		1
Total	63		22

stress condition at the end of the longitudinal. The new Navy oilers have a deep bracket extending through the bulkhead to provide continuity for the longitudinal.

Bilge Keels. In the troublesome bilge keels on T-2 tankers, most failures started at faulty butt welds and where the ends of the keels terminated abruptly at the middle of a plate panel. To alleviate this situation, scallops were cut in the web of the bilge keel in way of the welds. Several Group I casualties have originated at these scallops, which were introduced at the ends of the bilge keel in way of an added doubler plate. New directives for structural modification of T-2 tankers require that bilge keels be riveted to the hull plating and that bilge keel scallops be eliminated. With other types of tankers very few shell cracks have started from a welded bilge keel attachment; the trouble has been largely confined to T-2 tankers.

Bulwarks. Defective welds in bulwarks have started several serious failures. Bulwarks have been separated from the hull and supported by brackets to prevent cracks from spreading into the main hull plating.

Light Welds. Several serious cases of failure have occurred in which cracks originated at small fillet welds. This has not been a major problem but has been serious enough for the Navy and the American

Bureau of Shipping to change the requirements to a heavy fillet instead of permitting a light one when welding to heavy plate.

CORRELATION BETWEEN LABORATORY TESTS AND SERVICE FAILURES

Samples of steel were collected from approximately 100 fractured ships and submitted to the National Bureau of Standards for examination and tests. This particular study has resulted in the collection of the most complete body of data now in existence relative to the failure of large engineering structures. A study of these data and an understanding of the more significant conclusions derived therefrom are basic to the comprehension of the present state of knowledge regarding brittle fracture in welded steel structures. The following paragraphs discuss only the major findings of the National Bureau of Standards work—the reader is urged to review the more detailed papers listed in the bibliography.[9–13]

The plates from fractured ships were divided into three groups: those containing or immediately adjacent to the origin of fracture in the ship, called the *source* plates; those through which the crack passed, called the *thru* plates; and those in which a ship fracture stopped, called the *end* plates. Examination of samples included metallographic inspection, determination of chemical composition, and behavior in V-notch Charpy and tensile tests.

The V-notch Charpy energy versus temperature curves for some *source* and *end* plates are shown in Fig. 12.11.[10,12] The 15 ft-lb level and the temperature at time of the service failure, if known, are indicated on the figure. The plates in this series ranged in thickness from 0.44 in. to 0.69 in. It is apparent that the 15 ft-lb transition temperatures of the source plates are higher than those of the end plates.

Figs. 12.12,[10] 12.13, and 12.14 [12] summarize, respectively, the energy absorbed at 70 F, the energy absorbed at failure temperature, and the 15 ft-lb transition temperature (all in the V-notch Charpy test) for plates studied at the National Bureau of Standards. The data are divided according to plate thickness and fracture category. The horizontal bars on these figures represent the range of values; the vertical lines in the bars represent the values for individual plates; and the circles above the bars represent the average for each thickness or fracture group. Fig. 12.15 [12] shows the data of Fig. 12.14 plotted as frequency distributions for *source, thru,* and *end* plates.

Inspection of these figures indicates a distinction between the plates in the three fracture categories. The nature of the difference is probably best illustrated in Fig. 12.15. The *source* plates have a high aver-

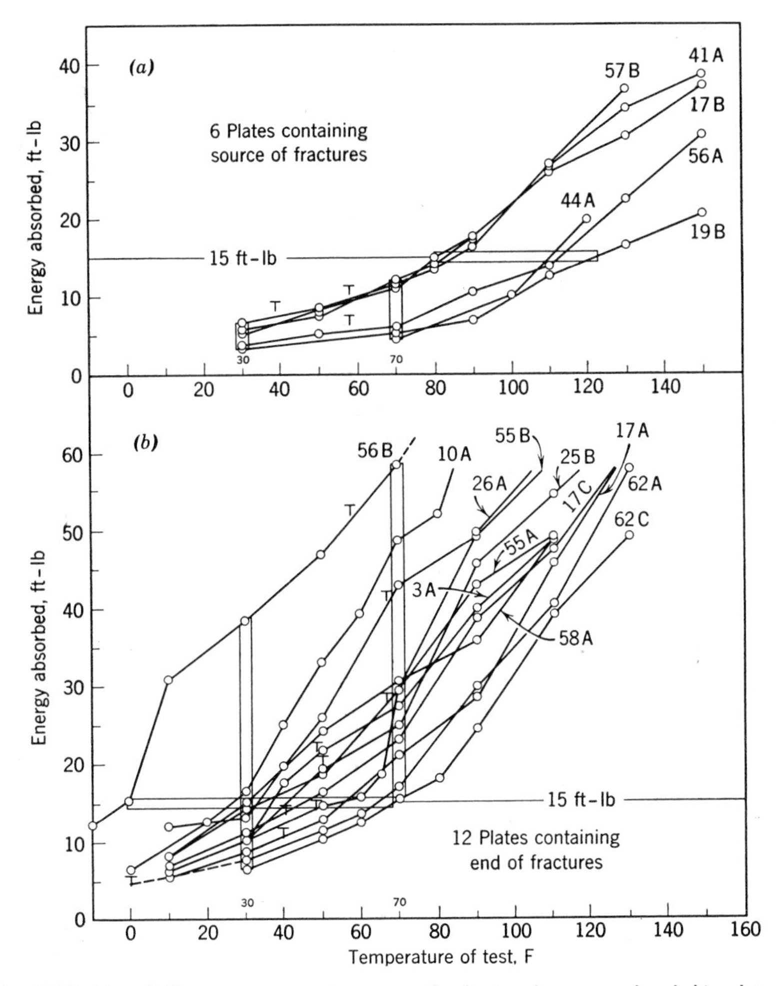

Fig. 12.11 V-notch Charpy vs. temperature curves for fractured source and end ship plates.[10] Plate thickness 0.44–0.69 in. Horizontal bars indicate range of 15 ft-lb transition temperature for (*a*) source plates, (*b*) end plates. Vertical bars indicate range of energy absorbed in tests at 30 F and 70 F. Temperatures at time of ship failure are indicated by letter T.

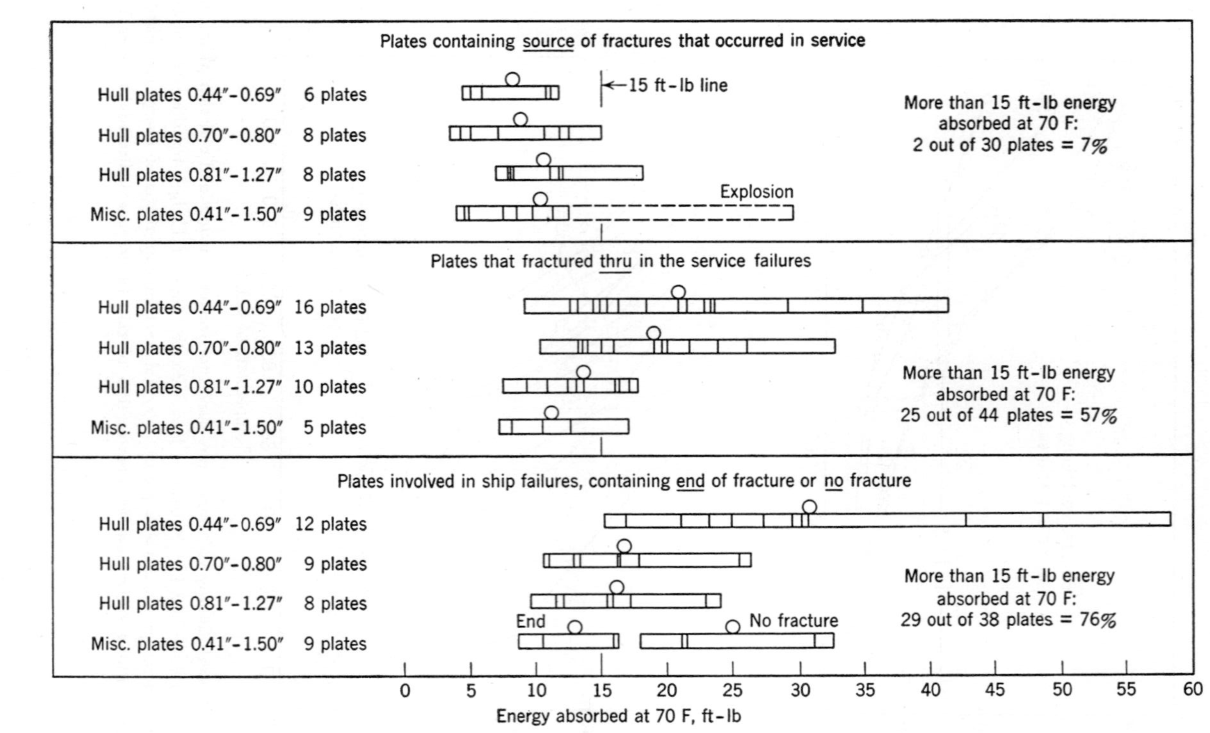

Fig. 12.12 Relation of energy absorbed by V-notch Charpy specimens to the nature of fracture in ship plates. Test temperature 70 F.[10]

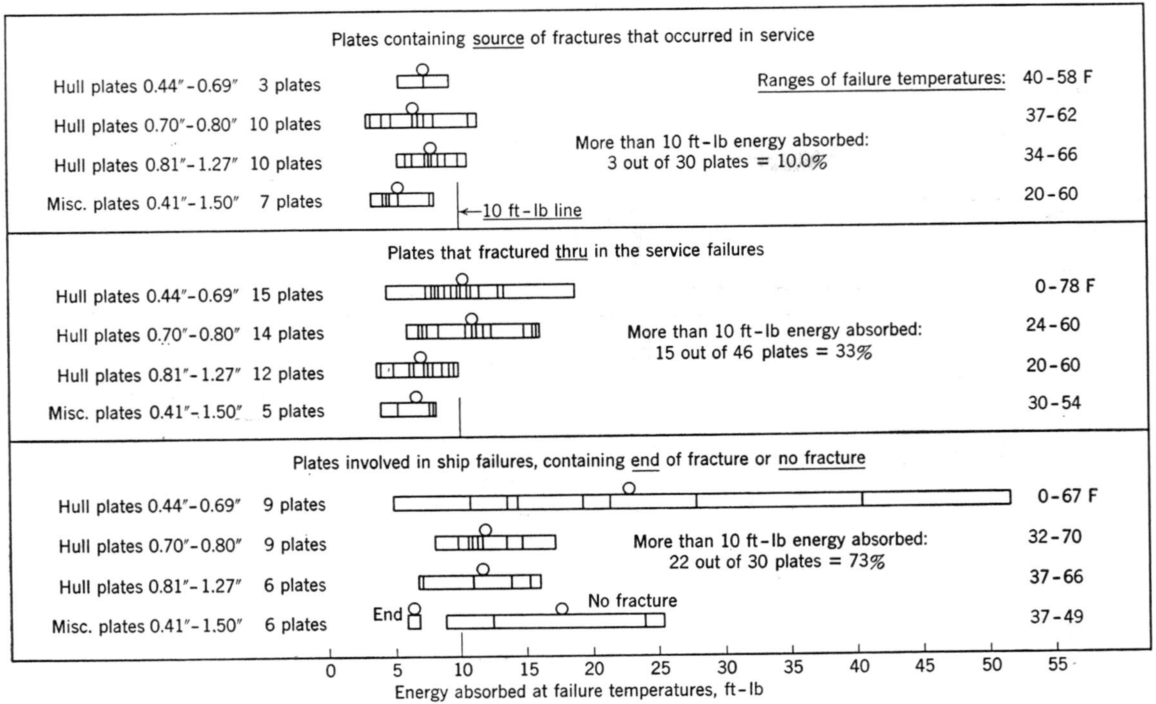

Plates containing source of fractures that occurred in service

Ranges of failure temperatures:

Hull plates 0.44″-0.69″	3 plates	40-58 F
Hull plates 0.70″-0.80″	10 plates	37-62
Hull plates 0.81″-1.27″	10 plates	34-66
Misc. plates 0.41″-1.50″	7 plates	20-60

More than 10 ft-lb energy absorbed:
3 out of 30 plates = 10.0%

10 ft-lb line

Plates that fractured thru in the service failures

Hull plates 0.44″-0.69″	15 plates	0-78 F
Hull plates 0.70″-0.80″	14 plates	24-60
Hull plates 0.81″-1.27″	12 plates	20-60
Misc. plates 0.41″-1.50″	5 plates	30-54

More than 10 ft-lb energy absorbed:
15 out of 46 plates = 33%

Plates involved in ship failures, containing end of fracture or no fracture

Hull plates 0.44″-0.69″	9 plates	0-67 F
Hull plates 0.70″-0.80″	9 plates	32-70
Hull plates 0.81″-1.27″	6 plates	37-66
Misc. plates 0.41″-1.50″	6 plates	37-49

More than 10 ft-lb energy absorbed:
22 out of 30 plates = 73%

No fracture

End

0 5 10 15 20 25 30 35 40 45 50 55

Energy absorbed at failure temperatures, ft-lb

Fig. 12.13 Relation of energy absorbed by V-notch Charpy specimens at the temperature of ship failure to the nature of the fractures in ship plates.[12]

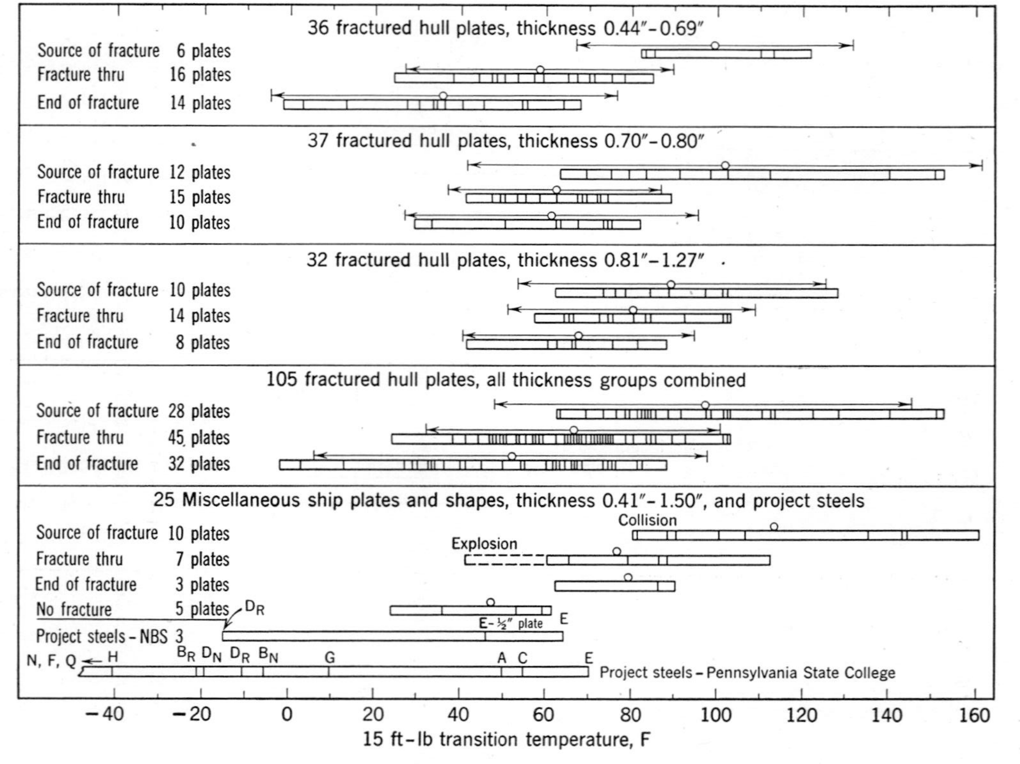

Fig. 12.14 Relation of 15 ft-lb transition temperature to the nature of the fractures in ship plates and comparison of transition temperatures of fractured ship plates and project steels. Arrows represent the range of plus or minus twice the standard deviation of the transition temperatures for each group of plates.[10]

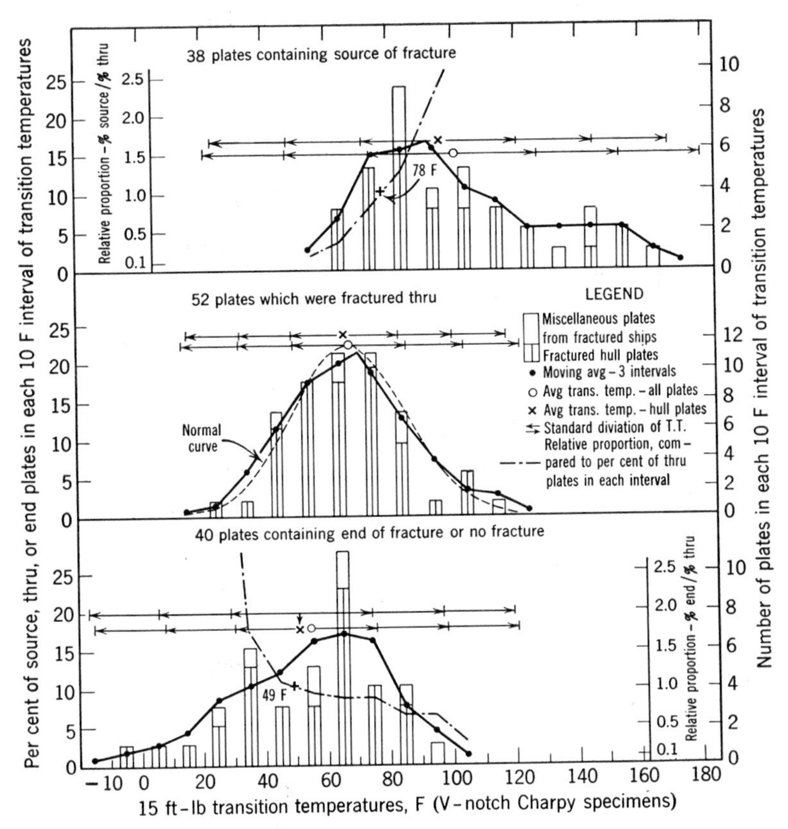

Fig. 12.15 Frequency distribution of 15 ft-lb V-notch Charpy transition temperatures for fractured ship plates.[10]

age transition temperature and a distribution that is unbalanced on the high side; the *thru* plates have a more normal and intermediate distribution; and the *end* plates have a low average transition temperature and a distribution with a long tail at lower transition temperature. The character of these distribution curves was not wholly unanticipated; one would suspect that the *thru* plates would be most representative of all ship plates and hence might tend toward a normal distribution, whereas the *source* and *end* plates were "selected" for their role in the fracturing of the ship. A factor in this selection is the notch toughness of the plate as measured in the Charpy test; the overlapping of the *source* and *end* plate distributions with the *thru* plate distribution can be explained by factors involved in the fracturing in addition to the notch toughness of the plate. For example, a plate in the fracture *thru* category having a transition temperature between about 60 F and 90 F (Fig. 12.15) might have been a fracture *source* plate under more severe stress conditions such as those in the region of a notch; under less severe conditions of average stress it might have been an *end* plate. Even though factors other than notch toughness contributed to the "selection" of a plate for its role in fracturing, it should be pointed out that statistical analyses have indicated that the differences in transition temperature and energy at failure temperature between the *source* and *thru,* and *thru* and *end* plates are not due to chance.

The extremely low probability of the differences in Charpy properties of plates in the three fracture categories being due to chance permits the development of several criteria that are very important to engineers. Fig. 12.13 shows that only 10% of the *source* plates absorbed more than 10 ft-lb in the V-notch Charpy test at the failure temperature; the highest value encountered in this category was 11.4 ft-lb. At the other extreme 73% of the *end* plates absorbed more than 10 ft-lb at the failure temperature. It can therefore be stated, based on these data—and for steels of this quality—that in a large structure brittle fractures are not likely to initiate in a plate that absorbs more than 10 ft-lb in the V-notch Charpy test performed at the anticipated operating temperature. This is another reason, independent in derivation from those listed in Chapter V, for the trend toward interpretation of Charpy tests at low energy levels.

Extreme caution must be exercised in extending a 10 ft-lb criterion to steels other than the nominal 0.25% C, 0.45% Mn semikilled materials studied at the National Bureau of Standards. A group at the Naval Research Laboratory have used their recently developed "drop-weight" test to study the properties of plates in the above composition range from fractured ships and of currently produced ship plate, including killed and low alloy types.[14, 15, 16] It was found that in all 17 ship fracture plates tested, the drop-weight transition temperature * occurred at a level on the Charpy curve of 10 ft-lb or less—the average for these plates was 6.1 ft-lb.[14, 15] However, when drop-weight tests were performed on semikilled steels containing 0.60–0.90% Mn, on killed structural steels, and on low alloy-high strength structural steels, it was found that the critical fracture initiation temperature (drop-weight transition temperature) was related to appreciably higher energy values on the V-notch Charpy curve. The applicability of this shift in performance level on the Charpy curve to the prediction of service per-

* Defined as the highest temperature at which the specimen is unable to withstand 2° of bend in the presence of a sharp crack. This transition is therefore of the "nil ductility" type described in Chapter V.

formance of steel structures is as yet not established, since there have been no reported major failures in structures fabricated from the superior steels. There exists, however, ample justification for the exercise of care in extrapolating the basic National Bureau of Standards data.

The tensile tests performed on samples of fractured plates disclosed that there was no correlation between tensile properties and service performance. Chemical composition, however, was found to be an important factor. The transition temperature was raised by carbon and phosphorus and lowered by manganese and silicon (within the range examined) and by finer grain size.

REFERENCES

1. H. G. Acker, "Review of Welded Ship Failures," Ship Structure Committee Report, Serial No. SSC-63, December 15, 1953.
2. D. P. Brown, "Observations on Experience with Welded Ships," *Welding J.*, pp. 765–782 (September 1952).
3. *Final Report of a Board of Investigation to Inquire into the Design and Methods of Construction of Welded Steel Merchant Vessels.* Washington, D. C.: Government Printing Office, 1947.
4. "Technical Progress Report of the Ship Structure Committee," March 1, 1948. Reprinted in *Welding J.*, Res. Suppl., pp. 377-s–384-s (July 1948).
5. "Second Technical Progress Report of the Ship Structure Committee," July 1, 1950. Reprinted in *Welding J.*, Res. Suppl., pp. 169-s–181-s (April 1951).
6. "Third Technical Progress Report of the Ship Structure Committee," August 1, 1953. Reprinted in *Welding Research Council Bull. No. 16,* pp. 1–21 (November 1953).
7. E. A. Wright, F. Jonassen, and H. G. Acker, "Research under the Ship Structure Committee," presented at the annual meeting of the Society of Naval Architects and Marine Engineers in New York City, November 13 and 14, 1952. Reprinted in *Welding Research Council Bull. No. 16,* 1953, pp. 22–64. Also reprinted in *Trans. Soc. Naval Architects Marine Engrs., 60,* 223–247 (1952).
8. F. Jonassen, "A Résumé of the Ship Fracture Problem," *Welding J.*, Res. Suppl., pp. 316-s–318-s (June 1952).
9. M. L. Williams and G. A. Ellinger, "Investigation of Fractured Steel Plates Removed from Welded Ships," Ship Structure Committee Report, Serial No. NBS-1, February 25. 1949.
10. M. L. Williams, M. R. Meyerson, G. L. Kluge, and L. R. Dale, "Investigation of Fractured Steel Plates Removed from Welded Ships," Ship Structure Committee Report, Serial No. NBS-3, June 1, 1951.
11. M. L. Williams, "Examination and Tests of Fractured Steel Plates Removed from Welded Ships," Ship Structure Committee Report, Serial No. NBS-4, April 2, 1953.
12. M. L. Williams and G. A. Ellinger, "Investigation of Structural Failures of Welded Ships," *Welding J.*, Res. Suppl., pp. 498-s–527-s (October 1953).

13. M. L. Williams, "Analysis of Brittle Behavior in Ship Plates," Ship Structure Committee Report, Serial No. NBS-5, February 7, 1955. (Also presented in A. S. T. M. Spec. Tech. Pub. No. 158, 1954.)

14. P. P. Puzak, M. E. Schuster, and W. S. Pellini, "Part I: Crack-Starter Tests of Ship Fracture and Project Steels," Ship Structure Committee Report, Serial No. SSC-77, June 18, 1954.

15. P. P. Puzak, M. E. Schuster, and W. S. Pellini, "Crack-Starter Tests of Ship Fracture and Project Steels," *Welding J.*, Res. Suppl., pp. 481-s–495-s (October 1954).

16. P. P. Puzak, M. E. Schuster, and W. S. Pellini, "Applicability of Charpy Test Data," *Welding J.*, Res. Suppl., pp. 433-s–441-s (September 1954).

CHAPTER

Summary

Brittle behavior of engineering structures has been a serious problem to engineers for almost a century. The technical literature of the late 1800's contains references to the brittle behavior of steel members and structures, with particular reference being made to the brittleness of Bessemer steel. These early failures were in riveted structures—welding being a Twentieth Century development. Failures were invariably associated with low ambient temperatures and frequently started at punched rivet holes. Excessive cold work embrittles steel and has been responsible for a number of service failures. With few exceptions the nominal stresses in the riveted structures at the time of failure were moderate, and the designs conformed to standard engineering practice.

With the turn of the century, reports of serious failures gradually became more frequent, and in the mid-forties, when welded steel merchant ships suffered many casualties, the incidence of such failures reached a peak. This high incidence of brittle fractures was the result of a combination of circumstances. One important factor was the exceptionally great number of large welded structures being built. The requirements for merchant vessels were so great during World War II that production rates skyrocketed. In order to maintain production schedules, it was necessary to employ unskilled and inexperienced workmen to prepare structural components and to weld them together. As a consequence, the structures frequently contained welding and structural defects that acted as stress concentrators and under certain conditions, such as low ambient temperature, could initiate a fracture. Typical examples of defects responsible for failures are shown in Chapter X. Very rarely have failures started in regions where there was no obvious defect in design or workmanship.

Weld defects provide notches, and notches have the capacity to transform uniaxial stresses into dangerous triaxial tensile stresses. At the apex of a notch, the tensile stress due to the load is several times the average value, and secondary tensile stresses acting perpendicularly to the main stress are present. It is sometimes thought that the stress-raising action of the notch is the primary cause of trouble. This is not so, however, as tests on geometrically similar specimens have shown. Thin plates with sharp notches are tough and ductile at ordinary temperatures, whereas thicker plates with similar notches are brittle. It is the components of stress in the width and thickness directions that induce brittle behavior. These secondary stresses are higher, the thicker the plate and the sharper and the deeper the notch. Results from experiments with plates of various thickness indicate that the thickness effect becomes important when the plate thickness exceeds about $\frac{1}{4}$ in.

Plastic flow (and hence ductility) is dependent only on the shear stresses, and the maximum shear stress is equal to one half of the difference between the maximum and the minimum principal stresses. It is therefore evident that in a triaxial stress system the ratio of maximum shear stress to maximum tensile stress can range from zero to more than one. It is this ratio that determines whether a given steel will behave in a ductile or a brittle manner.

This principle can be simply demonstrated. When an unnotched cylindrical specimen of mild steel is tested at liquid nitrogen temperature, it will be as brittle as cast iron if subjected to tensile loading but as ductile as copper if loaded in torsion. The difference in behavior is due entirely to the difference in the ratio of maximum shear stress to maximum tensile stress. In the tension specimen this ratio is one half, and in the torsion specimen it is one.

Brittleness at ordinary temperatures requires much lower stress ratios. There is no means known for lowering this ratio below one half other than to use a notch; the value of the ratio depends upon the sharpness of the notch and upon the plate thickness. Thus the relative brittleness of steels at ordinary temperatures can best be evaluated with notched specimens. Since the number of notched specimens that can be designed is infinite and since they all act somewhat alike, it is not surprising that the number in current use is large. Two of the problems that arise then are the valuation of specimens and tests and the selection of appropriate tests to evaluate potential service performance of steel. Although more will be said about this, it is worthy of note that the only notched bar test that has as yet been directly correlated with service performance is the V-notch Charpy. Extensive tests on plates removed from fractured ships have shown that the plates containing the fracture origins had V-notch Charpy values of about 10 ft-lb or less at the temperature of failure. Similar results were also found for a small number of nonship structures, but such data are much less complete than those for ships. This correlation is valid only for the class of steel involved and should not be accepted as having general validity for all classes of steel.

When steel fractures in a ductile manner, the physical mechanism of failure is different from that associated with brittle behavior. Steel can fail by either of two modes—shear or cleavage. Shear failures are a natural consequence of plastic flow and represent the terminus of the flow process. Plastic flow creates voids of atomic dimensions that gradually increase in size as the flow progresses. These voids eventually grow to microscopic size and then quickly enlarge to form a macroscopic fracture surface. The fracture follows a path diagonally across the cubic structure of the ferrite crystals; the crystallographic direction of a shear fracture is governed by the slip mechanism and is different from the path of a cleavage fracture.

Brittle behavior is associated with a cleavage fracture mechanism in which the fracture follows the cube planes in the ferrite crystals. Theoretically cleavage failure does not require nor involve plastic flow; for example, sheets of mica can easily be peeled apart without causing any displacement to occur in the plane of the sheets. Iron, being somewhat ductile by nature, generally undergoes some deformation prior to failure even under very adverse circumstances. Many cases have been observed, however, where the flow was so small as to be undetectable with a micrometer in plates that ranged from ½ in. to 1 in. in thickness. Furthermore, there have been a number of cracks formed in structures and structural components due entirely to residual stresses. Thus, the evidence indicates that the amount of flow associated with a cleavage fracture may be only a fraction of one per cent. However, it is generally found to be one per cent or more.

The existence of two modes of fracture accounts for the change from ductile behavior at high temperatures to the relatively brittle behavior at low temperatures. At high temperatures the cleavage strength is high relative to the shear fracture strength, whereas at low temperatures the reverse is true. The temperature at which the transition from one mode to the other occurs thus depends upon the ratio of the maximum shear to the maximum tensile stress as previously pointed out. When the ratio is one (torsion loading), the transition is below −300 F for mild steel; when it is one half, the transition occurs at about −250 F; with the lower ratios present in notched specimens, the transition occurs in the normal ambient range.

The two basic types of separation produce fractures that differ markedly in appearance. Shear failures appear gray and silky; cleavage fractures appear bright and granular. When the cleavage mode of fracture occurs in a plate of steel, it often produces a chevron or herringbone structure on the fracture surface. The chevrons point toward the origin of fracture, thus making positive identification of the fracture source possible.

The rate of loading also has a considerable effect upon the behavior of medium carbon structural steel. This effect is probably due mainly to the fact that plastic flow requires time to initiate. The faster the steel is loaded, the higher the stress reached before yielding begins. Thus, at a given temperature the maximum tensile stress can rise to a higher value when the load is applied rapidly. The higher the tensile stress rises before flow starts, the greater the probability of a cleavage fracture. As a practical example of the effectiveness of high loading rates, "hammer testing" of a structure occasionally causes a fracture to initiate (even though the nominal stress is thereby increased by only a very small amount) in a structure that would not otherwise fail.

There are 30 or 40 types of notched specimens in current use. With the diversity of specimen designs, testing procedures, and interpretations that presently exist, it is difficult to make any meaningful comparisons of the results obtained in different investigations. Probably a single standard test and a uniform interpretation of the test data will never be adopted because of the variations in service conditions, fabrication procedures, and designs from one application to another. When a particular type of test, however, is used to evaluate behavior in a specific service, an effort should be made to avoid nonstandard specimen designs and testing procedures. Such changes may preclude accurate comparison or correlation of the test results with other data. It is to the advantage of all concerned to use, whenever possible, generally accepted specimen designs and testing procedures rather than modifications thereof and also to employ standard methods of interpreting the test data. Two of the most commonly used and most discriminating tests are the V-notch Charpy (for an individual material) and the slow notch-bend (Kinzel or Lehigh) test (for a weld-plate combination). It is specifically recommended that V-notch Charpy tests always be made in addition to any other desired tests for purposes of comparison.

The literature on the brittle behavior of steel is extensive and contains vast amounts of data based on different types of tests and on different methods of evaluation. Despite the many papers presented on the subject, few contain critical analyses or summaries useful for clarifying and correlating the results. Hence, it is important to dwell at some length on this subject.

Notch bar tests are conducted at various temperatures to determine the temperature range over which an appreciable change takes place in some measured value, such as energy absorption, ductility, or fracture appearance. This change frequently occurs rather abruptly; for example, the energy absorbed to failure may drop abruptly from a high value to a much lower one within a narrow temperature range. The width of the transition range varies with the test conditions, the specimen geometry, and the chemical composition of the steel. In certain cases it is only a few degrees; in others it is several hundred. With any particular test specimen the transition range can be determined from any one of several different measurements having to do with energy absorption, ductility, or the appearance of the fracture. These measurements, however, will not all necessarily give the same transition range even in a single type of test. This is an important fact that is not universally recognized.

Transitions from "ductile" to "brittle" behavior based upon fracture appearance always yield higher values of transition temperature range than do those based on ductility measurements at the notch. This is a consequence of the observed physical behavior of the specimens and of the manner in which the fracture appearance and ductility transitions have been defined. The fracture appearance criterion is, as the name implies, based upon the appearance of the fracture surface. The temperature at which the surface is 50 per cent granular and 50 per cent fibrous is defined as the *fracture appearance (or fracture) transition temperature*. Below this temperature the energy to failure may be appreciably below the maximum, but the ductility at the base of the notch is usually high (e.g., 5 to 30 per cent). The *ductility transition* is almost always at a lower temperature because this criterion is based on an arbitrarily selected low value of notch ductility (e.g., one per cent lateral contraction at the notch apex). With V-notch Charpy specimens this corresponds to the 10 to 15 ft-lb energy level for semi-killed structural carbon steels.

Either transition can be measured by any of several variables; for example, the fracture appearance transition can be determined by fracture appearance or by energy absorption, and the ductility transition can be determined by ductility or energy measurements. The fracture transition cannot, however, be determined by notch ductility measurements, and the ductility transition cannot readily be established by observing the nature of the fracture surface.

Variations in specimen geometry affect the ductility and the fracture appearance transition temperatures quite differently. The evidence shows that the ductility transition temperature varies markedly with notch geometry and with specimen shape, whereas the fracture appearance transition temperature is relatively insensitive to changes in specimen geometry, particularly in specimens more than ½ in. thick. As the notch is made sharper and deeper, the strains are more localized; the strain rates are higher for a given loading rate; and the degree of triaxial tension becomes greater. These factors favor higher ductility transition temperatures. The fracture appearance transition depends upon how the crack, once formed, progresses rather than upon the amount of plastic flow that precedes the initiation of the crack. Once the first crack forms, the fracture characteristics no longer depend upon the geometry of the original notch. Rounded notches, of course, permit more local ductility than sharp ones before a crack forms and are thus associated with low ductility transition temperatures. Specimens with different sizes and shapes of notches often show widely different ductility transitions and yet show about the same fracture appearance transition temperature.

Ductility transition temperatures are sensitive to variations in notch geometry, rate of loading, and conditions of welding; fracture appearance transitions are considerably less sensitive to such variations. Since "transition temperature" is so dependent upon the criterion selected and upon the test method used, it is obvious that no exact correlation between results from widely varying tests is possible unless great care is taken to obtain comparable data, such as data based upon ductility at the notch apex. Any correlation based upon fracture appearance will not, in general, hold for the ductility transitions in the same series of tests. There may, indeed, even be reversals in the order of rating. There are two reasons for this: (1) the fracture appearance transitions are near the top of the energy-temperature curves, whereas the ductility transitions are near the bottom; and (2) the slope of the steeply rising portion of the curve varies with the type of test and with the type of steel.

Some reasonably good correlations between ductility transitions have been established. For example, the 10 ft-lb V-notch Charpy transition temperature (for a number of steels of the same general class) was found to be related to the ductility transition for keyhole Charpy specimens (as defined by the temperature at the middle of the scatter zone). Another correlation of value was found between the 10 ft-lb V-notch Charpy temperature and the temperature at the 20,000 in-lb level for internally notched 12-in. wide plates.

The only available direct correlation between service failures and notched bar tests is with the V-notch Charpy specimen. It was found that the 7 or 8 ft-lb transition temperature for V-notch Charpy specimens made from plates in which fracture initiated in service corresponded approximately to the temperature of the service failure. Fracture appearance transitions do not appear to correlate with the temperatures at which cracks initiate in service. They do, however, seem to correlate with the temperatures at which cracks are arrested.

Chemical composition and manufacturing practice are known to have large effects on transition temperatures of structural carbon steel. Fortunately, there have been a few comprehensive investigations of the effect of variations in chemical composition on the transition temperatures of hot-rolled structural carbon steel. On the basis of the information available, it appears that carbon raises all transition temperatures, but its effect differs with the criterion selected. A 0.1% increase in carbon raises the fracture appearance transition about 33 F, but the 15 ft-lb V-notch Charpy transition is raised only 25 F. Manganese lowers the transition temperature but at a much slower rate than carbon raises it. An increase of 0.1% in the manganese content lowers the fracture transition 4 F and the 15 ft-lb V-notch Charpy transition by 10 F. Silicon acts in a complex manner, apparently lowering the transition as the silicon content increases up to about 0.3% and raising it above that level. Phosphorus increases both transitions at rates greatly exceeding those for carbon. Sulphur has little effect, and the effect of nitrogen varies greatly with the criterion selected and with the composition of the steel. The effect of nitrogen seems to depend largely upon the deoxidation practice employed during melting and casting. The embrittling effect was found to be largely overcome by the aluminum in normalized steels that had been fully deoxidized with both silicon and aluminum. In semikilled steels nitrogen was found to be very effective in raising both fracture appearance and ductility transitions. Aluminum acts as a grain refiner in normalized silicon killed steels and is therefore effective in lowering the transition temperatures.

Welding is known to have a profound effect on the brittle behavior of engineering structures. Defective welds have often provided the notches necessary to start brittle fractures, and welds have provided the plate-to-plate continuity necessary for continuous crack propagation.

The transition temperature of weld metal varies over a wide range, depending upon the welding conditions, the type of electrode used, and the design of the specimen employed for the test. Fast cooling greatly decreases notch ductility. Consequently, small fast stringer beads or light fillet welds should be avoided. Preheating retards cooling and hence generally lowers the ductility transition temperature. Postheating to 1100–1200 F generally produces a substantial improvement in the notch ductility of weld metal or in weldments made without preheat. Deposits made with low-hydrogen electrodes (EXX15 or EXX16) or by the submerged arc process generally have lower ductility transitions than those made with other types of electrodes (without preheat).

Fracture appearance transitions have been shown to be relatively insensitive to variations in welding conditions, since this criterion reflects the propensity of the base plate to fail by cleavage once a crack starts. However, the amount of ductility prior to crack formation, which the ductility transition reflects, is strongly dependent upon the welding conditions. Thus, the ductility transition is more suitable for evaluating the performance of weldments than is the fracture appearance transition.

The performance of a weldment is best indicated by specimens that contain the entire weld zone as well as a portion of the base plate. These specimens should be notched, with the notch extending across the weld, the heat-affected zone, and the base plate. Specimens having notches parallel to the direction of the weld reflect only the properties of the particular zone of the weldment that contains the notch. Such tests, however, are particularly useful for disclosing the zone with the highest ductility transition temperature.

Welding is responsible for a further complication in that it introduces residual stresses. These stresses generally approach the yield strength of the metal in magnitude and arise because of the temperature gradients created by the welding operation. The existence of residual stresses is well established, but the effect of such stresses on the behavior of welded structures is still a matter of debate. It is argued by many that a slight amount of plastic flow will relieve the residual welding stresses and that therefore they cannot be harmful. Experiments on welded specimens free from defects have seemed to bear this out. However, there have been many fractures in unloaded components and in full-scale structures that were caused by residual stresses or by a combination of residual and thermal stresses.

Numerous attempts have been made to demonstrate the effects of residual stresses by means of laboratory tests, but most of these have failed in their objective. Only those tests in which notches were introduced before or during welding have shown any effect of the residual stresses.

Welding stresses can be substantially reduced or eliminated by mechanical or thermal means. Furnace "stress relieving" at 1100–1200 F produces an unquestionably beneficial effect. The major portion of this effect is undoubtedly due to the favorable changes in microstructure accruing from the heat treatment and is not due to the relaxation of stress. Low-temperature stress relieving, on the other hand, does not alter the microstructure but does relax the stress. Certain tests have shown that low-temperature stress relieving produces a substantial improvement, but in other tests no benefit was found. Only those tests in which a notch was present prior to welding or was created during welding showed improvement due to low-temperature stress relieving.

Some recent investigations have shown that cracks, once started, will propagate spontaneously when the nominal stress is above about 10,000 psi and the temperature is below that for the ductility transition. Since most codes governing the use of medium carbon structural steel permit stresses in excess of 10,000 psi, it is imperative that brittle fractures be prevented from starting. Unfortunately, attempts to determine why and how such fractures initiate in statically loaded structures have met with little success. This problem, therefore, remains to be solved.

Considerable progress has been made in the design of structural components. In an ideal structural design, all component parts of a structure should behave in a parallel manner insofar as stress and strain are concerned, and at the maximum load all components should be just on the verge of failure. To emphasize this point, the behavior of a ship hatch corner will be used as an illustration. A hatch corner that exhibits a high ultimate stress but a low energy absorption will accumulate higher stress in proportion to its elongation than will the adjacent components; such a corner will be likely to initiate a fracture. Another design of hatch corner that exhibits low strength but high energy will not carry its share of the applied load. Such a corner would not be likely to initiate a fracture, but because of the extra load transferred to other structural components, might cause a failure to start elsewhere. The use of such considerations does not, however lead to a direct solution of the design problem because the behavior of complex welded structures cannot be analyzed simply. Hatch corner design must, therefore, involve the intelligent use of good basic principles and the performance records of previous designs. The advancement in hatch corner design has reduced the hatch corner fractures per 100 ship years from 10.6 (based on 2110 ship years) to 0.70 (based on 4400 ship years). Improvements are also being made in the design of other structural components.

Advancement has been made in controlling the notch toughness of steel, and additional improvements can be expected. Semikilled ship plate steel made to the former ABS (American Bureau of Shipping) specification had 20 ft-lb keyhole Charpy transition temperatures that averaged about 30 F higher than the more recent ABS Class B steel. Furthermore, a substantial additional improvement has been made in plates over 1 in. thick by silicon killing and treating this steel with aluminum.

There is ample evidence to prove that poor workmanship has, in many cases, been responsible for fractures that have occurred in welded vessels. Weld defects have provided the notches responsible for initiating brittle fractures. The need for completely sound welds has been repeatedly demonstrated.

The brittle behavior of steel will be a plague to engineers for some time to come. With the recent accumulation of knowledge, however, the curtain of fear and uncertainty that has long obscured the brittle fracture problem has been lifted. Improvements in steel, in design, in welding, and in workmanship have gone far to reduce disastrous failures. Perhaps such failures can never be completely eliminated, but proper precautions can at the present time reduce the incidence of failure to a very low figure.

Author Index

Subject Index